Biological Membranes

A series covering selected areas of biology at advanced undergraduate level. While designed specifically for course options at this level within Universities and Polytechnics, the series will be of great value to specialists and research workers in other fields who require a knowledge of the essentials of a subject

Other titles in the series:

Experimentation in Biology	Ridgman
Methods in Experimental Biology	Ralph
Visceral Muscle	Huddart and Hunt
Comparative Immunobiology	Manning and Turner
Water and Plants	Meidner and Sheriff

TERTIARY LEVEL BIOLOGY

Biological Membranes

Their Structure and Function

ROGER HARRISON, M.A., Ph.D.

Lecturer in Biochemistry
School of Biological Sciences
University of Bath

GEORGE G. LUNT, B.Sc., Ph.D.

Lecturer in Biochemistry
School of Biological Sciences
University of Bath

Blackie

Glasgow and London

Blackie & Son Limited
Bishopbriggs
Glasgow G64 2NZ

5 Fitzhardinge Street
London W1H 0DL

First published 1975

International Standard Book Numbers

Paperback 0 216 90072 7
Hardback 0 216 90073 5

Printed in Great Britain by
Thomson Litho Ltd, East Kilbride, Scotland

Preface

THE STUDY OF MEMBRANES HAS EMERGED AS A MAJOR AREA OF BIOLOGICAL research and this has been reflected in the increased attention which has been devoted to the topic in undergraduate courses in Biology and Biochemistry. Despite a corresponding increase in the literature at research level, no advanced undergraduate text is currently available to serve what is clearly a growing need. It is to meet this demand that we have written the present book.

A major stimulus to research over the last three years has been the clarification of ideas on membrane structure, and we have attempted to outline the molecular basis of such ideas and to relate them to functional activities of biological membranes. Attention has been concentrated largely on those aspects of membrane function which can be discussed in molecular terms. Thus emphasis is given to the role of membrane carbohydrate in cellular interactions, which is presently an area of intensive activity in view of its medical implications, and yet which has received only cursory treatment in undergraduate textbooks.

In view of the major part played by physical techniques in the elucidation of membrane structure, we have included a final chapter dealing with these methods. We hope that this will serve both to provide for the student a convenient revision of the principles involved and to indicate the particular nature of their application to artificial and biological membranes.

A list of suggested reading, sub-divided by chapter, is included at the end of the book. This will direct the student towards the relevant specialist literature.

We gratefully acknowledge the help of our colleagues R. Eisenthal, A. H. Rose, A. W. Flegman and P. Squires and several of our undergraduate and postgraduate students who read and criticised parts of the manuscript. We would also like to thank J. Lightfoot and A. Dynamo for many carefully produced diagrams. Our thanks are also due to the many scientists throughout the world who have generously supplied original micrographs.

R. HARRISON
G. G. LUNT
School of Biological Sciences
University of Bath

Contents

CHAPTER 1

THE CELL

ALL STUDENTS OF BIOLOGY ARE FAMILIAR WITH THE OBSERVATIONS OF THE English microscopist Robert Hooke. In an account of his investigations published in 1665, Hooke described the microscopic appearance of cork and used the word *cell* to identify the small box-like compartments that he saw. Some 10 years later Antoni van Leeuwenhoek published numerous drawings of bacteria, spermatozoa, protozoa and red blood cells. It was not until the early nineteenth century, however—over 100 years after the observations of Hooke and van Leeuwenhoek—that the anatomist Theodor Schwann announced that 'the elemental parts of tissues are cells, similar in general but diverse in form and function'. Other scientists quickly accepted the new cellular theory, and the scientific world witnessed the beginnings of an explosion in cell science.

The cell membrane

At about the time of Schwann's announcement of the cellular organization of tissues, new microscopes were being developed with compound lenses. These were free from the chromatic aberration that had always bedevilled users of earlier instruments. With the widespread use of the new instruments, and the parallel development of staining procedures for improving the contrast of the various parts of tissues, it became apparent that within the cell, in addition to the nucleus, there was a whole range of hitherto unstudied bodies. Thus in the late nineteenth century mitochondria, Golgi bodies, and a variety of vacuoles and granules, were seen and characterized morphologically. However, in spite of rapid improvements in staining and sectioning, and in the design of lenses and microscopes, no information emerged on the nature of the cell boundary.

In 1855 Carl Nägeli observed differences in the penetration of pigments into damaged and undamaged plant cells, and examined the cell boundary, to which he gave the name *plasma membrane*. He also carried out experiments in conjunction with Cramer which showed cells to be osmotically sensitive, i.e. cells could change their volume depending on the osmotic strength of the surrounding medium. Nägeli suggested that it was the cell boundary which was responsible for these osmotic properties.

Information now began to appear on the function of the still unseen cell boundary or membrane. The German botanist Wilhelm Pfeffer carried out numerous experiments on the osmotic behaviour of plant cells, and in a publication in 1897 put forward two major conclusions: firstly, that 'the cell is enclosed by a plasma membrane' and, secondly, that 'this membrane is a universal barrier to the passage of water and of solutes'. However, it was soon found that although the cell membrane was indeed a barrier, some substances would cross the membrane very easily, whereas others would hardly cross at all. Charles Overton in 1899 published the results of his observations on the entry into cells of a wide range of compounds. He found that the more polar a molecule, the lower the rate of entry into the cell, whereas the addition of non-polar groups such as alkyl chains increased the rate of entry. Overton concluded that the cell membrane, which controlled the rate of entry of substances into the cell, was lipoidal in nature, and that cholesterol and other lipids were involved. Thus in 1899 the foundations for the idea of a *lipid membrane* surrounding the cell were laid. In 1925, Gorter and Grendel suggested that the lipid was in the form of a bilayer. This arrangement was later to be proposed by Danielli and Davson, and to form the basis of a model of membrane structure which is accepted today (see chapter 6).

Yet Gorter, Grendel, Danielli and all the membrane workers who had gone before had never seen the cell membrane. Despite the developments in this period in the fixing and staining of tissue specimens, and even with the development of phase contrast and interference microscopy, the cell membrane was still unresolved, and it remained unresolved until the advent of electron microscopy. The best light microscopes cannot resolve structures separated by less than half the wavelength of light (about 250 nm, using white light). An ordinary electron microscope has a limit of resolution of about 1 nm.

Figure 1.1. An electron micrograph of a longitudinal section of a prokaryotic cell, the bacterium *Streptococcus faecalis.* The thick cell wall CW, with the underlying plasma membrane PM, is clearly visible. The membranous invaginations which form the mesosomes M are the only intracellular organelles. The cells were prefixed in 3% glutaraldehyde and counterfixed in 1% osmium tetroxide. From M. L. Higgins and L. Daneo-Moore, *J. Cell. Biol.* (1974), **61,** 288–300. Original micrograph by courtesy of Drs. M. L. Higgins and L. Daneo-Moore, Temple University School of Medicine.

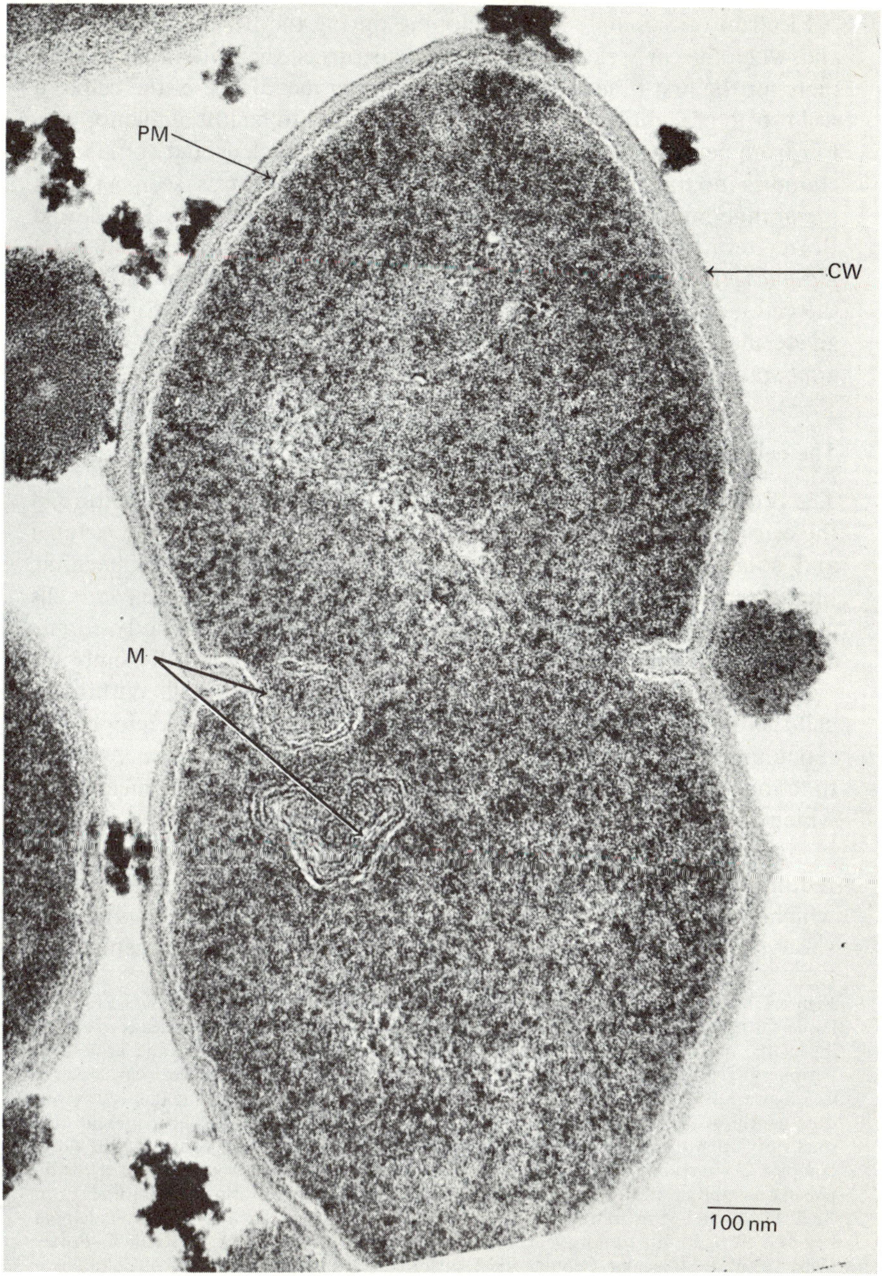
PM
CW
M
100 nm

Electron microscopy was developing during the period 1930 to 1950 and, when the early electron microscopists turned their attention to cells, there for the first time they saw the boundary membrane of the cell as a solid structural entity. But the whole cell seemed to be full of membranes. Far from being a membrane-bound sack with a nucleus and some mitochondria floating in a protoplasmic jelly, the cell was seen to be a membrane-bound collection of membranes. In the early 1950s, Palade and Porter termed this extensive intracellular membrane system the *endoplasmic reticulum.* Rather surprisingly, all the various membranes within the cell looked very much alike to the early electron microscopists, and all seemed to have the now familiar 'tramline' or 'railroad track' appearance of the plasma membrane (see chapters 3 and 6).

The cell and its membraneous contents

The profusion of intracellular membranes described above is a feature of the cells of higher organisms (plants and animals) and of protozoa, fungi and some algae. Such cells are said to be *eukaryotic.* The bacteria, blue-green algae, and several other micro-organisms are *prokaryotic* cells and have little or no membraneous structure within the cell body. Figure 1.1 shows an electron micrograph of a prokaryotic cell. The cell membrane may be seen clearly with its thick exterior coat or cell wall. Within the cell there is little visible structure; there is for example, no endoplasmic reticulum, no mitochondrion and no discrete nucleus. Many of the functions of these organelles are taken over by the plasma membrane, which has associated with it the electron transport chain and the enzymes of oxidative phosphorylation. The synthesis of many of the molecules required by the cell also takes place at the plasma membrane surface, which may have ribosomes attached to it. The plasma membrane may show some invaginations giving rise to an organelle-like structure, the

---

Figure 1.2. An electron micrograph of a plasma cell from the submucosa of the rat. The tissue has been fixed in glutaraldehyde followed by osmium. This procedure leads to clumping of the dense granular chromatin C at the centre of the nucleus N, and around its periphery. The less-dense euchromatin extends to the pores P in the nuclear envelope NE (see figure 3.2). The well-developed endoplasmic reticulum ER, which in this cell is predominantly of the rough type, is clearly seen. Free ribosomes R are also present. The stacks of flattened membraneous discs and associated vesicles which constitute the Golgi complex G are readily recognized, as are the mitochondria M. Surrounding the cell is the plasma membrane PM, which, at this magnification, appears as a single dense line. From K. R. Porter and M. A. Bonneville, *Fine Structure of Cells and Tissues*, 1973, Philadelphia, Lea and Febiger, 4th ed. Original micrograph by courtesy of Professor Keith R. Porter, Department of Molecular, Cellular and Developmental Biology, University of Colorado.

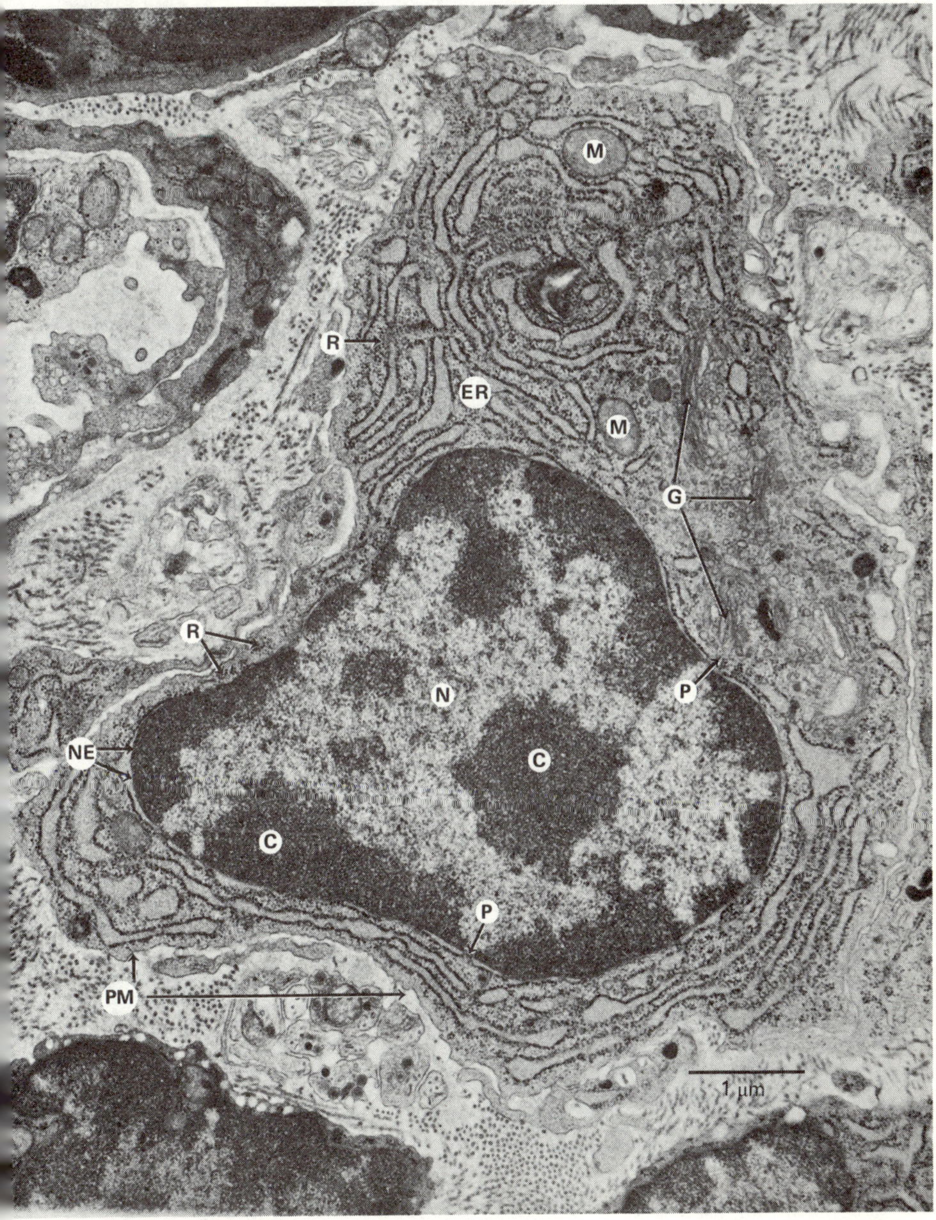
M
R
ER
M
G
R
N
P
NE
C
C
P
PM
1 μm

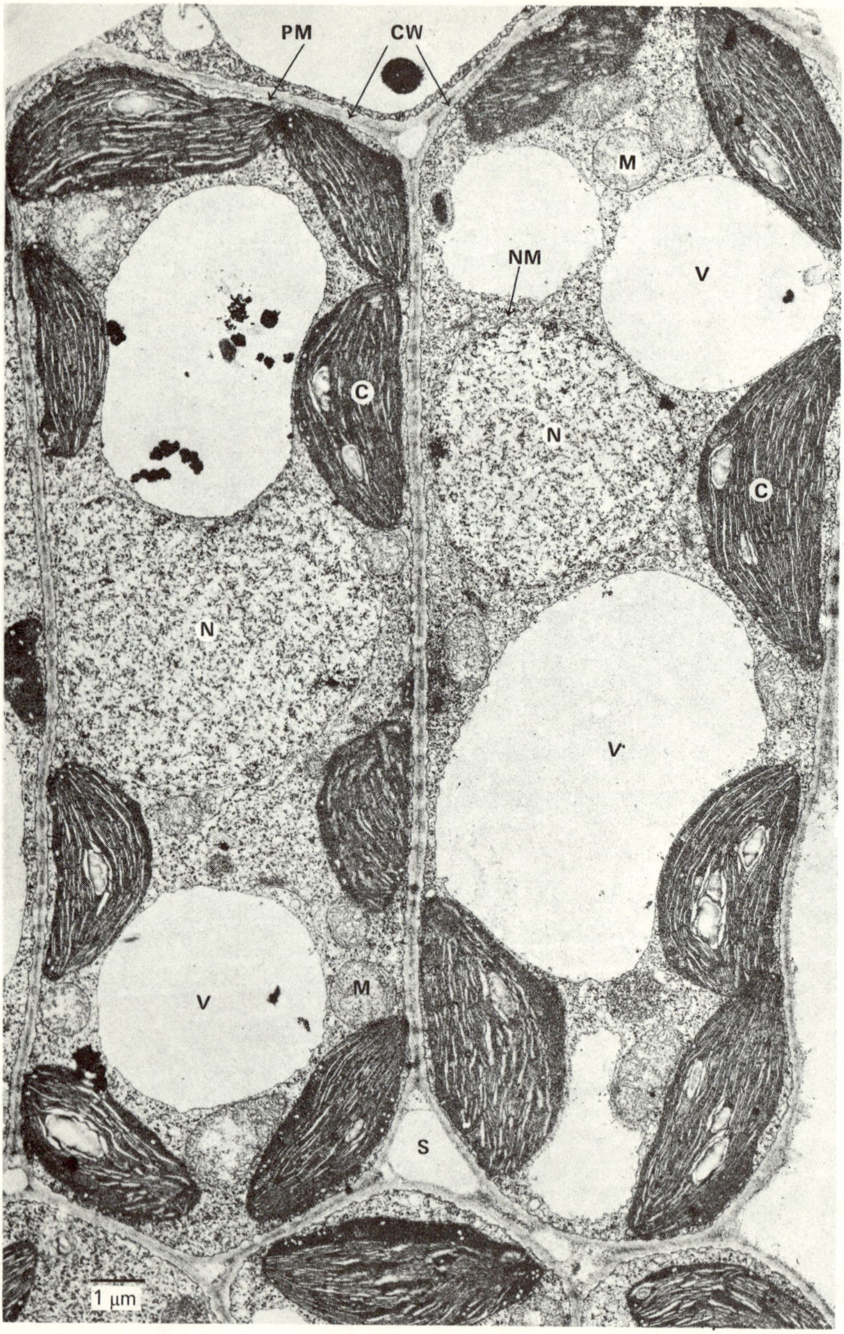
PM
CW
M
NM
V
C
N
C
N
V
V
M
S
1 μm

mesosome (figure 1.1). It has been suggested that synthesis of membrane and cell-wall components may occur at these sites.

The eukaryotic cells present a much more complex picture. Figure 1.2 shows an electron micrograph of a plasma cell from the submucosa of the rat with its wealth of intracellular membraneous structures. In figure 1.3, a photosynthetic leaf-cell is seen. Many of the subcellular organelles in plant and animal cells are similar: thus the nucleus, endoplasmic reticulum, mitochondria and Golgi bodies are comparable. The plant cell is characterized by its outer cell wall (a structure similar to that found in the prokaryotes), the large central vacuole, and the chloroplasts—all of which can be seen clearly in figure 1.3. The functions of the subcellular organelles vary widely; and yet early observations of the intracellular membranes, which are the structural elements of the organelles, suggested that they had a common structure. It is reasonable to suppose, however, that variations in membrane ultrastructure will occur, and that in the final analysis membrane structure will be seen to be inseparably linked to membrane function. Indeed, many examples of this are now being found and, as analytical techniques improve, it becomes increasingly clear that each membrane has a unique composition and structure, both of which are dictated by its cellular function.

SUMMARY

1. Cellular theory and the existence of a cell boundary were firmly established in the early nineteenth century.
2. The existence of the cell membrane, its permeability characteristics and its lipid-like nature, were all established before the ultrastructure of the membrane was known.
3. The advent of electron microscopy showed the structure of the cell membrane for the first time.
4. Prokaryotic cells contain little or no intracellular membrane, whereas eukaryotic cells contain abundant membraneous structures.
5. The cell membrane and all the intracellular membranes appear to have the same basic structure.

Figure 1.3. A vertical section through a photosynthetic leaf cell of *Betula verrucosa.* The thick cell wall CW, with the underlying plasma membrane PM, is reminiscent of the structure in figure 1.1. Within the cells, the chloroplasts C and the large vacuoles V are particularly apparent. The nucleus N, with its surrounding nuclear membrane NM, and the mitochondria M, are similar to their animal cell counterparts seen in figure 1.2. Intercellular spaces S are seen. The leaves were fixed in 3% glutaraldehyde and post-fixed in 1% osmium tetroxide; sections were stained with uranyl acetate and lead citrate. From J. D. Dodge, *Ann. Bot.* (1970), **34,** 817–824. Original micrograph by courtesy of Dr. J. D. Dodge, Birbeck College, University of London.

CHAPTER 2

MEMBRANE FUNCTION

The plasma membrane

We have read how Wilhelm Pfeffer proposed that the plasma membrane is a 'universal barrier to the passage of water and of solutes'. Let us examine the cellular role of such a barrier. The fundamental function of the plasma membrane is that of *protection.* Thus the cell can maintain a constant internal environment, irrespective of changes that may occur outside. However, the membrane must not be absolutely protective, and Pfeffer's 'universal barrier' does not fulfil the requirements of the living cell. The cell membrane, while protecting the cell from a variable external environment, must allow selective communication with the exterior. Arrangements must be made for the controlled passage of nutrients into the cell, and the removal of waste products from it. Plasma membranes, therefore, have associated with them a range of *transfer systems* which enable molecules to pass through the membrane in a specific manner. In the case of prokaryotic cells, no intracellular membranes are present, and the cell interior is a single compartment bounded only by the plasma membrane. Eukaryotic cells, however, have numerous intracellular membrane systems which form a series of intracellular compartments, within which many of the processes of metabolism occur.

Compartmentalization

Some 10 years ago, E. Pollard proposed that any cell with dimensions greater than 1 μm must have within it regions of submicroscopic order, so that interacting components may approach sufficiently closely for reactions to proceed. Many prokaryotic cells have dimensions of this order, while eukaryotic cells are invariably larger. The intracellular membranes of the eukaryotic cells provide the means for ensuring high local concentrations of substrates, by compartmentalizing them within organelles.

The compartmentalization of substrates and products has important implications for metabolic control. The rate of entry of substrate into a compartment and, therefore, the rate of a particular metabolic process, depend on the permeability characteristics of the boundary membrane of that compartment. Thus membranes can exert a controlling influence on the metabolic steps proceeding within the organelles. Processes which compete for a common metabolite may be separated by having the enzyme systems in different compartments, and their relative rates controlled by varying the rate of entry of the metabolite. Thus metabolic control is greatly facilitated by a well-developed intracellular membrane system.

Transfer systems

A corollary of the confinement of the cell contents within a plasma membrane and the further compartmentalization of metabolism within the cell is an abundance of membrane transfer systems. These allow for the selective movements of molecules between the cell and its external environment, and between the intracellular compartments. Such transfer systems often mediate unidirectional processes and this asymmetry of function is reflected in an asymmetric structure of the membrane (chapter 6).

Most biology students have seen an amoeba under the light microscope and observed it engulfing water or small particles. This process—*pinocytosis* in the case of liquid, *phagocytosis* if solids are engulfed—is a method for the *bulk transfer* of material into or, if reversed, out of the cell. Transfer of material in this way is not dependent on selective changes in the permeability of the membrane, and does not involve the passage of molecules through its molecular structure. The bulk-transfer system is not a characteristic of all cells, whereas the transfer of material at the molecular level is a universal feature of membranes.

Individual molecules may cross membranes in a variety of ways, which may be classified into two groups. There are those processes which do not require a direct supply of energy, *passive transfer*, and those which directly consume energy, *active transfer*. Passive transfer involves the movement of molecules down a concentration gradient across the membrane to a low-concentration region. Active-transfer systems usually move molecules in the opposite direction, i.e. from regions of low concentration to regions of high concentration. Both systems involve selectivity in that some molecules will cross the membrane more easily than others. In the case of passive-transfer systems, the selectivity can often be varied very considerably by changing the physical characteristics of the membrane.

Active-transfer systems involve the coupling of a transfer process to an energy-producing system. In several cases this is an *ATPase*, and it can be readily demonstrated that the transfer of many molecules across membranes is dependent on a supply of ATP. Classically this was demonstrated in the giant axon of the squid. These cellular extensions are sufficiently large to enable material to be injected into the cell interior without damaging the cell membrane. Using this preparation, it was possible to demonstrate that in axons that have been treated with cyanide in order to inhibit ATP synthesis, the extrusion of sodium ions is directly dependent on intracellular injections of ATP.

Both passive and active-transfer systems may involve the coupling of the transported molecules to a *carrier molecule* with very specific binding sites located at the membrane surface. The complexed molecule is then moved through the membrane and is released at the other surface. The nature of the carriers and the way in which they may be linked to an energy source is still not clear. The latest views on these problems are discussed in detail in chapter 9.

The cell membrane must allow selective communication between the contents of the cell and its exterior, by mediating the transfer not only of individual molecules but also of information. Thus in many cases, mechanisms exist for the reception of messenger molecules, such as neurotransmitters and hormones, and for the transmission of their information into the cell interior. These mechanisms are necessarily associated with the plasma membrane, and will be discussed in chapter 8.

Membranes and enzymes

Membranes are the structural elements of cells and, therefore, in multicellular organisms, of the tissues. The non-membranous constituents of cells form an aqueous phase which of itself is unable to take on and maintain a characteristic form; only by surrounding the aqueous phase with a membrane can constant shape and form be maintained. A close correlation between membrane morphology and function can be seen; examples are discussed in the next chapter. For the present, let us look beyond this toward the molecular level of organization, where we find that membranes also fulfil an important role as structural supports. Many of the chemical processes of biological systems involve long series of co-ordinated reactions. A is converted to B, which is converted to C, and so on, through many steps. Such sequences will not proceed efficiently if the reactants are simply dissolved in the cytoplasm. Suppose, however, that the various enzymes involved in the sequence are bound in an orderly fashion to the surface of a membrane, as shown in figure 2.1.

The membrane maintains a constant spatial relationship between the enzymes, allowing the product of enzyme 1 to be passed on to enzyme 2, and so on, along a series. In this way the enzyme-catalyzed reaction becomes *vectorial*—a condition which cannot be achieved when the enzymes and other reactants are free in solution. The reaction sequence will proceed more efficiently when organized in a membrane, and numerous examples are to be found, one of the most well characterized being the arrangement of the electron transport chain on the inner mitochondrial membrane (chapter 8). Enzymes which are associated with membranes in this way are said to be *membrane-bound*.

The membrane-bound form of an enzyme frequently shows properties different from those of a soluble preparation. The differences may be expressed as changes in substrate specificity, inhibitor sensitivity, optimum pH, K_m and general stability. The phenomenon is termed *allotopy*, and was first noted with the ATPase of the inner mitochondrial membrane (chapter 8). This enzyme is inhibited by both dicyclohexylcarbodiimide and oligomycin when attached to the membrane, whereas the solubilized enzyme is unaffected. Furthermore, the soluble enzyme is cold-labile, while no such effect is observed with the membrane-bound form. A

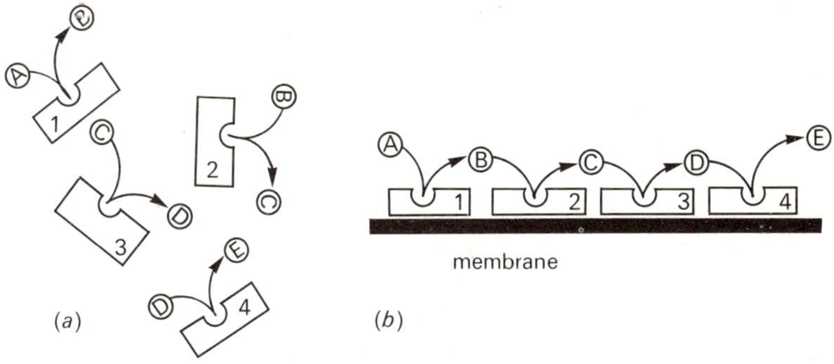

Figure 2.1. Membrane-bound enzymes. In (*a*) enzymes 1–4 and substrates, products A-E are free in solution. When the enzymes are spatially fixed by attachment to a membrane surface, as in (*b*), the conversion of A to E proceeds more readily.

further example is the enzyme xanthine oxidase, which is associated with the milk-fat-globule membrane (chapter 4). The enzyme is anchored to the membrane by a hydrophobic protein tail, which can be cleaved by tryptic digestion. The cleaved enzyme is still active, but shows a characteristically different substrate specificity which reverts to the original pattern on reassociation with the membrane.

If we consider the great differences in the environments of a soluble enzyme and a membrane-bound enzyme, it is not too surprising that the properties of the enzyme may change. Thus the soluble enzyme is in a polar hydrophilic environment of high dielectric constant. A variety of molecules including substrates, other metabolites and ions can approach the enzyme easily and may interact with groups on its surface. In contrast, the membrane-bound enzyme may be largely embedded in a lipophilic region of low dielectric constant, with little opportunity for interaction with small polar molecules. The membrane-bound enzyme exists in a relatively stable microenvironment, the nature of which is determined by the molecular arrangement of the membrane. Changes in membrane compostion or structure will modify the environment of the enzyme and may constitute a regulatory system.

Cellular recognition

Cells recognize each other. Thus the leucocytes of the higher animals recognize foreign cells, such as bacteria in the blood, and engulf them. The leucocytes make no attempt to engulf any of the several types of cells legitimately circulating in the blood stream. On the other hand, the macrophages of the spleen can recognize worn-out erythrocytes and remove them from the circulation by phagocytosis, while healthy erythrocytes are left untouched.

Cells from higher organisms frequently exhibit *contact inhibition.* In simple terms, this means that when cultured on a nutrient medium, individual cells will continue to grow and divide until they come into contact with other cells, at which point growth stops. It is now established that the recognition sites involved in the phenomena are on the outer surface of the plasma membrane, and that the chemical groupings involved are also responsible for immune responses. This area of membrane research has far-reaching medical implications. Thus the problems of tissue rejection, which at present bedevil the transplantation of organs, would disappear overnight if we knew how to modify the recognition sites on the surface membranes of the organs. The study of the role of the plasma membrane surface is probably the most rapidly expanding area of membrane research. It is discussed in depth in chapter 7.

SUMMARY

1. The plasma membrane ensures the maintenance of a constant internal environment within the cell.
2. The compartmentalization of metabolic processes within membrane-bound organelles enables high concentrations of reactants to be maintained at discrete sites.
3. Compartmentalization provides a means of regulating metabolism.
4. Membranes allow for the selective movement of materials across them. Movement across a membrane may be dependent only on concentration gradients (passive transfer) or may require an energy supply (active transfer).
5. Information carried by extracellular messenger molecules is transmitted by the plasma membrane into the cell interior.
6. Many enzymes are attached to membranes. Such enzymes are said to be membrane-bound. The activity of membrane-bound enzymes may be modified by the membrane.
7. Constituents of the plasma-membrane surface provide a highly sophisticated cellular recognition system.

CHAPTER 3

MORPHOLOGY OF MEMBRANES

The unit membrane

Early electron micrographs suggested that all membranes have the same basic structure. In the late 1950s and early 1960s, J. D. Robertson proposed his *unit membrane theory* of membrane structure. He suggested that all membranes, whether from plants, animals or micro-organisms have a common structural pattern based on a bimolecular lipid layer with protein associated with the two faces; the pattern, in fact proposed by Danielli and Davson (see chapter 6). Robertson's theory was based mainly on electron microscope studies of myelin, though in later work he examined a wide variety of membranes and found that they all appeared to have the same basic structure as myelin.

Unit membranes appeared in transverse section as *trilamellar structures* formed from two electron-dense bands separated by an electron-lucent band. This is the classical 'tramline' picture of early electron micrographs typified in figure 3.1.

Over the years however it has become increasingly apparent that the original concept of a universal membrane structure is inadequate (see chapter 6). Detailed examination of individual membranes reveals them to have unique structural features which are a reflection of their specific functions. Let us now examine in more detail the ultrastructure of some specialized membranes in which a clear correlation between structure and function has emerged.

The nuclear membrane

The nucleus was the first organelle to be clearly recognized using light microscopy and was described by Robert Brown in 1831. It was not until

Figure 3.1. Electron micrograph of a section of a human erythrocyte fixed in permanganate. The trilamellar unit membrane bounding the cell is clearly defined. From J. D. Robertson in *Cellular Membranes in Development*, (1964), (M. Locke, ed.), Academic Press, New York, p. 3. Original micrograph by courtesy of Professor J. David Robertson, Department of Anatomy, Duke University Medical Centre.

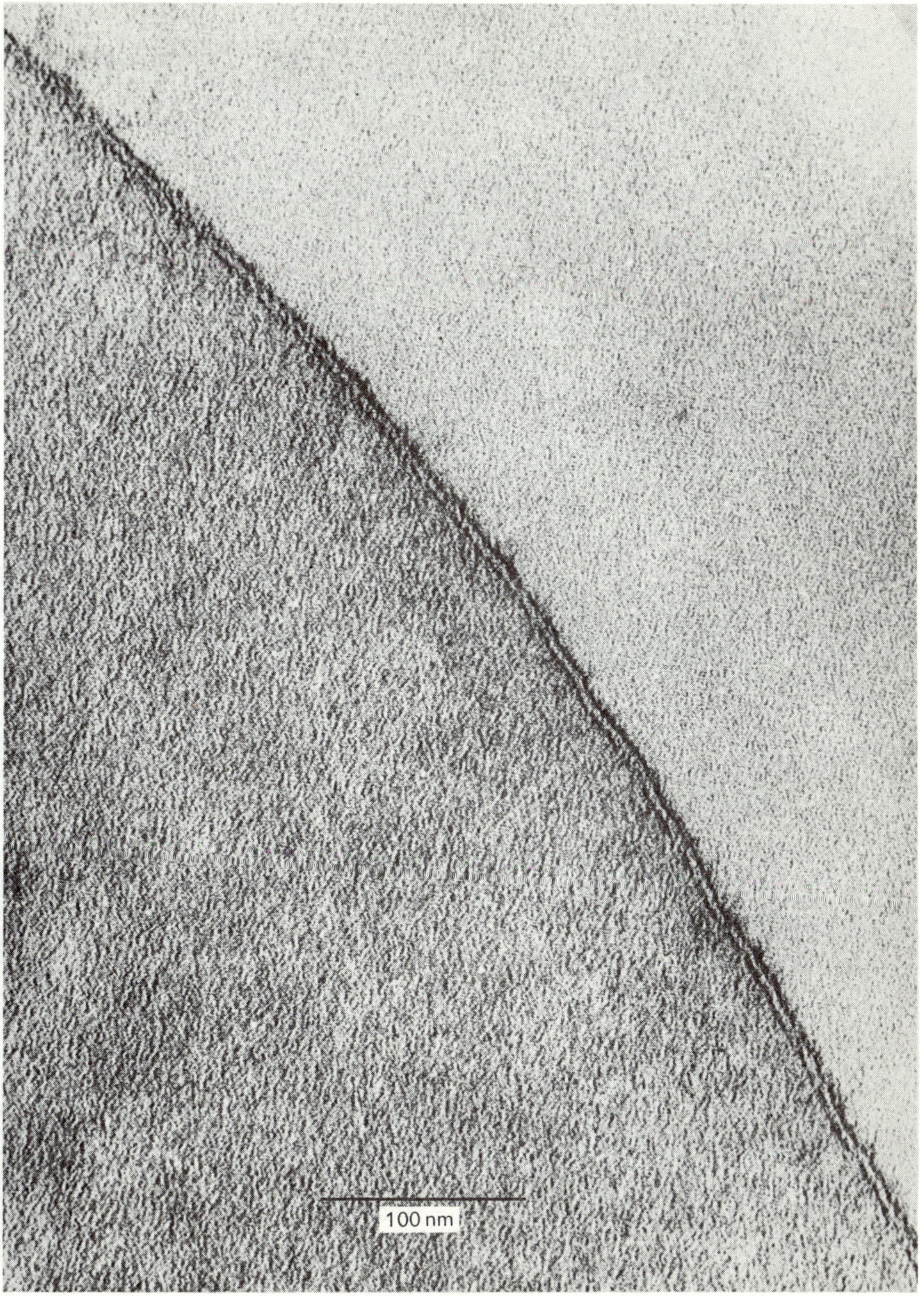
100 nm

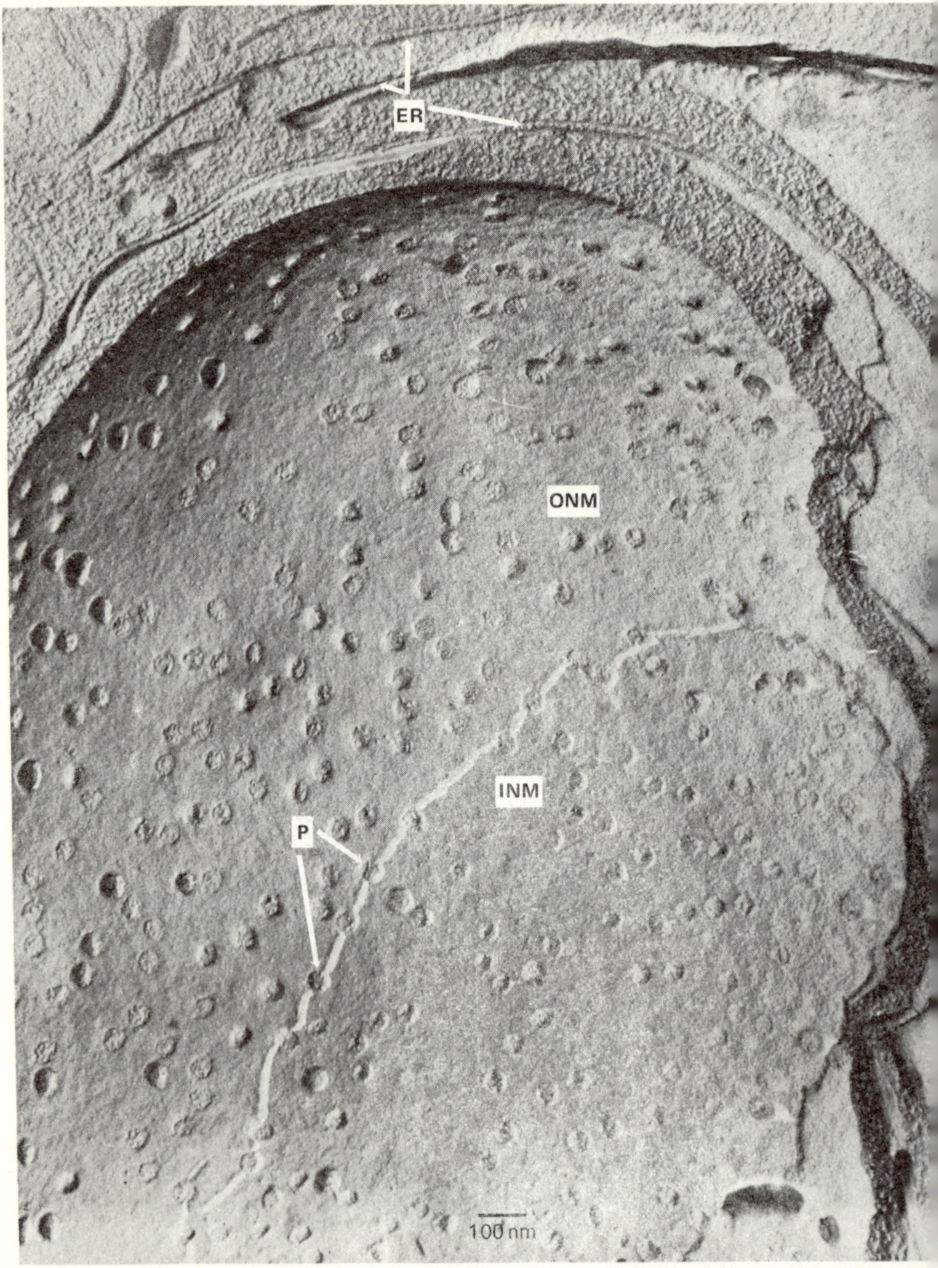
ER
ONM
INM
P
100 nm

the advent of electron microscopy that the detailed ultrastructure of the boundary separating nuclear material from cytoplasm was elucidated. A major finding was that in eukaryotic cells the nuclear envelope or membrane consists of two concentric layers of membranes. Each layer has the usual tramline appearance, but the membranes are frequently pierced by large pores of between 40 nm and 60 nm diameter. Furthermore, the outer layer of the membrane seems to be continuous with the endoplasmic reticulum, and detailed examination of electron micrographs shows the two membrane systems to be continuous at many points. Bacteria have no intracellular membranes, and no membrane surrounds the nuclear material. In fungi and cells of higher organisms, the appearance of the nuclear envelope parallels the development of the endoplasmic reticulum. The large pores penetrating the envelope have been studied in detail, and have been found to be very similar in plant and animal cells (see figure 3.2). Frequently granular material may be seen in the centre of the pores, linked by a system of fibrils to granular bodies, thought by some to be ribosomes, on the periphery of the pore. It is suggested that this material may be an RNA-protein complex being transported between the nucleus and the cytoplasm. Messenger RNA must pass from its intranuclear site of synthesis to the areas of protein synthesis on the ribosomes, and it is attractive to postulate that the role of the pores in the nuclear envelope is to mediate this transfer.

The mitochondrion

Mitochondria are seen in the light microscope as small granular bodies present in all cells of higher organisms. While the contents of the mitochondria are obviously different and separate from the cytoplasm, the nature of the boundary is not at all clear. Electron microscopy reveals the mitochondrion to be a highly-organized membraneous structure. It has an outer membrane surrounding the entire organelle, but within this is another complex membrane system enclosing an inner compartment. Thus the mitochondrion contains two quite separate compartments: an

---

Figure 3.2. Electron micrograph of a platinum replica of a freeze-etched (see page 102) section of a pea-root cell. The inner and outer nuclear membranes, INM and ONM respectively, are seen. The pores P distributed over the nuclear surface, are particularly apparent and can be seen to pass right through both membranes (arrows). Sheets of endoplasmic reticulum ER encircle the nucleus. From D. H. Northcote, *Brit. Med. Bull.* (1968), **24,** 107–112. Original micrograph by courtesy of Dr. D. H. Northcote, Department of Biochemistry, University of Cambridge.

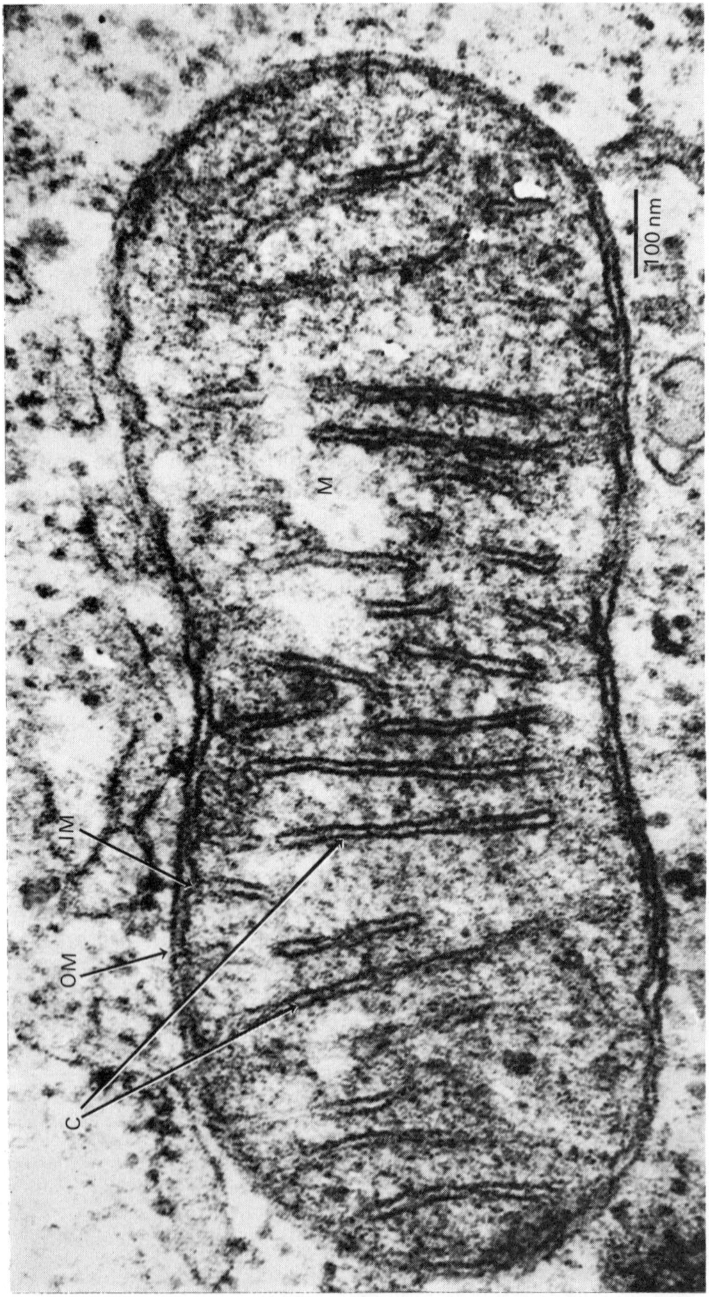

Figure 3.3. Electron micrograph of a section through a mitochondrion in a piglet intestinal cell. The separate outer and inner membrane systems, OM and IM, are clearly visible. The inner membrane is elaborately folded, giving rise to the cristae C, which penetrate deeply into the matrix M. The tissue was fixed in glutaraldehyde, treated with osmium tetroxide, and stained with uranyl acetate and lead citrate. From E. A. Munn, *The Structure of Mitochondria* (1974), Academic Press, London, p. 3. Original micrograph by courtesy of Dr. E. A. Munn, Agricultural Research Council, Institute of Animal Physiology, Babraham, Cambridge.

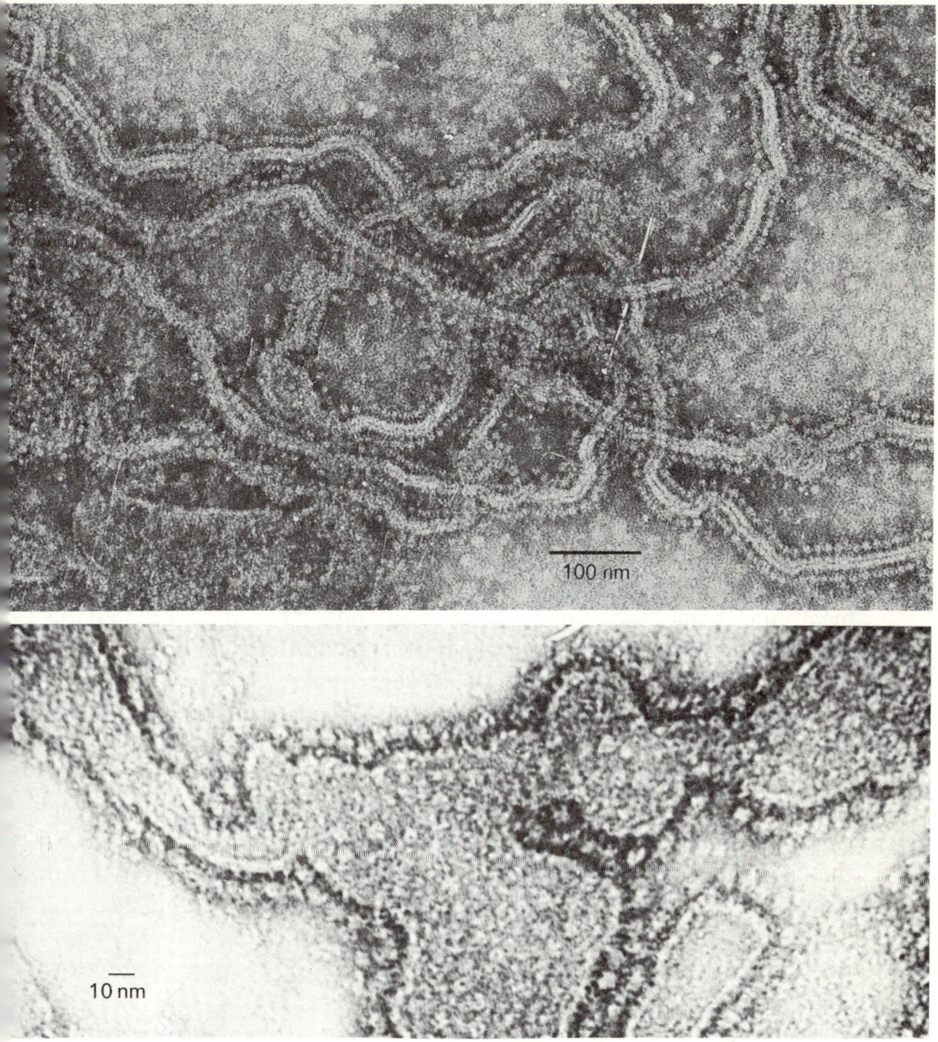

Figure 3.4. Electron micrographs of negatively stained fragments of cristae membranes. The upper micrograph shows a preparation from the flight of muscle *Calliphora* and, in the lower micrograph, rat liver cristae membranes are seen at higher magnification. The stalked particles are clearly visible in both preparations. The upper micrograph is from E. A. Munn, *The Structure of Mitochondria* (1974), Academic Press, London, p. 126. Both original micrographs by courtesy of Dr. E. A. Munn, Agricultural Research Council Institute of Animal Physiology, Babraham.

outer chamber or *perimitochondrial space*, bounded by two different membranes, and an inner chamber bounded by the inner membrane. The inner chamber frequently contains fibrillar and granular material, and is referred to as the *matrix*. Figure 3.3 shows a mitochondrion from a piglet intestinal cell, and the two membrane systems can be clearly seen.

Examination of electron micrographs reveals that the outer membrane is usually rather thicker than the inner membrane, and frequently shows ordered arrays of small particles. In plant mitochondria, the outer surface of the outer membrane is pitted, and it has been claimed that the pits penetrate to the perimitochondrial space. A redistribution of the particles in the outer membrane has been seen to occur during energization of the electron transport system of the inner membrane, suggesting that structural-functional changes in the one membrane may be transmitted to the other. The significance of such changes is not yet known.

The inner membrane is a highly convoluted system with numerous infoldings termed *mitochondrial crests* or more usually *cristae* (see figure 3.3). Osmotic rupture of mitochondria under hypotonic conditions, followed by detailed examination of the broken mitochondria in the electron microscope, reveals ultrastructural features unique to the inner membrane. Under these conditions H. Fernandez-Moran showed that the inner surface of the inner membrane is covered with small knobs, 8–10 nm in diameter, linked to the membrane by short stalks. The particles project into the matrix and can be clearly seen in the electron micrographs in figure 3.4.

The biochemical activities of the inner membrane have been shown to be those of *electron transport* and *oxidative phosphorylation*. It has been suggested that the projections from the inner membrane correspond to the mitochondrial ATPase-ATP synthetase (see chapter 8). The two membrane systems of the mitochondrion have quite different biochemical activities associated with them (see chapters 4 and 8) but exact correlations between ultrastructure and function have yet to be established.

The chloroplast

Chloroplasts are the most common of the cellular organelles in the plant kingdom. Their average diameter is in the range 4–10 μm, and they are

Figure 3.5. Electron micrograph of a transverse section through a single chloroplast from a corn marigold leaf cell. The lamellae membranes L are stacked together to form the grana G; single lamellae can be seen crossing the stroma S to connect with other grana. Original micrograph by courtesy of Dr. J. D. Dodge, Birbeck College, University of London.

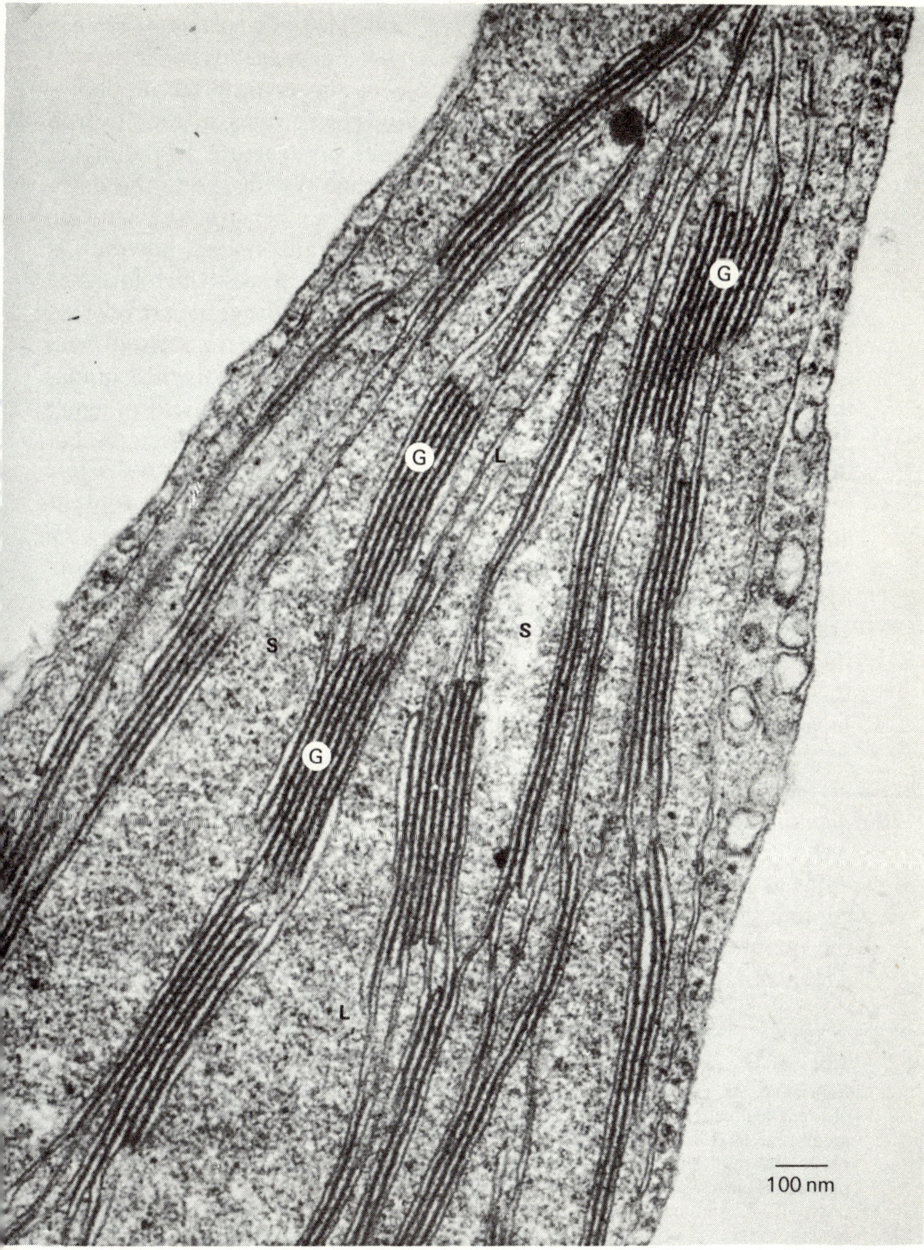
G
G
L
S
S
G
L
100 nm

thus readily visible in the light microscope; they are seen to contain numerous small granules termed *grana* embedded in a matrix or *stroma.* The pigments, such as chlorophyll, can be distinguished in the grana and in the late nineteenth century the role of the chloroplast in photosynthesis was established. Examination of chloroplasts in the electron microscope reveals a complex membraneous substructure. In the higher plants there are two concentric unit-membrane systems, as in the mitochondrion. The outer membrane is a relatively simple structure showing no foldings or invaginations. The inner membrane system, however, is elaborately folded into stacks of flattened cylindrical sacs which form the grana. The individual sacs that collectively make up the grana are referred to as *thylakoid discs.* A tubular membrane system, again derived from the inner membrane, is frequently seen connecting the individual grana; this system can be seen in the electron micrograph reproduced in figure 3.5. The multilaminar system is also seen in photosynthetic bacteria, but in this case no boundary membrane is found, and therefore no discrete photosynthetic organelle is present. It is possible to disrupt chloroplasts and to recover both complete grana and individual thylakoid discs by a series of centrifugation procedures, when it can be shown that both fractions can carry out the light reactions of photosynthesis. Thus the grana contain both the light-trapping pigments and the enzyme systems involved in the initial light reactions (chapter 8). Attempts to correlate these specific functions of the thylakoid membranes with their structure have met with some success. High-power electron microscopy, particularly of freeze-etched specimens (see chapter 6) has revealed paracrystalline arrays of particles in the thylakoid membrane. These particles are termed *quantosomes* and are about 10–15 nm in diameter, with an estimated weight of some 2×10^6 daltons* (see figure 3.6).

It has proved possible to isolate quantosomes and to show that they contain pigments, lipids, electron carriers and an ATPase system. Thus the quantosome represents a small self-contained photosynthetic unit. The arrangement of the quantosomes immediately brings to mind the

* 1 dalton = 1 atomic mass unit = $\frac{1}{12}$ of the mass of an atom of the nuclide ^{12}C.

Figure 3.6. An electron micrograph of a platinum replica of a freeze-etched preparation of a pea-leaf cell. A chloroplast CH is seen lying beneath the inner surface of the plasma membrane PI. Particulate units (arrowed) are seen on the inner membranes of the chloroplast. The inset shows this region at a higher magnification, and the ordered array of particles is clearly seen. From D. H. Northcote, *Brit. Med. Bull.* (1968), **24,** 107–112. Original micrograph by courtesy of Dr. D. H. Northcote, Department of Biochemistry, University of Cambridge.

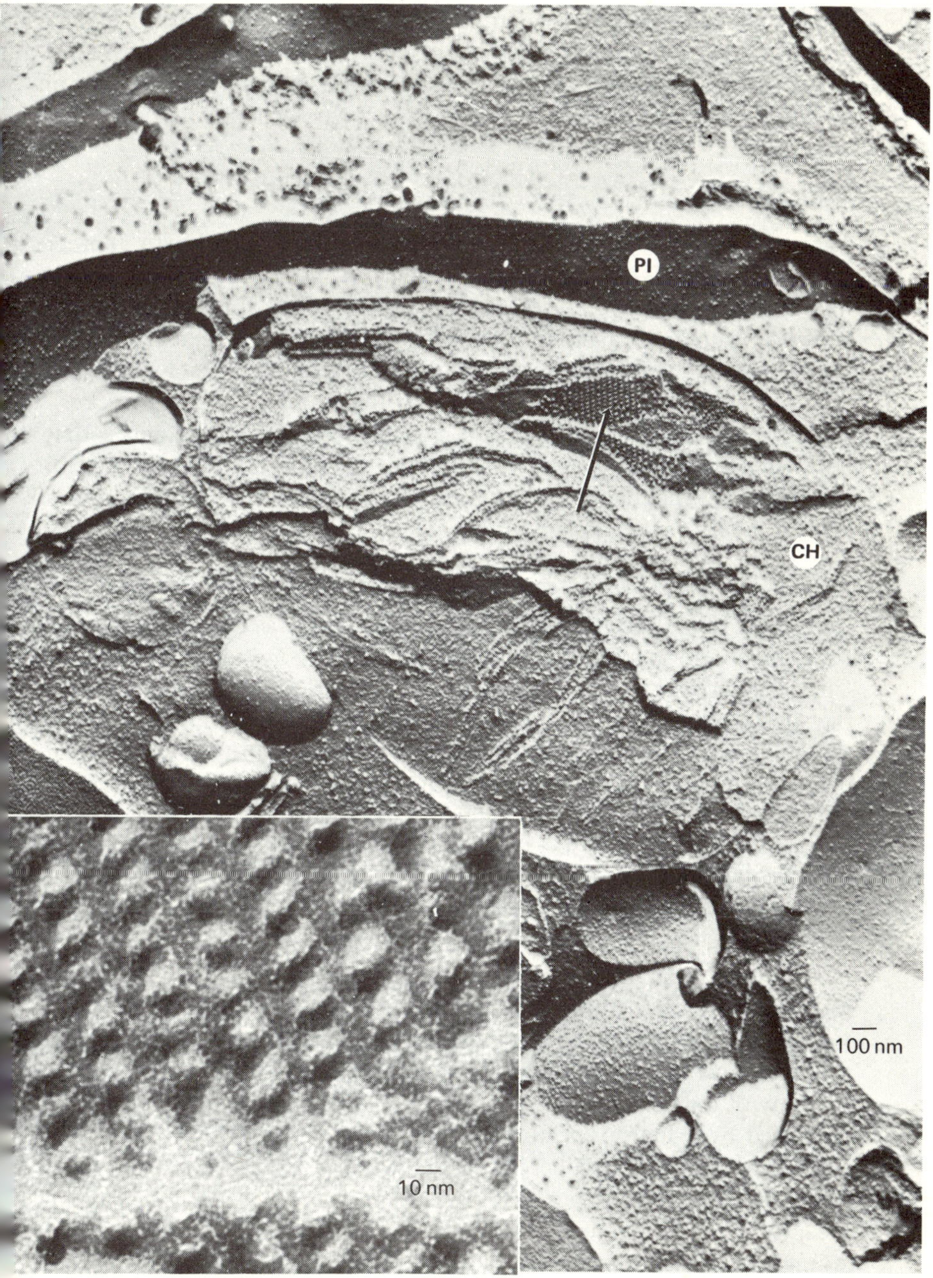
PI
CH
100 nm
10 nm

knobs and stalks of the inner mitochondrial membrane, and it may well be that similar macromolecular organizations of membrane constituents have evolved in the two organelles to carry out the similar processes of photosynthetic and oxidative phosphorylation (see chapter 8).

The synapse

The point at which a nerve cell or neurone makes contact with another cell is termed the *synapse.* The importance of these specialized contacts was recognized at the end of last century by the Spanish histologist Santiago Ramon y Cajal. Until the late 1930s Ramon y Cajal expounded his theory that neurones were discrete cells, and that contact between them occurred only at specialized sites, the synapses. There was considerable opposition to this theory, and many histologists claimed that the nervous system was a continuous network of filaments with thickenings at the points where several filaments joined. The thickenings formed the nerve-cell bodies which were so clearly visible when nervous tissue was stained and examined in the light microscope. Electron microscopy showed Ramon y Cajal to have been quite correct. Neurones were seen to be discrete cells, and it was firmly established that the nervous system is a contiguous rather than a continuous system. Sir Charles Sherrington, a contemporary of Ramon y Cajal, proposed that the sites of specialized contact (or synapses) were key control points in the nerve network, and he put forward the view that at these points a definite separation of the surfaces of the two cells occurs. Again electron microscopy has shown Sherrington to have been correct. Thus at the synapse a distinct gap called the *synaptic cleft* is seen between the surface membranes of the two cells. We now know that molecules of *neurotransmitter* are released into the cleft and diffuse across it to interact with specific receptors in the membrane of the other cell. This vital link in the nerve pathway has long attracted the attention of histologists, and many ultrastructural features of the membranes have been found which can be related to their unique functions. Figure 3.7 shows typical synaptic junctions in the cerebral cortex of the rat.

Many of the ultrastructural features of the synaptic region were first described by Eduardo De Robertis, and in the mid 1950s De Robertis and Bennett gave the first description of *synaptic vesicles.* These are small unit membrane-bound sacs that are seen exclusively in the pre-synaptic area. It did not take long before the vesicles were shown to be the sites of storage of neurotransmitter, and De Robertis and his co-workers demonstrated that under conditions of prolonged transmitter release the number of vesicles is diminished.

The precise mechanisms of transmitter release have been the subject of considerable research, and much progress has been made using combinations of biochemical and histological techniques. Careful examination

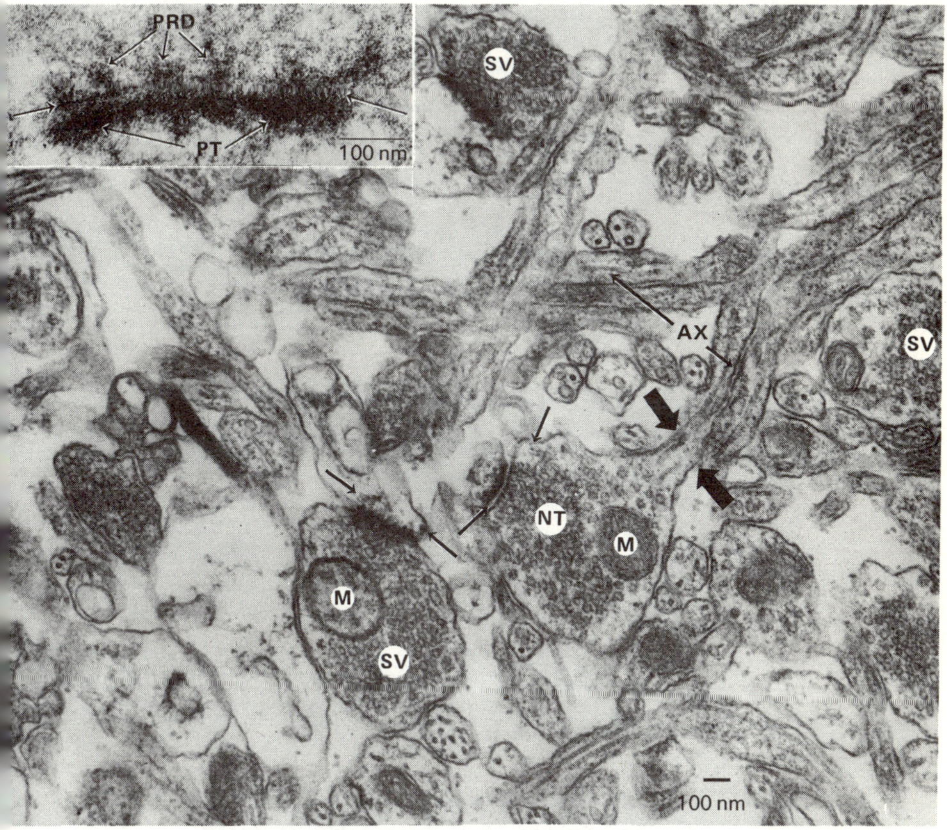

Figure 3.7. Electron micrograph of a section of a slice of rat cerebral cortex. The slice has been incubated at 37 °C for 2 hours in Krebs-Ringer buffer solution which has resulted in a considerable enlargement of the extracellular space; the nerve terminals NT are particularly well defined. The terminals are filled with synaptic vesicles SV, and contain some mitochondria M. The synaptic junctions are arrowed. The detailed structure of the junction is seen in the inset enlargement. The synaptic cleft is arrowed and the presynaptic dense projections PRD and postsynaptic thickenings PT are clearly seen. Homogenization of the tissue breaks the axons AX at the point shown by heavy arrows, and the detached terminal may be isolated as a discrete fraction. From G. G. Lunt and E. G. Lapetina (1970) *Brain Res.*, **18,** 451–458.

of the presynaptic membrane has revealed a unique structural organization. Thus it seems that the presynaptic dense projections seen in figure 3.7 are part of a complex structure termed the *presynaptic vesicular grid*. Professor K. Akert and his colleagues have suggested that this structure may serve to guide synaptic vesicles down to specific openings or *synaptopores* in the presynaptic membrane. The probable arrangement of the membrane specializations can be seen in figure 3.8.

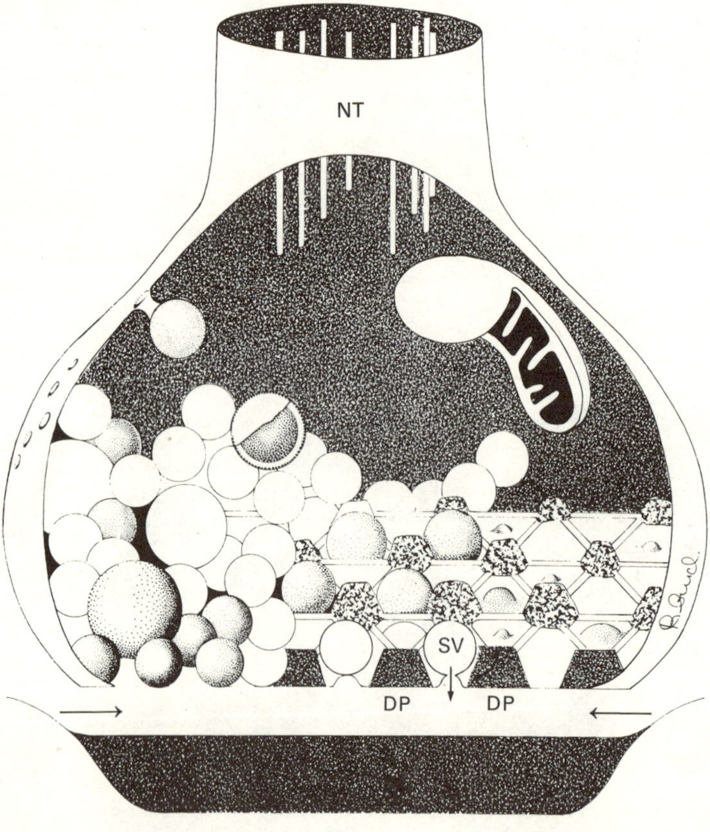

Figure 3.8. Schematic diagram of a presynaptic nerve terminal NT, with presynaptic dense projections DP, forming the vesicular grid with synaptopores through which synaptic vesicles SV could discharge their contents (arrow) into the synaptic cleft (arrowed). Compare with the micrograph in figure 3.7. From K. Akert *et al.* (1972). Freeze-etching and cytochemistry of vesicles and membrane complexes in synapses of the central nervous system in *Structure and Function of Synapses* (ed. G. D. Pappas and D. P. Purpura) Raven Press, New York, pp. 67–86. Original diagram kindly supplied by Professor K. Akert, Brain Research Institute, University of Zurich.

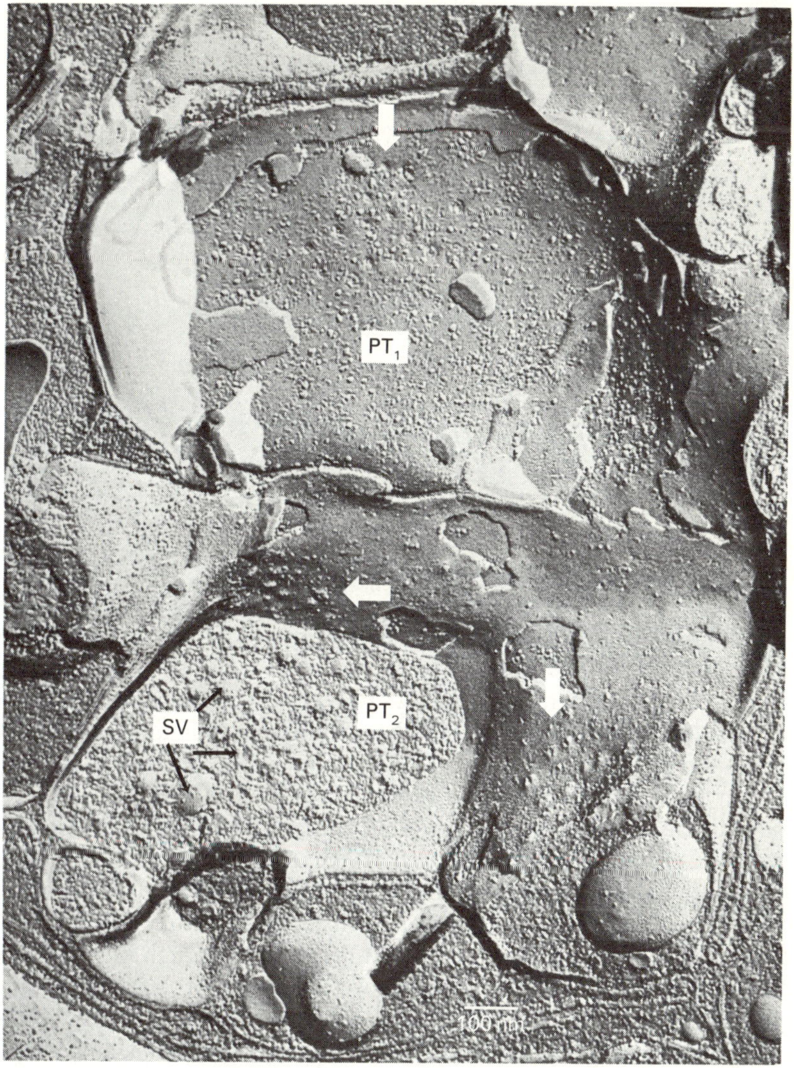

Figure 3.9. Freeze-etched section of pigeon optic tectum. PT_1 is a presynaptic nerve terminal viewed from the external surface and PT_2 is another terminal viewed from the inside. Synaptic vesicles SV are seen in terminal PT_2. Structures are seen in both terminals (heavy arrows) which may correspond to the synaptopores in Figure 3.8. From K. Akert *et al.* (1972). Freeze-etching and cytochemistry of vesicles and membrane complexes in synapses of the central nervous system in *Structure and Function of Synapses* (ed. G. D. Pappas and D. P. Purpura), Raven Press, New York. Original micrograph by courtesy of Professor K. Akert, Brain Research Institute, University of Zurich.

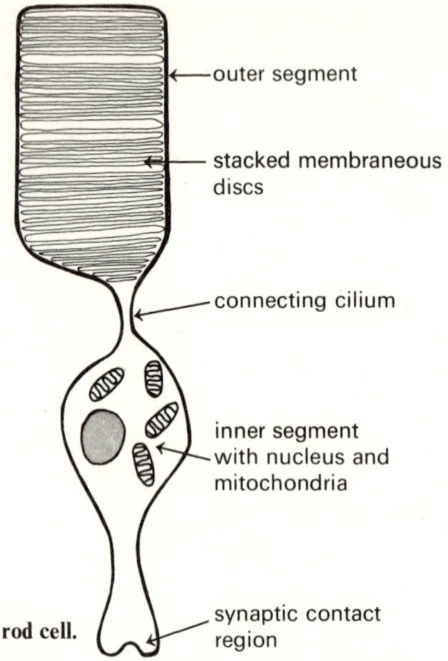

Figure 3.10*a*. A retinal rod cell.

Examination of freeze-etched preparations of nerve terminals has revealed areas in the membrane which correspond closely with the structures shown diagrammatically in figure 3.8. Thus in figure 3.9 arrays of small crater-like openings in the membranes bounding the nerve terminal may be seen.

Many years ago Sir Bernard Katz showed that the release of neurotransmitters was a *quantal* process, *i.e.* discrete amounts of transmitter are released into the synaptic cleft. It has always been an attractive idea that the quanta of neurotransmitter correspond to the synaptic vesicles, and when the latter were described by De Robertis, numerous workers sought unequivocal proof that this is so. Although it now seems that no direct correlation exists between quanta of transmitter and synaptic vesicles, it is likely that the structural organization of the presynaptic membrane provides a mechanism for channelling single vesicles to sites where they can release their contents into the synaptic cleft.

The retinal sacs

The rods and cones of the vertebrate retina are highly-specialized cells which detect and convert light energy into an electrical impulse. Figures

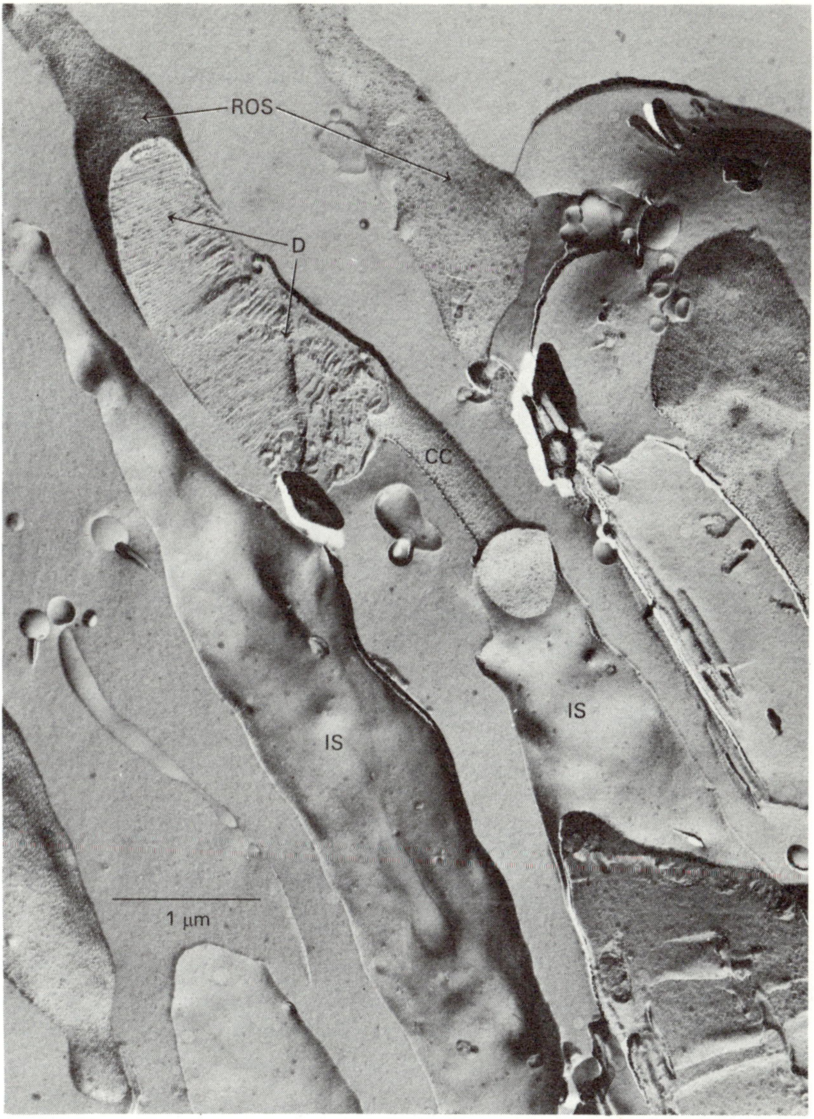

Figure 3.10*b*. Electron micrograph of freeze-fractured mouse retina showing portions of the rod cell inner segment IS, the connecting cilium cc, and the rod outer segment ROS. The outer segment contains the stacked membraneous discs which are seen in cross-fracture D. From L. Y. Jan and J.-P. Revel, *J. Cell. Biol.* (1974), **62,** 257–273. Original micrograph by courtesy of Dr. Lily Yeh Jan, California Institute of Biology, Pasadena.

3.10*a* and *b* show the main features of a retinal rod cell. The cone cell is essentially the same, except that the outer segment is short and compact.

The outer segment of the cells is concerned with the detection of light, and examination of this part of the cell with the polarization light microscope suggests the presence of a multilaminar structure not unlike that seen in myelin. Electron microscopy reveals that the pattern seen in the polarization microscope results from membraneous sacs stacked longitudinally along the segment axis. The sacs are formed from two-unit membranes which surround a space 3–5 nm wide (figure 3.11). These sacs can be shown to be osmotically sensitive and will swell under hypotonic conditions.

It has been demonstrated that the retinal sacs are derived from the plasma membrane of the cell. In the cones of the frog retina, the plasma membrane undergoes repeated invaginations which lead to the build-up

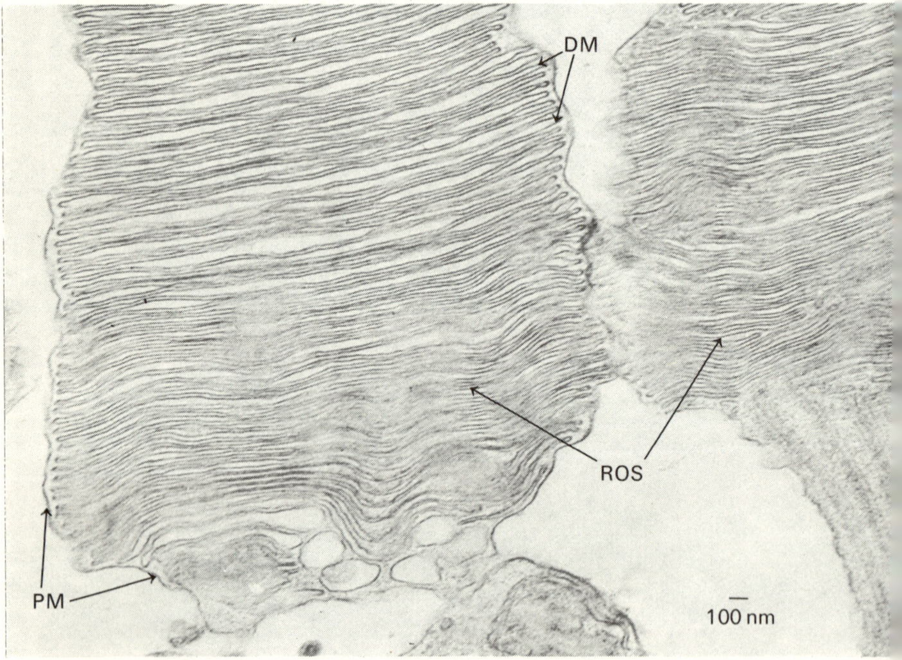

Figure 3.11. Electron micrograph of rat retinal rod cells. The stacked arrangement of discs within the rod outer segment ROS is clearly illustrated, and the disc membranes DM are seen to be quite separate from the plasma membrane PM of the cell. Original micrograph by courtesy of Dr. E. De Robertis, Instituto de Biologia Celular, Universidad de Buenos Aires.

of a series of disc-like structures. In the rods the discs develop in a similar manner, i.e. by the invagination of the plasma membrane, but the resultant sacs seem to pinch off producing stacks of discs completely separated from the bounding plasma membrane (see figure 3.11). It has been shown that the discs contain the visual pigment rhodopsin, made

Figure 3.12. Electron micrograph of freeze-fractured retinal disc membranes from the mouse. The stacked arrangement of the discs is clearly seen. The cytoplasmic leaflet of the disc membrane CL contains numerous particles which are thought to represent the sites of rhodopsin molecules. The intra-disc leaflet IL of the disc membrane shows no such particles, suggesting that rhodopsin is located in the outer or cytoplasmic half of the disc membrane bilayer. From L. Y. Jan and J.-P. Revel, *J. Cell Biol.* (1974), **62,** 257–273. Original micrograph by courtesy of Dr. Lily Yeh Jan, California Institute of Biology, Pasadena.

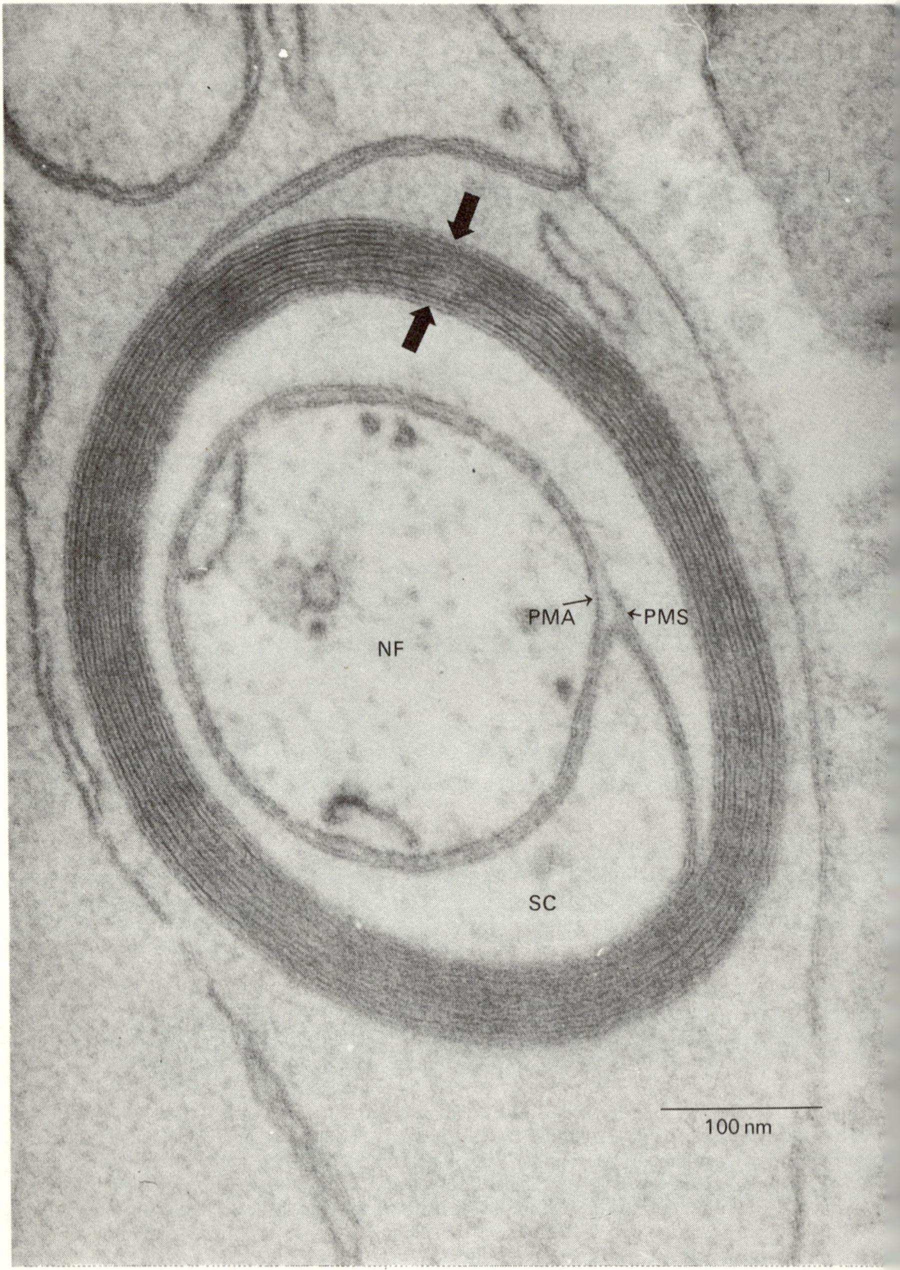
PMA
PMS
NF
SC
100 nm

up from a protein, opsin, and a chromophore, 11-*cis* retinal (chapter 8). It is suggested that the rhodopsin is synthesized in the inner portion of the cell and is then transported, via the connecting cilium, to the base of the outer segment, where it is incorporated into developing retinal discs. The protein is a major structural element of the disc membrane and may comprise 80% of the total membrane protein. There is good evidence that the light-induced isomerization of the chromophore, 11-*cis* retinal, induces a conformational change in the protein of the disc membrane, resulting in a permeability change, which triggers off the nervous impulse (see chapter 8).

The arrangment of flat sacs with light-trapping pigments incorporated into the membrane is reminiscent of the grana of chloroplasts, and freeze-etched preparations of both membranes show a similar granular appearance (see figure 3.12). Both the retina and the chloroplast are concerned with absorbing the maximum amount of light, and conversion of the light energy to some other form. It seems that the multilayered membranes provide a system which is able to do this most effectively.

Myelin

A considerable amount of our knowledge on membrane ultrastructure has been obtained from studies on myelin. In 1936 W. J. Schmidt produced models of the structure of myelin membranes based on studies with the polarization light microscope. The structure proposed by Schmidt was very similar to the contemporary model of Danielli and Davson for the plasma membrane. Later studies of myelin using X-ray diffraction confirmed the early prediction of Schmidt, and in 1954 Geren published electron micrographs of myelin which clearly showed the myelin membrane to be continuous with the plasma membrane of the Schwann cell. It is now well known that the myelin sheath which surrounds axons is produced by the Schwann cells, in the case of peripheral nerves, and by oligodendroglial cells in central nerves. The process involves a gradual spiralling of the myelin-producing cell around the axon, thereby producing the characteristic multilayered sheath shown in the electron micrograph of figure 3.13.

Figure 3.13. Electron micrograph of a young mouse sciatic fibre with a developing myelin sheath. The nerve fibre NF is enveloped in the multilaminar myelin sheath (heavy arrows). The separate plasma membranes of the axon PMA and of the Schwann cell (SC), PMS, can be clearly distinguished. From *Neurosciences Res. Prog. Bull.* (1971), **9**, p. 520, (ed. L. C. Mokrasch, R. S. Bear and F. O. Schmitt). Original micrograph by courtesy of Professor J. David Robertson, Department of Anatomy, Duke University Medical Centre.

Electron microscopy of myelin has revealed no characteristic ultrastructural features. It is, it seems, the nearest approach to a model 'unit membrane'; its main function is to act as an insulator for the axons, a purpose for which its multilayered lipid-protein structure of low dielectric constant makes it ideally suited.

SUMMARY

1. Early electron microscopy of membranes led to the formation of the *unit membrane* theory.
2. Unit membranes are characterized by their *tramline* appearance—two electron-dense bands bounding an electron-lucent zone.
3. As techniques improved, many examples of membranes having *unique ultrastructural features* were found. These are seen to be closely linked to the characteristic *function* of the membrane.

CHAPTER 4

ISOLATED MEMBRANE PREPARATIONS

THE ULTRASTRUCTURE OF CELL MEMBRANES CAN BE STUDIED WITHOUT separating them from other cell constituents. Similarly, their permeability properties and many transport phenomena can be investigated using intact cells or even whole tissue. However, before we can hope to understand the many functions of membranes in molecular terms, we need to know their precise chemical composition. In order that the chemical analyses are meaningful, it is essential that they are carried out on a pure membrane. This is where the problems begin. Firstly, procedures must be devised which allow the complete separation of a particular membrane system from a wide range of other cell constituents. Having achieved this, it is then necessary to show that the isolated membrane is not substantially different from the intact membrane *in situ*. What we hope to do is to use our knowledge of the isolated membrane *in vitro* to explain and understand its function and behaviour *in vivo*.

The first isolation of a subcellular organelle was achieved by Friedrich Miescher, who in 1871 isolated nuclei from broken cells by a centrifugation procedure. Later workers improved upon Miescher's methods, and in the late 1930s R. R. Bensley and his colleagues isolated mitochondria. It was Albert Claude, however, who, during the period 1937 to 1945, laid the foundations of present-day subcellular fractional schemes. The earlier workers had concentrated only on the isolation of a single subcellular organelle, and paid no regard to the many other cell constituents. Claude's approach was quite different in that he introduced the concept of a quantitative analysis of the cell contents. Thus analyses were carried out on all the cell fractions. A final balance sheet was drawn up, thereby allowing an assessment of the contribution made by each fraction to the intact tissue. Claude also introduced the idea of characterizing the fractions by measuring enzymic activities, and thus paved the way for the establishment of *marker enzymes* which are now widely used. Many workers now characterize a subcellular fraction solely on the basis of measurements of enzymic activities, without pausing to think that in the first instance a strict correlation between morphology and enzymic activity had to be established.

Even though it is now almost thirty years since Claude developed his tissue fractionation scheme, there are very few isolated membrane fractions which fulfil simple criteria of purity. Thus the membranes whose chemical compositions are well established are the mammalian erythrocyte membrane, myelin, liver plasma membrane, and to a lesser extent the plasma membranes of Hela cells and Ascites tumour cells. There are, of course, many cell organelles whose isolation has been achieved, and we can readily obtain pure preparations of mitochondria, chloroplasts, lysosomes or nuclei, but each one of these organelles may contain a very heterogeneous collection of membranes. For example, we saw in chapter 3 that the mitochondrion very clearly consists of two quite different membrane systems. It is possible to separate these two membranes, when they are found to have different biochemical properties and to contain different lipids and proteins (see chapters 5 and 8). Any data we collect on the chemical composition of whole mitochondria provide only mean values for two distinct membranes. Consequently they are of limited use in aiding our understanding of the interrelations of structure, chemical composition and function.

Let us now look at some of the procedures that have been used to isolate and characterize membrane systems.

Animal cell membranes

The erythrocyte membrane

The mammalian erythrocyte membrane has long been the favoured material for studies on membrane composition and on structure-function relationships. There are several reasons for this: it is much easier to prepare in a pure and relatively intact form than most other membranes and, equally important, it is available cheaply in large quantities. The mammalian erythrocyte is an anuclear cell containing no organelles, and is in effect a plasma membrane containing only cytoplasm. This atypical situation has led many people to criticize the extensive use of the erythrocyte membrane as a model for plasma membranes. However it should be borne in mind that this membrane carries out many of the functions of a normal plasma membrane. It contains a wide range of enzymes, shows specific vectorial transport properties, and contains a range of lipids and proteins not greatly different from those of other plasma membrane preparations.

The preparation of the membrane involves removal of the cytoplasm with its high concentration of haemoglobin without damaging the membrane too much. Many methods have been developed for doing this, each group of workers having their own particular ideas on the best

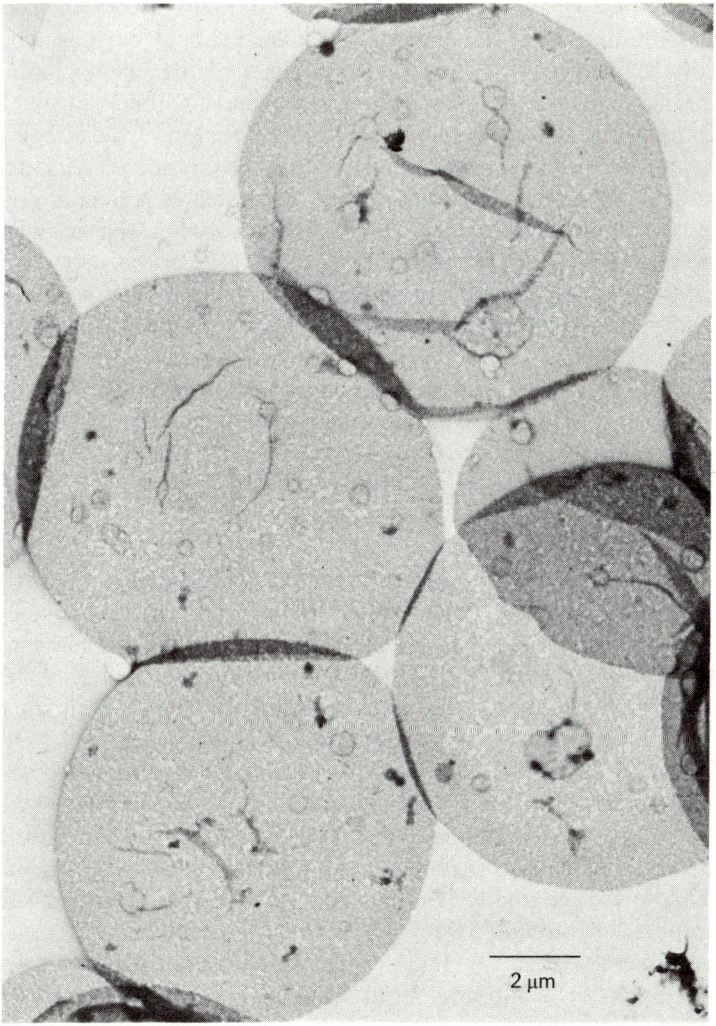

Figure 4.1. Electron micrograph of unstained human erythrocyte ghosts. The ghosts have the appearance of empty sacks with some slight 'crumpling' of the surface. From G. L. Nicolson, *J. Cell. Biol.* (1973), **57,** 373–387. Original micrograph by courtesy of Dr. J. R. Smith, Department of Cancer Biology, The Salk Institute for Biological Studies.

method, but basically all involve a controlled haemolysis of the cell. This is generally a hypotonic (20 mosM) lysis at a pH of about 7·6, the membranes being collected by sedimentation. This procedure may lead to a completely haemoglobin-free membrane which is the subject of considerable controversy. Many workers maintain that *in vivo* some haemoglobin is bound to the membrane, and indeed should be considered as part of the membrane structure. Proponents of the haemoglobin-free membrane preparations answer that some haemoglobin may well be associated with the membrane, but that it is only loosely adsorbed onto the membrane's inner surface, and should not be considered a membrane constituent. We have no way of knowing which view is correct at present, but it seems quite likely that no sharp division between what is and what is not a membrane constituent can be made. Certainly erythrocyte membrane preparations, with or without haemoglobin, show a wide range of enzyme activities. Morphologically they appear to be little changed and when resealed (see chapter 5) retain the osmotic characteristics of the intact erythrocyte. Thus the erythrocyte membrane or ghost as shown in figure 4.1 can be considered as a reasonable model for the natural membrane *in vivo*.

Other plasma membranes

The isolation of plasma membranes from cells other than the erythrocyte presents many problems, most of which have not yet been overcome. The cells of any organ are present as a solid structured mass which must be disrupted before the isolation of the membranes can begin. Organs invariably contain more than one type of cell, and in an ideal situation a cellular fractionation would precede any attempts at a subcellular fractionation. In practice this is hardly ever done, and the heterogeneity of cell types within the organ in question is usually conveniently forgotten. Further contamination of membrane fractions can arise from both the vascular and nervous systems associated with the organ, but again these are invariably ignored. Reported yields of purified plasma membranes are rarely above 10% of the theoretical figure. It must be realized, therefore, that in such a situation contamination of the final preparation with membranes from one or more of the several minor classes of cell in the starting organ is a very real possibility.

In spite of numerous pitfalls that lie in the path of the isolator of plasma membrane, many preparations have been made and characterized. The most popular starting material has been rat liver and, although the liver cell is frequently given as an example of a 'typical' animal cell, it should be borne in mind that liver is made up of roughly equal numbers of parenchymal and reticuloendothelial cells. With the notable exception of R. B. Howard and his colleagues, who prepared a cellular suspension of liver from which they isolated the parenchymal cells, most workers simply disrupt the whole liver tissue.

The disruption process can obviously greatly affect the nature of the ensuing subcellular fractions, and there are two aspects of the process which must be considered. These are the composition of the medium in which disruption occurs, and the physical nature of the process. By far the most common medium is a sucrose solution which is usually slightly hypotonic; 0·25 M sucrose is widely used in liver fractionations. The use of salt solutions, such as Krebs-Ringer bicarbonate and phosphate media, frequently causes the aggregation of subcellular particles, although

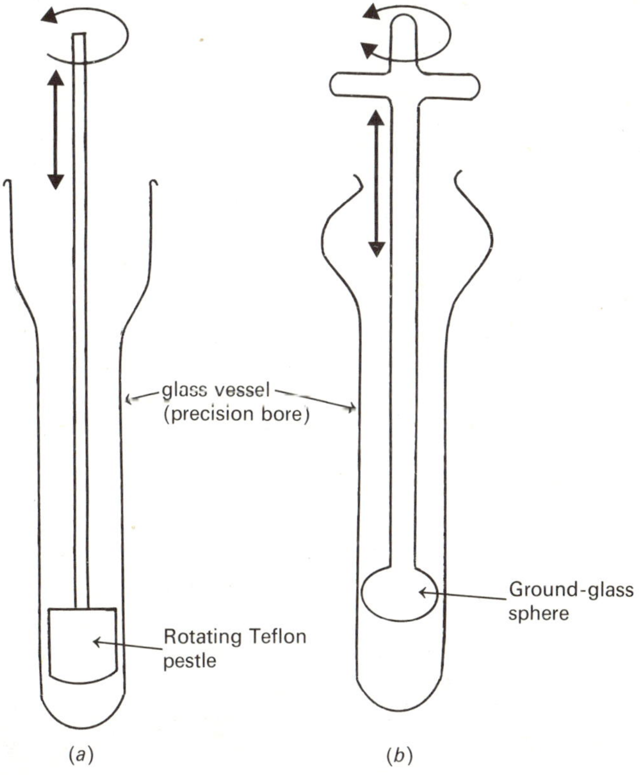

Figure 4.2. (*a*) The Potter-Elvejhem and (*b*) the Dounce tissue homogenizers.

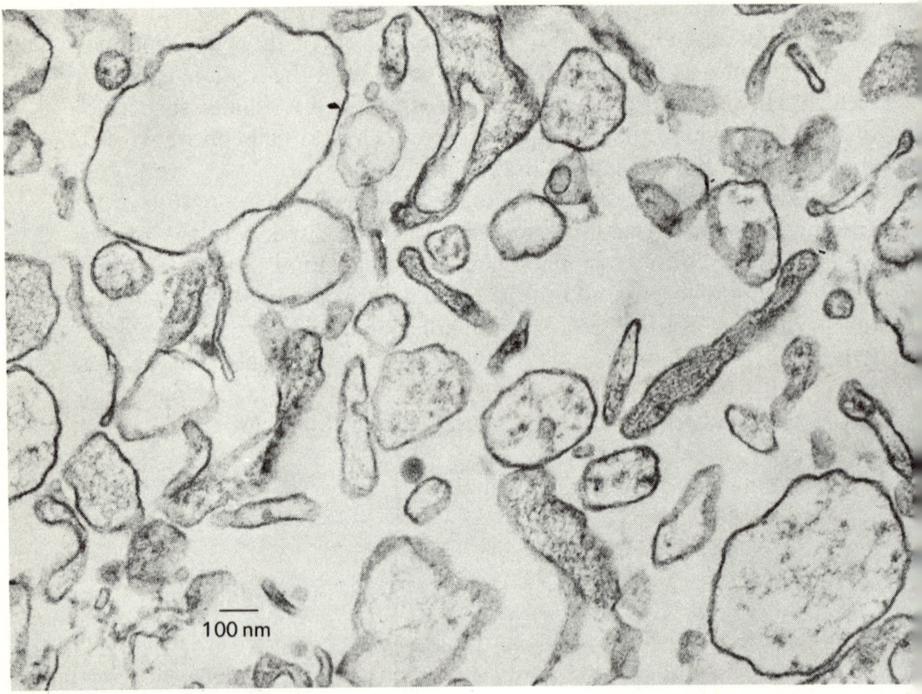

(*a*)

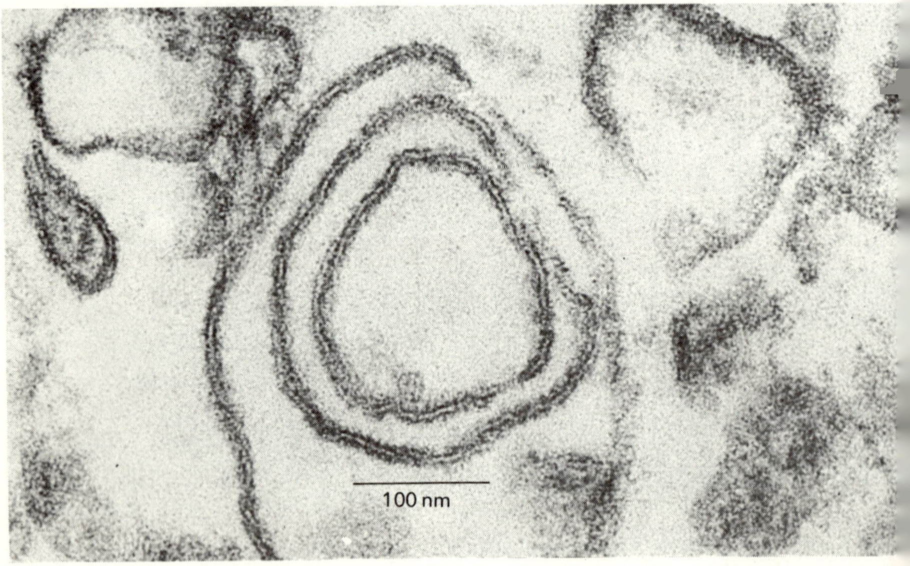

(*b*)

reports have been made that in certain tissues, such as spleen, sucrose promotes aggregation. In such cases salt solutions are the preferred media. The disruption or homogenization medium is usually buffered at pH 7·4, and there are many reports that at lower pH-values tissues become more difficult to homogenize.

The homogenization is usually done with a Potter-Elvejhem homogenizer. As shown in figure 4.2*a* this consists of a precision-bore glass tube with a close-fitting motor-driven pestle, originally of Perspex but now usually of Teflon. The tissue is cut into small pieces in the buffer, and is then forced between the rotating pestle and the wall of the tube by raising and lowering the glass tube. Thus the cells are subjected to a shear force and are torn open, releasing the subcellular organelles. The radial clearance between the pestle and the tube wall can vary between 0·05 and 0·5 mm, a value being chosen so that minimal damage occurs to nuclei, mitochondria and other organelles. Even with the widest clearances, about 10% of the mitochondria suffer damage to their outer membranes, and there is evidence that at least 15% of the lysosomes and peroxisomes may be broken. A similar disruption of cells can be achieved by using a Dounce homogenizer (figure 4.2*b*) which has a ground-glass tube with a close-fitting ground-glass plunger; this is operated by hand and is considered to be more gentle than the Potter-Elvejhem method. Homogenizers of the Waring-Blendor type, in which the tissue is chopped by rotating knives, are rarely used, as considerable damage usually occurs, particularly to the nuclei.

The mild-shear homogenization procedures produce a rather heterogeneous collection of plasma membrane fragments, ranging from large extended sheets to small pinched-off closed vesicles which can be separated from the other cell organelles using the standard procedures of combined differential and density-gradient centrifugation (see figure 4.3).

It is still difficult to characterize absolutely a plasma membrane fraction. The membrane vesiculates during the homogenization and appears similar to other intracellular membranes, though usually the

---

Figure 4.3. *a* and *b*. Electron micrographs of a washed preparation of plasma membranes from BRl 8 lymphoblastoid cells. In figure *a* the preparation is seen to be free from subcellular organelles such as lysosomes, mitochondria and nuclei, neither is there any contamination with ribosomes. It can be seen that the plasma membrane vesicles vary considerably in size. At higher magnification (figure *b*) the trilamellar appearance of the membrane is particularly distinct. From M. J. Crumpton and D. Snary (1974). Preparation and properties of lymphocyte plasma membrane, in *Contempory Topics in Molecular Immunology* (ed. G. L. Ada) **3,** Plenum, New York, pp. 27–56. Original micrographs by courtesy of Dr. M. J. Crumpton, National Institute for Medical Research, Mill Hill.

fragments are rather bigger. In the particular case of liver cells there are morphological features which assist in the identification of the isolated membrane. Thus there are characteristic membrane specializations—*junctional complexes*—which occur at the points where neighbouring cells make contact. These connections survive the homogenization procedure, and pieces of plasma membrane attached to the junctional complex can be recognized in the electron microscope (see figure 4.4). There are also reports that after negative staining, hexagonal arrays are visible on the plasma membrane, no such feature being visible on any of the intracellular membranes.

Once a membrane fraction has been identified morphologically, other factors may be sought which aid in its characterization. If an enzyme can be shown histochemically to be exclusively associated with a certain membrane fraction, it can be used as a *primary* marker. Although histochemistry has enabled the subcellular localization of a number of enzymes, there are relatively few which lend themselves to exploitation at the level of the electron microscope. However, the rat liver plasma membrane may be identified by the presence of the primary enzyme markers, 5′ nucleotidase, Na^+,K^+-ATPase and alkaline phosphatase. When the plasma membrane has been characterized in this way, other enzyme activities in the fraction may be used as *secondary* markers to identify the fraction in subsequent preparations. In rat liver plasma membranes, such secondary markers would be leucine aminopeptidase and adenylate cyclase.

Other methods of characterizing the plasma membrane which are not dependent on the presence of a particular enzyme have also been sought. One such approach has been to label the membranes, prior to cell disruption, with a fluorescent or radioactive molecule which is known to interact with membrane constituents, but which will not enter the cell. By following the distribution of the label throughout the fractionation procedure, we will hopefully also be following the plasma membrane. The criticism of this method is that once the membrane is labelled in this way it ceases to be the same structure as it was *in vivo*.

Other characteristics of plasma membranes that have been exploited in an attempt to characterize the isolated fractions are their surface

---

Figure 4.4. Electron micrograph of isolated plasma membranes of rat liver cells. The large sheets of plasma membranes from several cells are still attached to each other by way of the junctional complexes (arrowed). From P. Emmelot *et al.*, *Biochim. Biophys. Acta* (1964), **90,** 126–145. Original micrograph by courtesy of Professor P. Emmelot, Antoni Van Leeuwenhoekhuis Het Nederlands Kankerinstitut, Amsterdam.

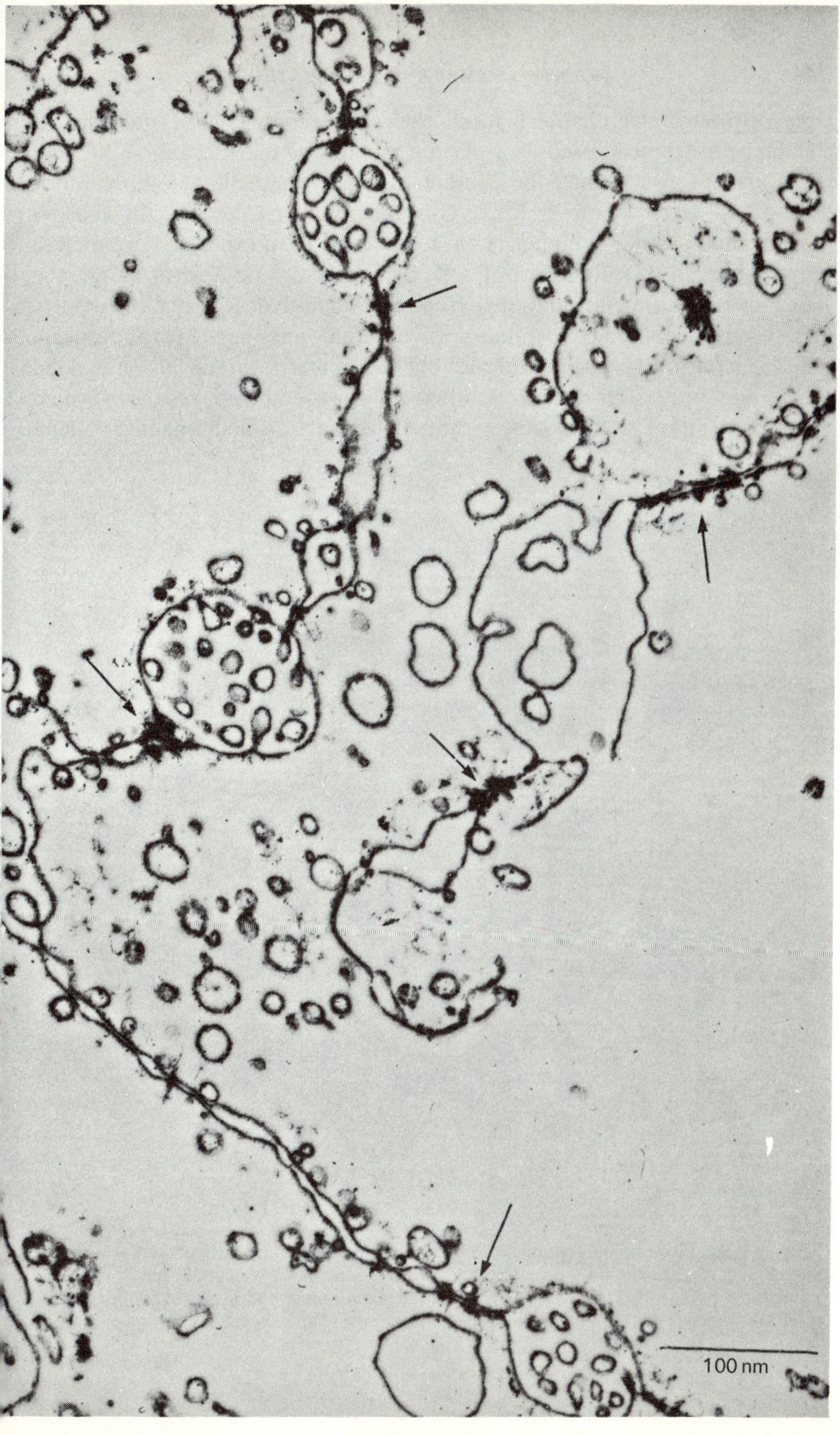
100 nm

glycoproteins (see chapter 7) and their lipid content. The presence of sialic acid has been used as a plasma membrane marker, but sialic acid has also been shown to be present in other organelles, notably mitochondria, albeit at rather lower concentrations. In general, the plasma membrane has much higher cholesterol levels than other cell organelles, though again this alone is not sufficient for us to be able to assign the title of plasma membrane to a fraction. Unequivocal proof of identity can come only from a number of different analyses. Morphological, histochemical, enzymological and chemical assays should all be carried out, and only after a consideration of the combined results of such complementary analyses should the isolated fraction be designated plasma membrane.

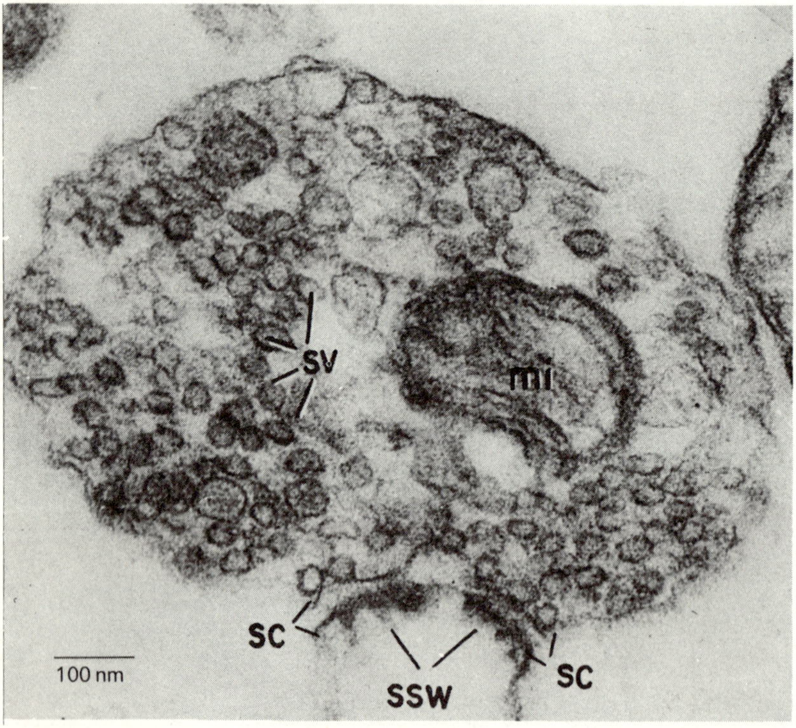

Figure 4.5*a*. Electron micrograph of an isolated nerve terminal (synaptosome) from rat cerebral cortex. The main morphological features of the intact terminals seen in figure 3.7 are still apparent: Synaptic vesicles SV; intraterminal mitochondria mi; synaptic cleft SC and the attached postsynaptic membrane with the subsynaptic web SSW.

Intracellular membranes

The membranes of the cell organelles are not as well characterized as the plasma membrane. In general, what we obtain is an organelle preparation which has been characterized morphologically and by the use of enzyme markers. In an exactly analogous manner to the development of markers for the plasma membrane, groups of characteristic enzymes have been established for the cell organelles. The most common marker enzymes are shown in Table 4.1.

In practice few of the enzymes in Table 4.1 have an absolutely clear-cut distribution. The identity of the membraneous fractions derived from

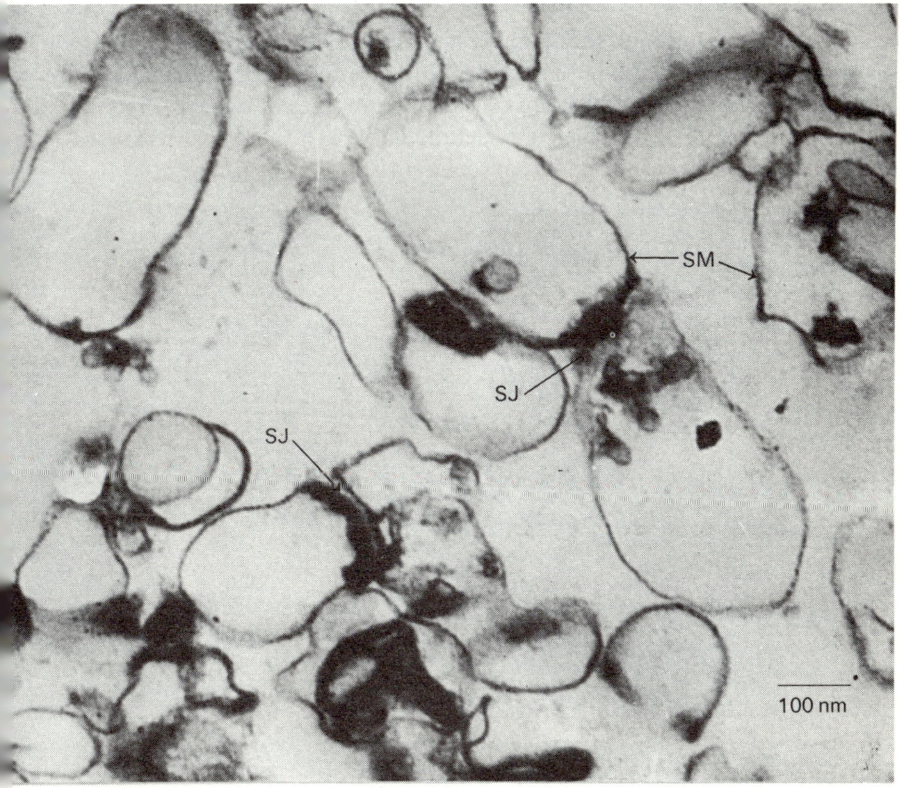

Figure 4.5*b*. Electron micrograph of isolated nerve terminals after hypo-osmotic shock. The empty synaptic membrane profiles SM still retain the intact synaptic junctions SJ. Original micrographs kindly supplied by Dr. E. De Robertis, Instituto de Biologia Celular, Universidad de Buenos Aires.

Table 4.1 Marker enzymes for subcellular organelles

Organelle	*Marker Enzyme*
Nuclei	NAD pyrophosphorylase (DNA for whole nuclei).
Mitochondria	Succinate dehydrogenase; cytochrome oxidase; monoamine oxidase; glutamate dehydrogenase.
Lysosomes	Arylsulphatase; β glucuronidase; acid phosphatase.
Golgi body membranes	UDP galactose; *N*-acetylglucosamine-galactosyl transferase; ADPase; thiamine pyrophosphatase.
Endoplasmic reticulum (microsomes)	glucose 6-phosphatase; arylesterase, NADH-cytochrome c reductase (rotenone insensitive). RNA (rough endoplasmic reticulum).
Peroxisomes	Catalase; urate oxidase.

a tissue homogenate should be established by assaying a number of markers and correlating their distribution pattern with the morphology of the fractions. In mammalian cells the membranes of two cell organelles have been studied in particular detail. These are the nerve terminal of central nervous tissue and the mitochondrion.

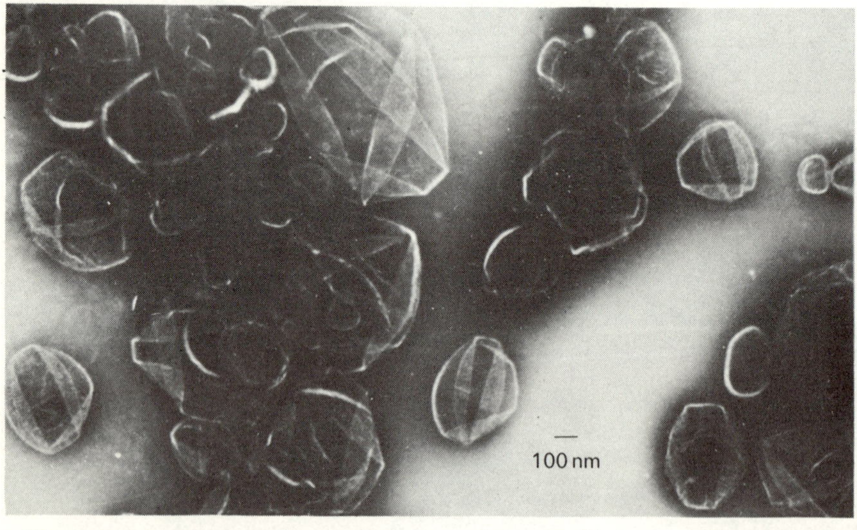

Figure 4.6a. An electron micrograph of an osmium tetroxide-fixed negatively-stained preparation of purified mitochondrial outer membranes from rat liver. The preparation consists almost entirely of folded collapsed bags, composed of a single membrane layer. There are no sub-units or particulate material associated with the membrane. From D. F. Parsons, G. R. Williams and B. Chance, *Ann. N.Y. Acad. Sci.* (1966), **137,** 643–666. Original micrograph by courtesy of Professor Donald F. Parsons, Roswell Park Memorial Institute, Buffalo.

In chapter 3 the specialized structure of the nerve terminal was described. During the low-shear conditions obtained in a Potter-Elvejhem homogenizer, the nerve terminal breaks off and forms a small sealed body containing synaptic vesicles and mitochondria. These broken-off nerve endings or *synaptosomes* may be isolated by differential and density-gradient centrifugation yielding a pure fraction. If the nerve ending fraction is then subjected to a hypo-osmotic shock, the contents are lost and the empty membrane sacs may be purified further on a density gradient. The appearance of the intact nerve terminal and of the empty membrane sacs may be compared in figure 4.5.

The empty membrane sacs still retain intact the structural elements of the synaptic junction which serves to identify them morphologically. A number of enzymes have been found to be associated with the membrane, and therefore provide a range of markers, the most widely used being acetylcholinesterase; Na^+,K^+-stimulated ATPase; glutamine synthetase; adenylate cyclase and phosphodiesterase.

Reference was made in chapter 3 to the two mitochondrial membrane systems. Intact mitochondria may be isolated from tissue homogenates by differential centrifugation. The subsequent separation of the two mitochondrial membranes has been achieved, and their biochemical properties found to be quite different. Several methods have been developed for separating the membranes, most of which are based on a treatment of the intact mitochondria with the glycoside *digitonin.* This compound interacts with the outer membrane, which may be then separated from the intact inner membrane and matrix or *mitoblast* by differential and/or density-gradient centrifugation (see figure 4.6).

Treatment of the mitoblast with a detergent allows the separation of the membrane from the soluble matrix. The outer membranes appear quite smooth, though some of the fine surface structure referred to in

Table 4.2. Enzymes of the inner and outer mitochondrial membranes

Outer membrane	*Inner membrane*
Monoamine oxidase	ATPase
NADH-cytochrome b_5 reductase	Carnitine acetyltransferase
Glycerophosphate acyltransferase	Steroid 11-β-hydroxylase
Hexokinase 2	Succinate dehydrogenase
Cholinephosphotransferase	Choline dehydrogenase
Acyl-Co synthetase	Cytochrome oxidase
	3-hydroxybutyrate dehydrogenase

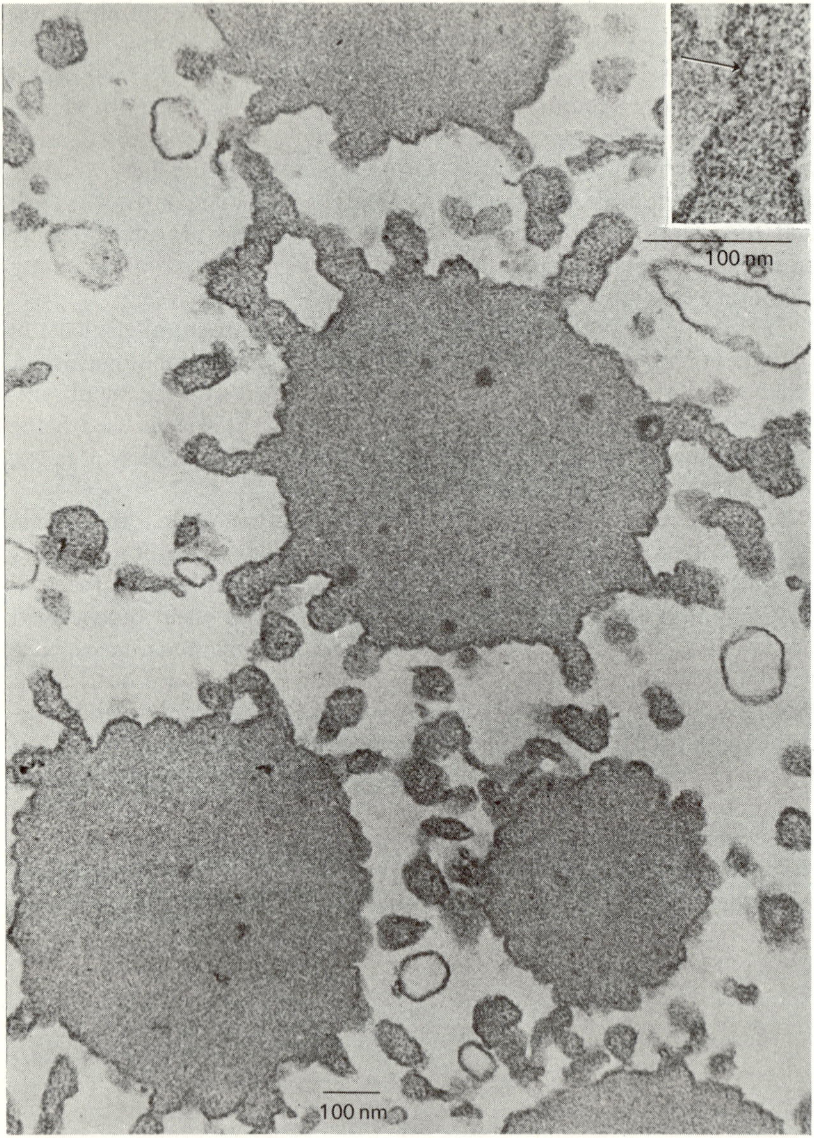

Figure 4.6b. An electron micrograph of a rat liver mitochondrial inner membrane-matrix preparation. The inner membrane appears intact, and in the inset the trilamellar nature of the membrane is seen (arrow). From C. Schnaitman and J. W. Greenawalt, *J. Cell. Biol.* (1968), **38,** 158–183. Original micrograph by courtesy of Professor John W. Greenawalt, Department of Physiological Chemistry, The Johns Hopkins School of Medicine.

chapter 3 may be seen, and the inner membrane shows the characteristic knobs and stalks that are seen in intact mitochondria. Analysis of the two membranes reveals major differences in enzyme activities as shown in Table 4.2.

The inner membrane is also found to contain most of the cardiolipin (see chapter 5), the phospholipid that is frequently said to be characteristic of mitochondria. Some workers have reported that the outer membrane is greatly enriched in phosphatidylinositol compared with the inner membrane, but others claim that this is not so. Indeed there is still considerable disagreement over the enzyme activities and composition of the two membranes, although their structural characteristics are well established.

Alternative preparative procedures

The low-shear homogenization procedures described above are, with minor modifications, applicable to a very wide range of animal tissues. Many other methods of cell disruption have been tried but have not been widely adopted. *Ultrasonication* of cell suspensions has been investigated, but this procedure invariably damages the plasma membrane and the cell organelles. *Gas-bubble nucleation*, in which cells are equilibrated with inert gas at very high pressures and then suddenly returned to atmospheric pressure, has been used quite successfully in the preparation of plasma membranes from tumour cells, but has not been widely used for other tissues. A major disadvantage of the technique is that the plasma membrane is fragmented into very small pieces which are difficult to separate from microsomes. *High-shear methods*, which usually involve forcing tissue suspensions (often frozen) through extremely small apertures under very high pressure, have been used for the preparation of organelles and membrane fragments from micro-organisms.

The milk-fat-globule membrane

The membrane surrounding fat droplets in fresh milk is derived from the mammary-cell plasma membrane during secretion. Fat globules are formed in the basal region of the mammary cell and migrate to the apical cell surface, through which they bulge, becoming progressively enveloped in the plasma membrane. Finally the protruberance is pinched off, resealing the cell, and leaving an intact membrane around the departing fat globule (see figure 4.7). In some 1–5% of the globules, small crescents of cytoplasm can be detected trapped between the fat droplet and the surrounding membrane, but very little cytoplasmic material is carried away by the fat globule in this way.

There is evidence that Golgi vesicle membrane is also directly incorporated into milk-fat-globule membrane during the secretion process. This does not necessarily imply that milk-fat-globule membrane differs

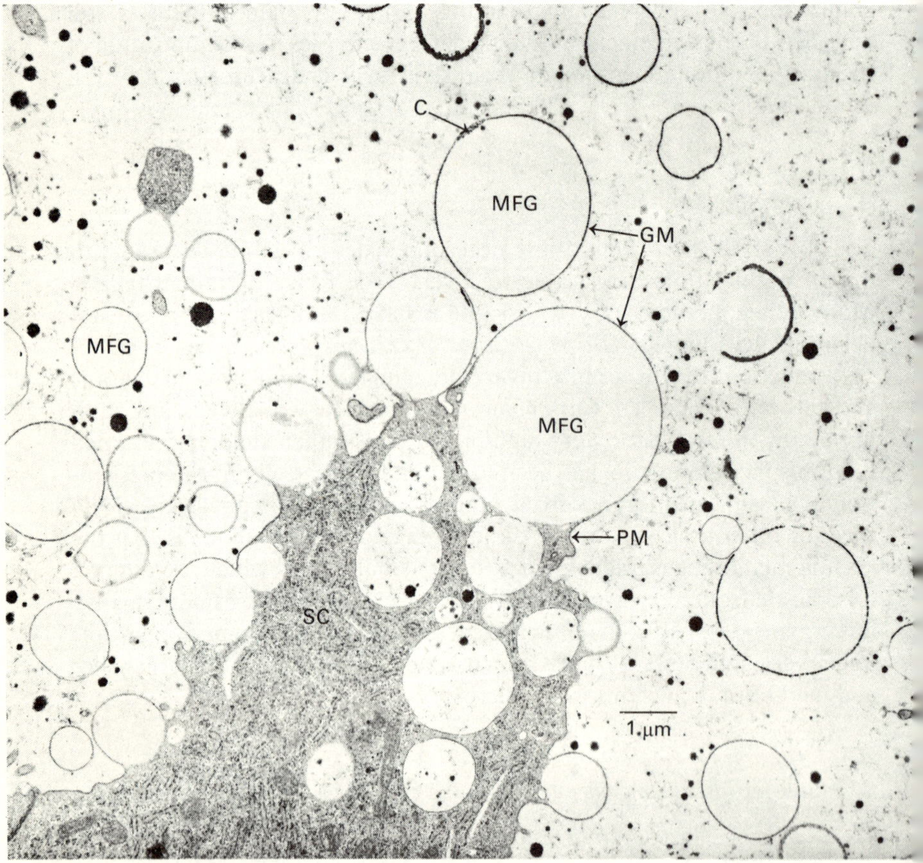

Figure 4.7a. An electron micrograph of a section of goat mammary tissue showing milk fat globules MFG, in the process of secretion. The globules approach the plasma membrane PM of the secretory cell SC, and bulge through it. The globule forms a protuberance, which pinches off, forming a free milk-fat globule with a boundary membrane GM. Small crescents of cytoplasm C are sometimes trapped in the globules.

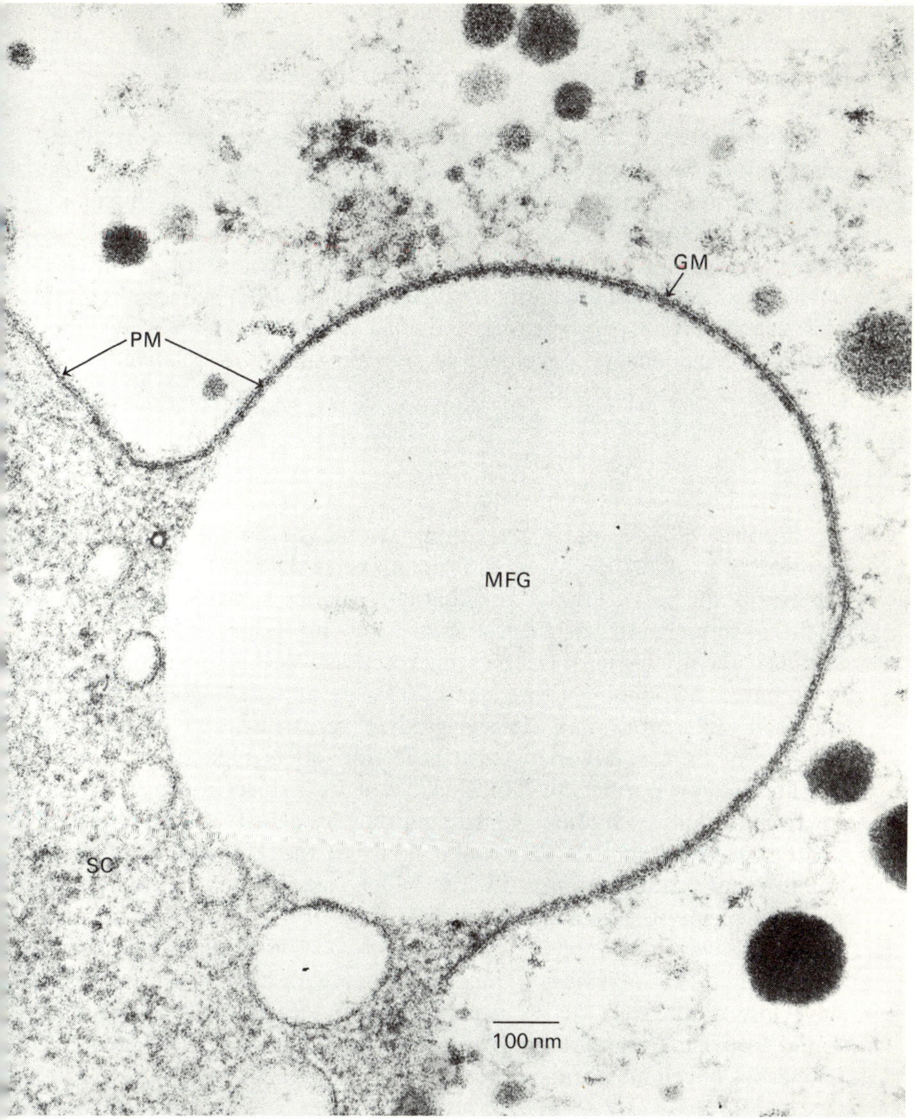

Figure 4.7b. At higher magnification it can be clearly seen that the trilamellar plasma membrane PM of the secretory cell SC is continuous with the globule membrane GM. Both original micrographs kindly supplied by Dr. F. B. P. Wooding, Agricultural Research Council, Institute of Animal Physiology, Babraham.

from the apical plasma membrane of the mammary cell, since this plasma membrane is also continually being replenished by Golgi vesicle membranes as the vesicles discharge their contents into the alveolar lumen.

The laboratory preparation of milk-fat-globule membranes from expressed milk is simple. Separated cream is well washed to remove soluble skim-milk components and shaken (the equivalent of churning); the fat-globule membranes rupture, allowing the fat to coagulate as butter, and leaving a suspension of membranes in the buttermilk. In view of the practical difficulties involved in obtaining clean mammalian-cell plasma-membrane preparations, the milk-fat-globule membrane constitutes a particularly convenient large-scale supply of relatively pure plasma-membrane material.

Myelin

No account of membrane preparation would be complete without a mention of myelin. Yet myelin is in many ways the most atypical of all the membrane preparations. The characteristic multilayered appearance of the myelin sheath has been known for many years and has always attracted the attention of electron microscopists (see chapter 3). Myelin is prepared by homogenizing nervous tissue and then going through standard differential and density-gradient centrifugation procedures. Because of its very low density, a reflection of its high lipid content, myelin is often purified by flotation, i.e. if we subject a crude myelin fraction to density-gradient centrifugation, the density of the gradient can be arranged so that the myelin floats to the top, well away from any other membraneous constituents. Much valuable information on the physical properties of membranes has come from studies on purified myelin. However, myelin tells us little of membrane function. It has few characteristic enzyme activities associated with it, and appears not to have any of the very active transporting and carrier systems usually found in plasma membranes. Thus, if we wish to look at the dynamic properties of cell membranes, the study of myelin will tell us little.

Plant cell membranes

In the case of plant cell membranes, the only system that has been looked at in any detail is the chloroplast, and to a lesser extent mitochondria. These are prepared in much the same way as animal cell organelles; i.e. the tissue is disrupted, and the resultant homogenate subjected to differential and density-gradient centrifugation. Preparation of plasma membranes from plant cells is greatly complicated by the presence of the thick polysaccharide cell wall, and so far no methods for the routine preparation of pure plant plasma membranes have emerged.

The cell membranes of micro-organisms

Micro-organisms can be produced in large quantities relatively easily and cheaply compared with animal cells. Furthermore, a homogeneous population of cell types is available, thereby circumventing many of the problems outlined above. Many micro-organisms have an extraneous coat or cell wall and, before isolation of the plasma membrane can be attempted, these outer barriers must be removed. The cells are usually very resistant to the sort of low-shear procedures used for disrupting animal cells, and attempts to separate the membrane from the wall by purely physical methods have met with little success. However, considerable progress has been made using enzyme preparations which digest away the outer wall leaving an intact protoplast bounded by the plasma membrane. The protoplast can be shown to be osmotically sensitive and, indeed, with careful removal of the wall retains the permeability characteristics of the original cell. Pure preparations of plasma membranes can be made from protoplasts in an analogous manner to the preparation of erythrocyte ghosts. The protoplasts are put into a hypotonic medium, and the empty plasma membrane sacs collected by sedimentation. Figure 4.8 shows plasma membrane fractions prepared from bakers' yeast (*Saccharomyces cerevisiae*) by treatment with an enzyme preparation from snail gut.

Once the problem of the cell wall has been overcome, the plasma membranes of certain micro-organisms have many attractions. The eukaryotic micro-organisms have cell membranes which show many similarities to those of plant and animal cells. One of the most convenient eukaryotic micro-organisms with which to work is yeast. Mutant strains of *Saccharomyces cerevisiae* (brewers' yeast) have been isolated which have a requirement for an unsaturated fatty acid, which, when supplied in the growth medium predominates in the membrane lipids. The dependence of molecular order on fatty acid composition has been studied using spin labels (chapter 11) in the membranes of such mutants. The possibility of varying the lipid composition of a natural membrane is clearly most attractive, and considerable effort is now being directed towards this end. Strains of *Saccharomyces cerevisiae* are found which, when grown under strictly anaerobic conditions, show a growth requirement not only for an unsaturated fatty acid but also for a sterol. Protoplasts with plasma membranes enriched in oleic, linoleic and linolenic acids have been obtained, and have been found to become increasingly susceptible to osmotic lysis as the degree of unsaturation

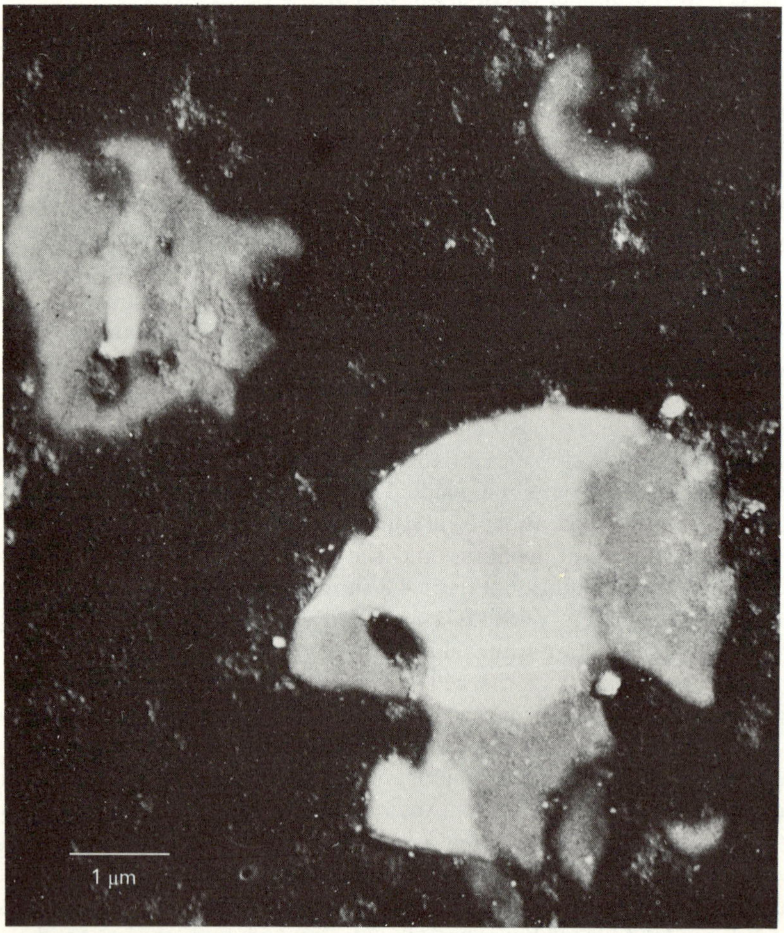

Figure 4.8a. Electron micrograph of a whole plasma membrane preparation from yeast obtained by enzymatic digestion of the cell wall. The preparation has been shadowed with platinum-palladium.

of the acyl chains, and therefore the fluidity of the membrane (see chapter 6) increases. Similarly membrane stability has been correlated with sterol composition, and the further possibility exists of simultaneously varying both sterol and fatty acid. This system presents the

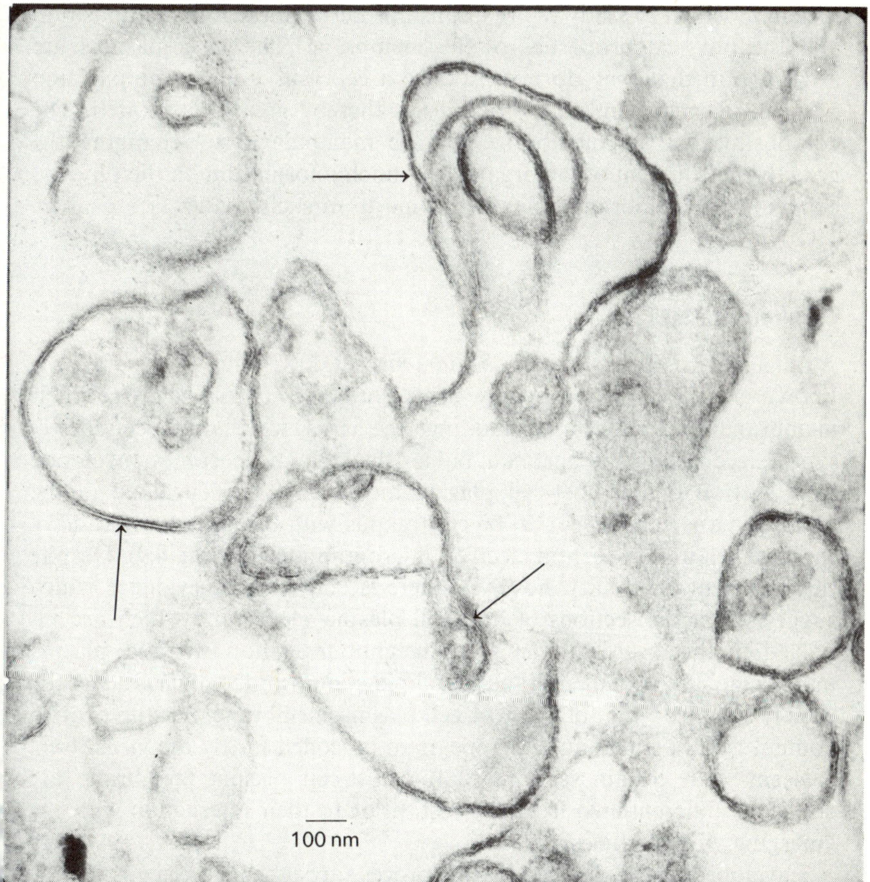

Figure 4.8b. Electron micrograph of a preparation of yeast plasma membranes purified by zonal centrifugation. The trilamellar structure of the membrane is clearly seen (arrows). Both micrographs from H. Suomalainen and T. Nurminen. 'Structure and Function of the Yeast Cell Envelope' in *Yeast, Mould and Plant Protoplasts. Proceedings of the Third International Symposium on Yeast Protoplasts, Salamanca, 1972,* (ed. J. R. Villanueva, I. Garcia-Acha, S. Gascon and F. Uruburu), Academic Press, London, pp. 167–185. Original micrographs by courtesy of Dr. Heikki Suomalainen, The Finnish State Alcohol Monopoly, Helsinki.

membrane researcher with opportunities that are not feasible with animal or higher-plant membrane preparations.

The prokaryotic micro-organisms have plasma membranes which differ widely in function and composition from those of eukaryotic cells (see chapters 1 and 5). The *mycoplasmas* have become a popular model system in which to study the relationships between the lipid composition and the physical properties of the membrane. The mycoplasmas are attractive in that they do not produce a cell wall, and the preparation of clean plasma membrane fractions is thereby greatly facilitated. The composition of the membrane may be manipulated by changing the growth environment of the organisms; much information on the physical behaviour of membrane lipids has come from such studies (see chapter 11).

Viral membranes

A range of viruses, particularly animal viruses, have a limiting membrane known as the *envelope*. Many such *enveloped viruses* acquire their membrane by a process of budding; the virus, which has been newly synthesized within the host cell, bulges through and becomes enveloped by a section of the host-cell plasma membrane. The envelope of the budding virus can be seen to be continuous with the unit membrane of the host cell in thin-section electron micrographs (see figure 4.9). Despite this apparent continuity, however, there is considerable evidence which suggests that the sections of host-cell plasma membrane which are involved in this process differ from neighbouring non-involved plasma membrane. The viral membrane has a lipid composition which is generally closely similar to that of the host-cell plasma membrane, but the protein content is quite different, and appears to be coded for by the virus itself. It seems that certain sections of the host-cell plasma membrane are somehow differentiated from the rest, prior to their interaction with the emerging virus particles.

Enveloped viruses formed by this process are excellent systems for the study of membrane structure and biosynthesis. Differential centrifugation in density gradients allows the preparation of pure virus particles which are free from cells and contain only protein and nucleic acid in addition to the limiting membrane. Moreover, the membrane composition can to some extent be manipulated. For instance, viral membranes with the same protein but different lipids can be obtained by growing a given virus in different types of host cell, while membranes with similar lipids

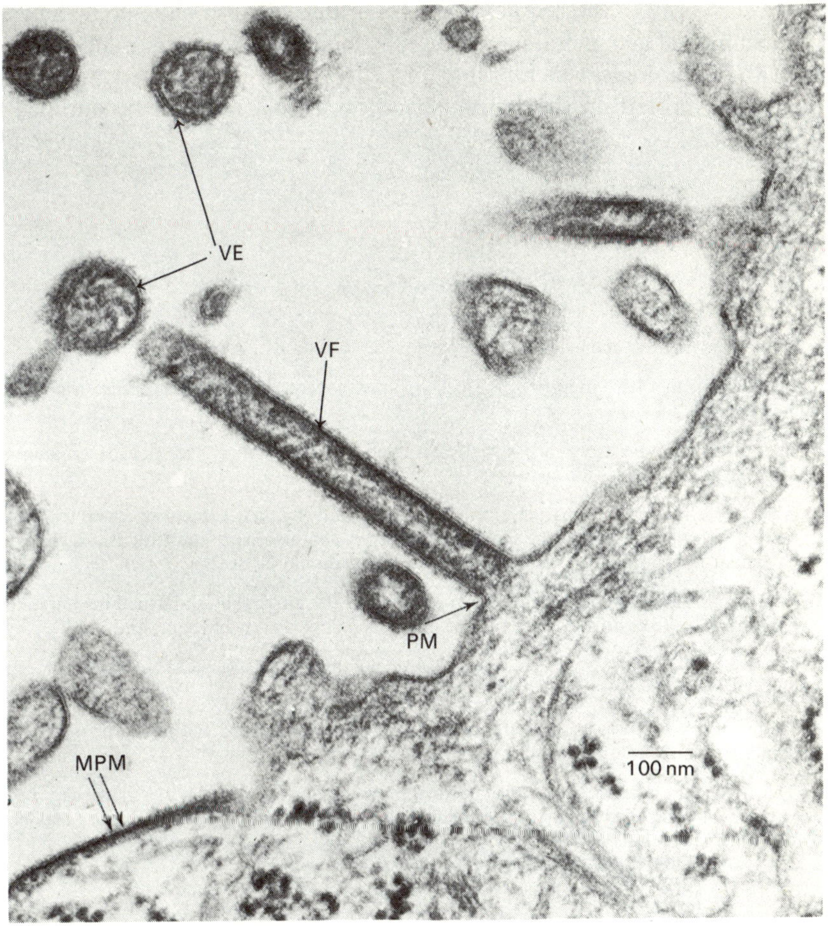

Figure 4.9. Electron micrograph of a portion of the cell surface with viral SV5 filaments, VF, in the process of budding. The circular profiles are released viral particles with a clearly defined viral membrane or envelope VE. It can be seen that the host-cell plasma membrane PM is continuous with the membrane of the viral filament. A portion of modified plasma membrane MPM is seen with surface projections and underlying nucleocapsid. From R. W. Compans and P. W. Choppin (1973). Ortho myxoviruses and Para myxoviruses in *Ultrastructure of Animal Viruses and Bacteriophages: An Atlas* (eds. A. J. Dlaton and F. Haguenau), Academic Press, New York, pp. 213–237. Original micrograph by courtesy of Dr. Richard W. Compans, The Rockefeller University, New York.

and different proteins arise from different virus types grown in the same host cell. Many of the physical techniques described in chapter 11 have been employed using viral membranes as model systems to gain information about biological membranes in general. The role played by viral membrane protein in the initial attack on a host cell will be outlined in chapter 7.

SUMMARY

1. Before carrying out chemical analyses pure membranes must be obtained.
2. Preparation involves rupturing the cell in such a way that the membranes are not damaged.
3. The membrane fractions are usually isolated by differential and density-gradient centrifugation.
4. Isolated membranes are characterized morphologically, by their content of characteristic marker enzymes, and by the presence of other characteristic constituents, such as particular lipids. Ideally a combination of analyses should be used.
5. Few membranes have been isolated in a pure form. The most well-established membrane preparations are erythrocyte membrane, the liver cell plasma membrane, and myelin.
6. The milk-fat-globule membrane constitutes a convenient large-scale preparation of plasma membranes.
7. The enveloped viruses present the opportunity of varying both the lipid and protein composition of a plasma membrane-derived fraction.
8. The lipid composition of the plasma membranes of certain micro-organisms may be varied in a controlled manner. The relative ease of isolation of such membranes makes them attractive model systems.

CHAPTER 5

MEMBRANE COMPONENTS

WHILE THE COMPOSITION OF MEMBRANES VARIES WITH THEIR SOURCE, THEY generally contain approximately 40% of their dry weight as *lipid* and 60% as *protein*, held together in a complex by non-bonded interactions. Usually carbohydrate is present to the extent of 1–10% of the total dry weight. This is covalently bonded either to lipid or to protein, and the carbohydrate-containing molecules will be considered as lipids or proteins as appropriate. In addition to the above components, membranes contain some 20% of their total weight as water, which is tightly bound and essential to the maintenance of their structure.

Lipids

Lipids are water-insoluble organic substances, extractable by non-polar solvents such as chloroform, ether and benzene. It is only relatively recently that the development of thin-layer chromatography, particularly using silicic acid, has allowed routine separation and analysis of individual lipids from their complex mixtures in biological systems.

Membrane lipids are polar lipids, containing both a hydrophobic tail and a hydrophilic head group within the molecule. Most of the polar lipids of cells are, in fact, localized in the membranes. The hydrophobic and hydrophilic regions can be bridged by a *glycerol* moiety, by a *sphinganine derivative* or homologue or, finally, within a *sterol* molecule.

In the glycerol derivatives, the hydrophobic tail commonly consists of two long-chain fatty acids esterified to two hydroxy-groups of glycerol, while the third, primary, hydroxy-group carries a hydrophilic grouping. Such a diacylglycerol derivative (or glyceride) is shown in figure 5.1. The hydrophobic tail can also contain long-chain fatty aldehyde and alcohol molecules, attached to the glycerol hydroxy-groups by other linkages, as shown in the legend to figure 5.1.

Sphinganine derivatives and homologues also contain a terminal

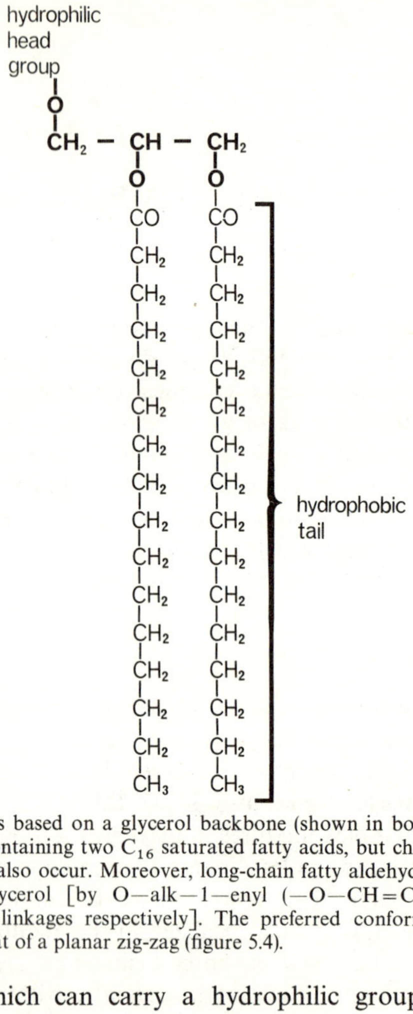

Figure 5.1. Polar lipids based on a glycerol backbone (shown in bold type). The hydrophobic tail is shown containing two C_{16} saturated fatty acids, but chain lengths may vary and unsaturated acids also occur. Moreover, long-chain fatty aldehydes and alcohols may also be linked to glycerol [by O—alk—1—enyl (—O—CH=CH—) and O—alkyl (—O—CH_2—CH_2—) linkages respectively]. The preferred conformation of the polymethylene chains is that of a planar zig-zag (figure 5.4).

hydroxy-group which can carry a hydrophilic grouping. They have additionally an amino group and a long aliphatic chain built into the basic structure, which together with a long-chain fatty acid (attached to the amino group via an amide linkage) constitute the hydrophobic tail of the molecule. Generalized structures of polar lipids based on sphinganine (dihydrosphingosine), 4-sphingenine (sphingosine) and 4-D-hydroxysphinganine (phytosphingosine), the three major sphinganine derivatives, are shown in figure 5.2. Such polar lipids are generally classed as *sphingolipids*.

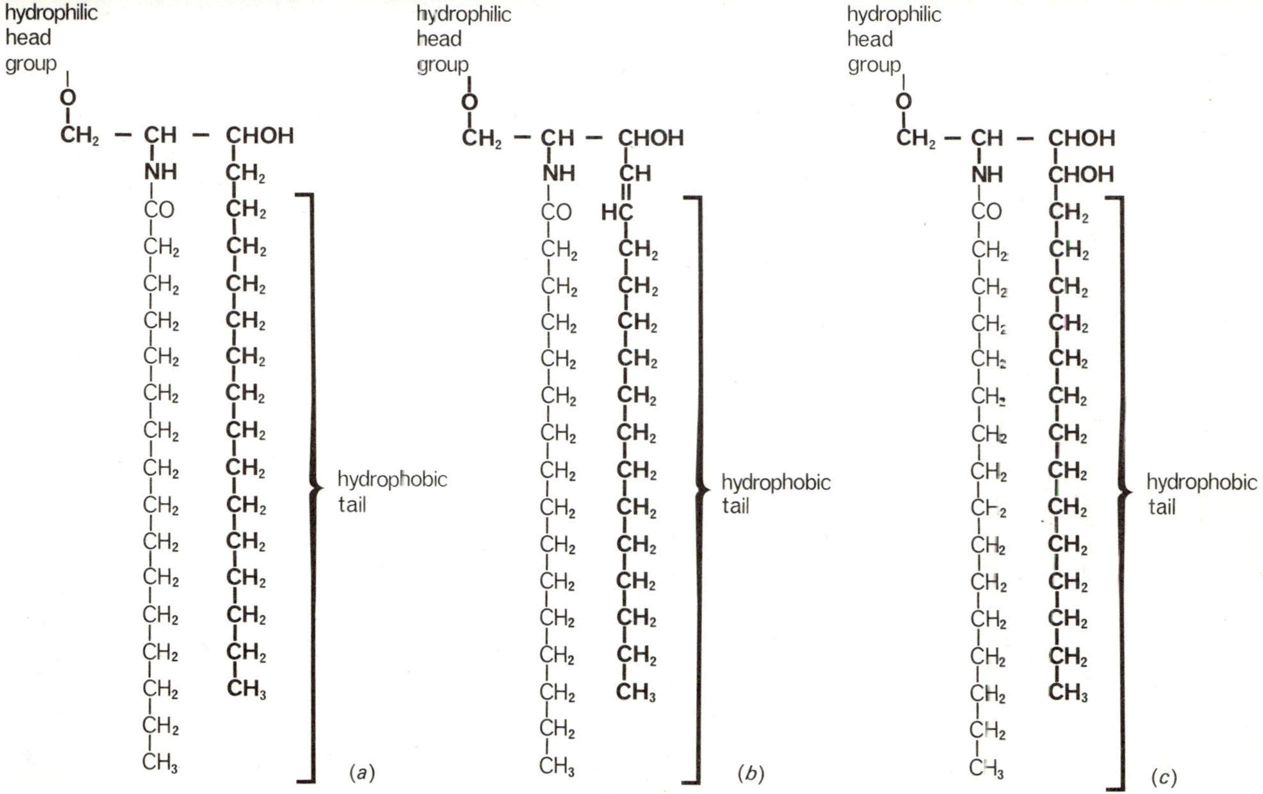

Figure 5.2. Polar lipids based on sphinganine derivatives (shown in bold type).
(*a*) sphinganine (dihydrosphingosine);
(*b*) 4-sphingenine;
(*c*) 4-D-hydroxysphinganine (phytosphingosine).
The fatty acids may be of various chain lengths and may be unsaturated. In addition, homologues of the sphinganine derivatives containing chains of different lengths and degrees of unsaturation occur.

The hydrophobic tails of polar lipids

Most models proposed for membrane structures (chapter 6) incorporate a lipid bilayer arrangement, such as that shown schematically in figure 5.3. There the long aliphatic chains are sequestered within the interior

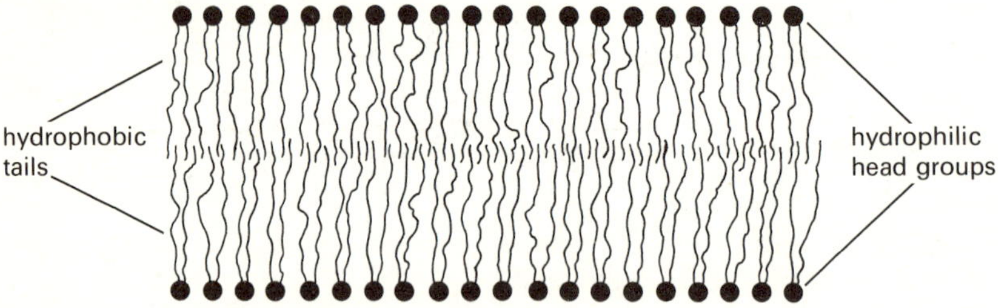

Figure 5.3. Bilayer arrangement of polar lipids.

of the membrane, and all the hydrophilic head groups face the aqueous environment. A hydrophobic or apolar group in water causes extensive rearrangement of water molecules in its vicinity, leading to a thermodynamically unfavourable loss of entropy. Accordingly, apolar groups tend to cluster together, excluding water, and so reduce the free energy of the system. The major driving force for this hydrophobic association results, therefore, from entropic factors rather than from specific apolar-apolar interactions.

Table 5.1. Fatty acids commonly occurring in higher plants and animals

Saturated fatty acids

Structure	*Notation*	*Systematic name*	*Trivial name*
$CH_3(CH_2)_{12}COOH$	14:0	*n*-tetradecanoic	myristic
$CH_3(CH_2)_{14}COOH$	16:0	*n*-hexadecanoic	palmitic
$CH_3(CH_2)_{16}COOH$	18:0	*n*-octadecanoic	stearic
$CH_3(CH_2)_{18}COOH$	20:0	*n*-eicosanoic	arachidic
$CH_3(CH_2)_{20}COOH$	22:0	*n*-docosanoic	behenic
$CH_3(CH_2)_{22}COOH$	24:0	*n*-tetracosanoic	lignoceric

Unsaturated fatty acids

Structure	*Notation*	*Trivial name*
$CH_3(CH_2)_5CH{=}CH(CH_2)_7COOH$	16:1	palmitoleic
$CH_3(CH_2)_7CH{=}CH(CH_2)_7COOH$	18:1	oleic
$CH_3(CH_2)_4CH{=}CHCH_2CH{=}$ $CH(CH_2)_7COOH$	18:2	linoleic
$CH_3CH_2CH{=}CHCH_2CH{=}CHCH_2CH{=}$ $CH(CH_2)_7COOH$	18:3	linolenic
$CH_3(CH_2)_4CH{=}CHCH_2CH{=}$ $CHCH_2CH{=}CHCH_2CH{=}$ $CH(CH_2)_3COOH$	20:4	arachidonic

The hydrophobic tails of polar lipids are made up of the long aliphatic chains of fatty acids, aldehydes or alcohols, of sphinganine derivatives, or of sterol molecules. The composition of the hydrophobic region of a bilayer of polar lipid is accordingly capable of considerable variation, and it is probable that the physical properties of the bilayer as a whole can be subtly controlled by structural variations in the hydrophobic tails. An indication of the different structural possibilities and of their effects on the membrane can be obtained from consideration of the long-chain fatty acids, which are the commonest components of the hydrophobic tails of polar lipids. Fatty acids of higher plants and animals contain 16–24 carbon atoms, with chains of 16 and 18 predominating, and can be saturated or unsaturated. Monounsaturated acids have a double bond between carbon atoms 9 and 10. Further double bonds, if present, usually occur in the chain between carbon 10 and the terminal methyl group in such a way that two double bonds are separated by a methylene group (i.e. $CH{=}CH{-}CH_2{-}CH{=}CH$) and never conjugated (as in $CH{=}CH{-}CH{=}CH{-}$). Commonly occurring fatty acids of higher organisms are shown in Table 5.1. Bacteria generally contain shorter fatty acids with no more than one double bond. When a double bond occurs, it is usually situated between carbons 7 and 8 (counting, in this case, from the terminal methyl group). Bacterial lipids also commonly contain branched-chain, as well as β-hydroxy and cyclopropane fatty acids, typical examples of which are shown in Table 5.2.

Table 5.2. Branched-chain, hydroxy and cyclopropane fatty acids commonly occurring in bacteria

CH_3 | $CH_3CH(CH_2)_nCOOH$	branched chain *iso* fatty acids
CH_3 | $CH_3CH_2CH(CH_2)_nCOOH$	branched chain *anteiso* fatty acids
OH | $CH_3(CH_2)_nCHCH_2COOH$	β-hydroxy fatty acids
CH_2 / \\ $CH_3(CH_2)_5C$ —— $C(CH_2)_9COOH$ | | H H	cyclopropane fatty acid (lactobacillic)
$CH_3(CH_2)_5CH{=}CH(CH_2)_9COOH$	*cis*-vaccenic acid

Although free rotation is possible about each carbon-carbon bond in saturated fatty acids, the minimum energy conformation is that of the planar zig-zag shown in figure 5.4*a*. Such extended chains might be expected to fit well into an ordered crystalline type of array within a bilayer structure. The presence of a *trans* double bond in the chain makes little difference to the overall conformation (figure 5.4*b*). Naturally-occurring unsaturated fatty acids almost always contain *cis* double bonds, however, which impart an overall bend of approximately 30° to the chain (figure 5.4*c*). Incorporation of such kinked molecules into the ordered array of a bilayer will disrupt the array and tend to make the membrane more fluid. This effect is apparent in the melting-points of naturally-occurring unsaturated fatty acids which, on average, melt 50 °C lower than those of the corresponding saturated acids (see also chapter 6). Similar effects on membrane fluidity may be brought about by the branched-chain and cyclopropane fatty acids of bacteria.

Phospholipids

When the hydrophilic head group of one of the generalized polar lipids, shown in figures 5.1 and 5.2, contains a phosphate moiety, the resulting compounds are classified as phospholipids.

Phosphoglycerides are phospholipids in which a primary phosphate of glycerol contains at least one O-acyl, O-alkyl or O-alk-1′-enyl residue attached to the glycerol moiety (see figure 5.1). The two primary groups of glycerol are not stereochemically identical, and it is almost always the same primary hydroxy-group which is esterified to phosphate in the phosphoglycerides. Which primary hydroxy-group is so involved is best designated by the *stereospecific numbering system.* In this system, when glycerol is drawn in the Fischer projection with the C-2 hydroxy-group on the left-hand side, the carbon atoms are numbered as shown in figure 5.5. When the stereospecific numbering system is being applied, the prefix *sn-* is used before the name of the compound. Phosphoglycerides usually contain an *sn*-glycerol 3-phosphate moiety in which the phosphate grouping exists either as the dibasic acid (figure 5.6, R=H) or as the diester, linked to one of the R groups listed in figure 5.6.

Phosphatidic acids contain no second alcohol grouping esterified to the *sn*-glycerol 3-phosphate moiety (figure 5.6, R=H). The diacyl derivative (figure 5.7) is usually simply referred to as phosphatidic acid and plays a key role in the biosynthesis of most phosphoglycerides. As such it is widely distributed, occurring at a low level (1–5% of total

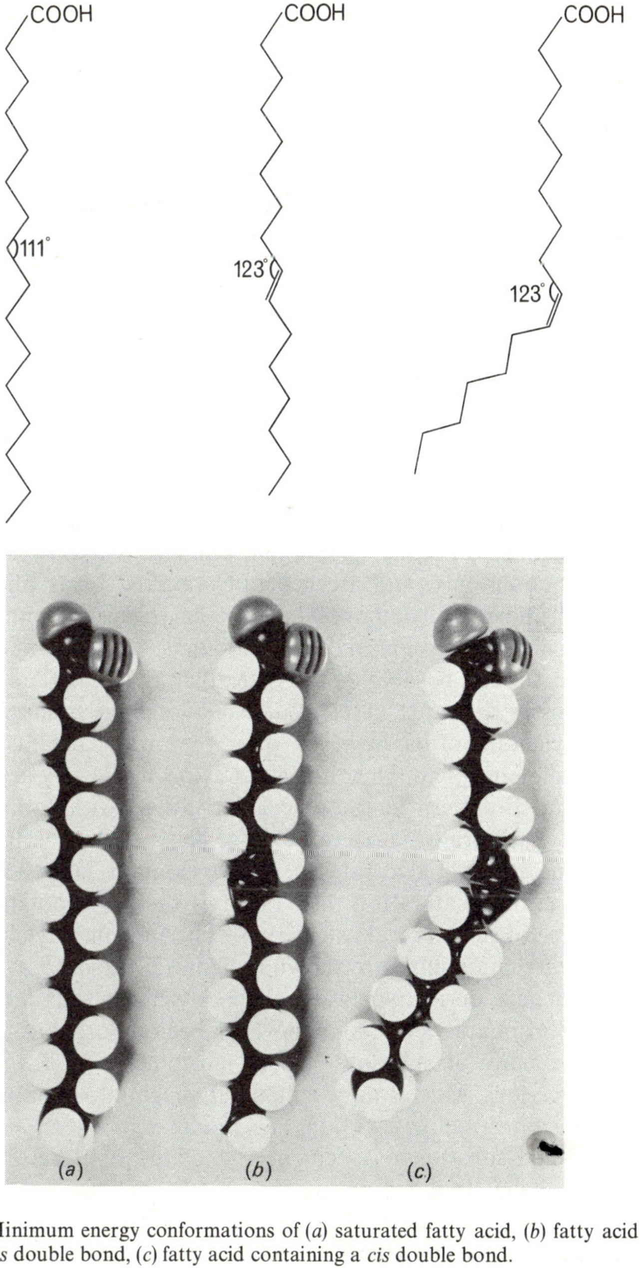

Figure 5.4. Minimum energy conformations of (*a*) saturated fatty acid, (*b*) fatty acid containing a *trans* double bond, (*c*) fatty acid containing a *cis* double bond.

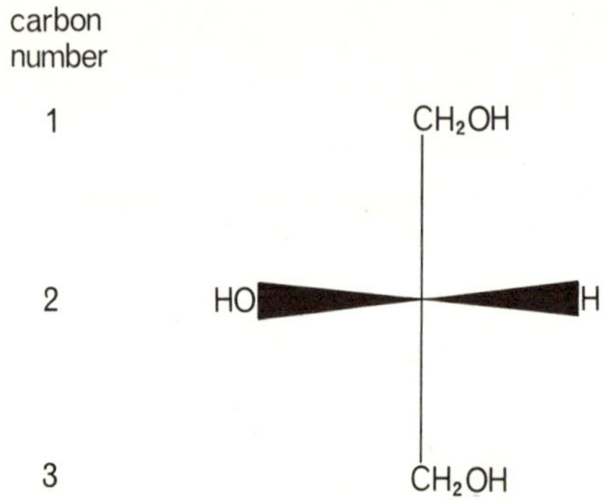

Figure 5.5. Stereospecific numbering of glycerol.

phospholipids) in many tissues. Alk-l′-enyl and alkyl derivatives have been detected but have not been widely characterized.

Choline and ethanolamine phosphoglycerides are the most abundant phosphoglycerides in higher plants and animals. The diacyl derivatives occur most commonly, and are generally referred to as phosphatidylcholine and phosphatidylethanolamine. It has been recommended that the old trivial names for these compounds, lecithin and cephalin respectively, should be abandoned. Phosphatidylethanolamine usually occurs in lesser amounts in mammalian and plant tissues than does phosphatidylcholine. It is, however, often the principal phospholipid of bacteria, while phosphatidylcholine is rarely present. Fatty acid substitution falls into a pattern in the diacyl derivatives with saturated acids at C-1 and unsaturated acids at C-2 of the *sn*-glycerol moiety. The ethanolamine phosphoglycerides generally contain fatty acids with a higher degree of unsaturation than those of the corresponding choline phosphoglycerides. General structures of phosphatidylcholine and phosphatidylethanolamine are shown in figures 5.8 and 5.9.

The monoacyl derivative lysophosphatidylcholine, and to a lesser extent lysophosphatidylethanolamine, have been reported as minor components of many membranes. There is some evidence that these phosphoglycerides, which can be actually damaging to membranes, arise from specific phospholipase action.

O-Alk-l′-enyl substituents occur at C-1 of the *sn*-glycerol moiety of phosphoglycerides in combination with an O-acyl residue at C-2, and the resulting compounds are known as plasmalogens. 1-O-Alk-1′-enyl-2-O-acyl choline phosphoglyceride and 1-O-alk-1′-enyl-2-O-acyl ethanol-

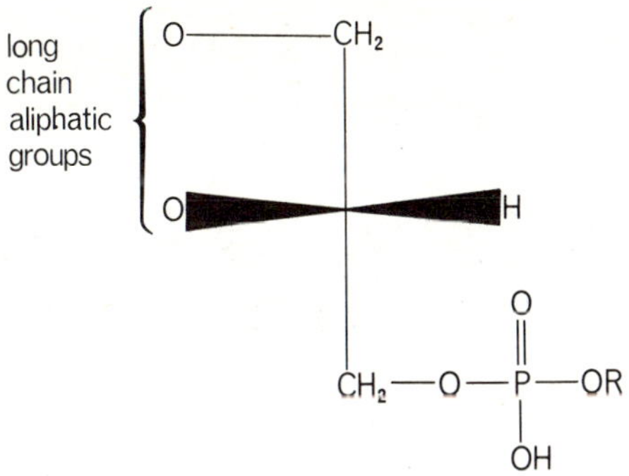

Phosphoglycerides	*R Group*
Phosphatidic acids	H
Choline phosphoglycerides	$—CH_2CH_2\overset{+}{N}(CH_3)_3$
Ethanolamine phosphoglycerides	$—CH_2CH_2NH_2$
Serine phosphoglycerides	$—CH_2CH(NH_2)COOH$
Inositol phosphoglyceride (phosphatidylinositol)	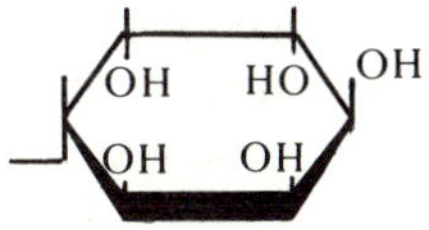
Glycerol phosphoglyceride (phosphatidylglycerol)	$—CH_2—CHOH—CH_2OH$
Phosphatidylglycerol phosphoglyceride (diphosphatidylglycerol or cardiolipin)	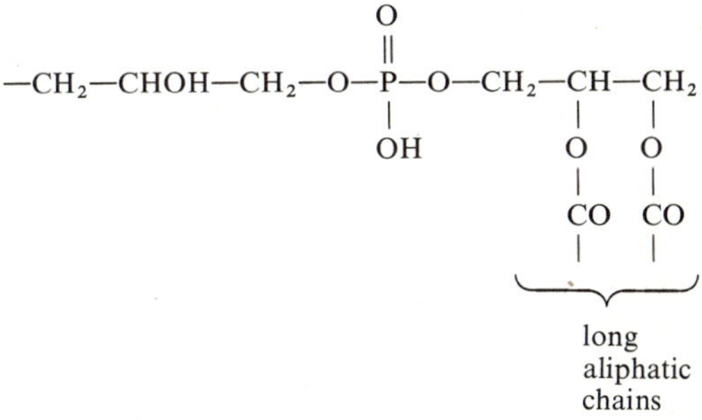
3-*O*-Aminoacyl-*sn*-glycerol phosphoglycerides (phosphatidyl-3-*O*-aminoacyl-*sn*-glycerol)	$—CH_2—CHOH—CH_2—OR^*$

Figure 5.6. The major phosphoglycerides are based on the general structure shown. Where only the diacyl derivative has been isolated, this is named in parenthesis. R* = L-alanyl, L-lysyl or L-ornithyl.

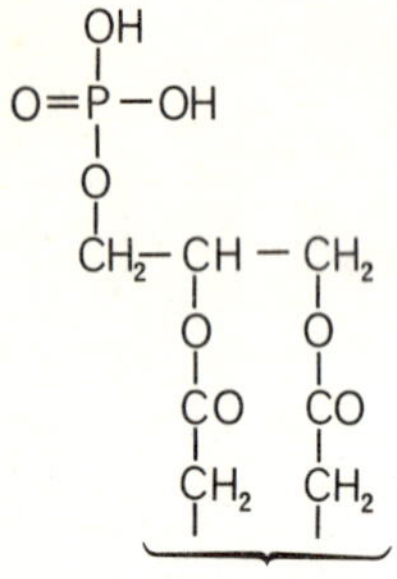

Figure 5.7.
Phosphatidic acid.

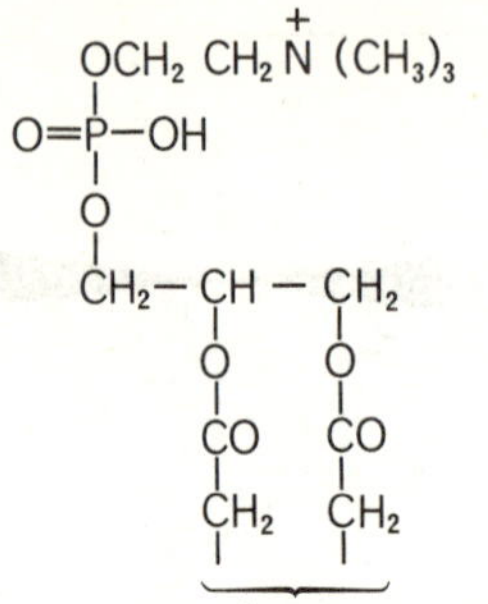

Figure 5.8.
Phosphatidylcholine (diacyl choline phosphoglyceride).

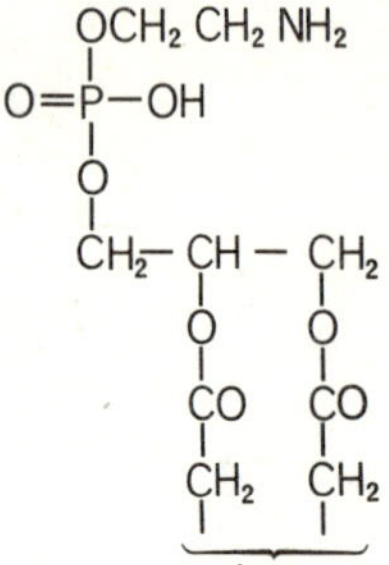

Figure 5.9.
Phosphatidylethanolamine (diacyl ethanolamine phosphoglyceride).

amine phosphoglycerides are accordingly choline plasmalogen (figure 5.10) and ethanolamine plasmalogen (figure 5.11) respectively. While plasmalogens have been shown to be widely distributed, they are difficult to separate from the corresponding acyl- and alkyl-substituted compounds and are often not specifically looked for. Relatively high concentrations of ethanolamine plasmalogen have been reported in myelin, and lesser amounts in heart muscle, where choline plasmalogen is particularly abundant. Bacteria also show a widely variable content of plasmalogens, which appear to be largely confined to anaerobes.

1-O-Alkyl-2-O-acyl choline phosphoglyceride and its ethanolamine analogue, as well as the di-O-alkyl derivatives, have been detected accompanying the corresponding diacyl phosphoglycerides in many tissues. Again separation of the analogues is difficult, and it may be that the ether derivatives are more common than has been reported.

Diacyl, monoacyl, alk-l′-enyl and alkyl serine phosphoglycerides occur with similar substitution patterns to those of their choline and ethanolamine analogues. The diacyl derivative phosphatidylserine (figure 5.12) is widely distributed, but usually in concentrations less than 10% of total phospholipid.

Phosphatidylinositol (diacyl inositol phosphoglyceride) (figure 5.13) is also commonly found as a minor (5–10%) phospholipid component. Its 4-phosphate and 4,5-diphosphate occur, and have been reported in highest concentration in nervous tissue (largely myelin).

Concentrations of phosphatidylglycerol (diacyl glycerol phospho-

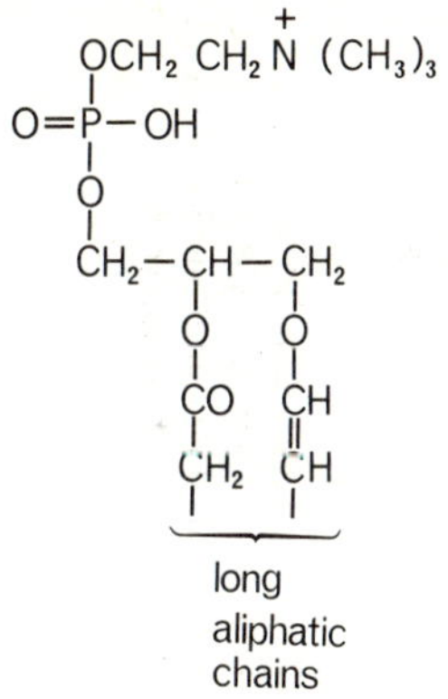

Figure 5.10. Choline plasmalogen.

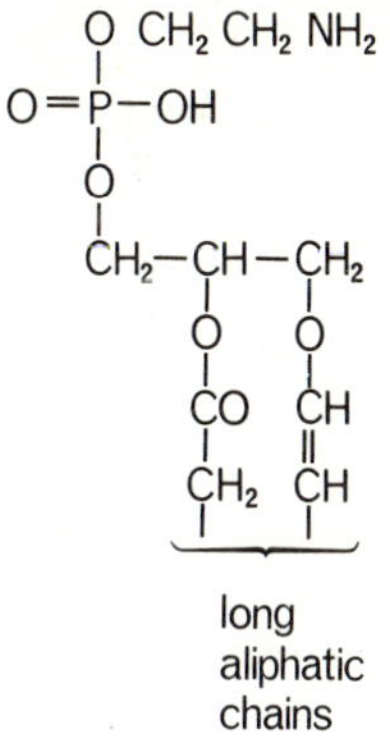

Figure 5.11. Ethanolamine plasmalogen.

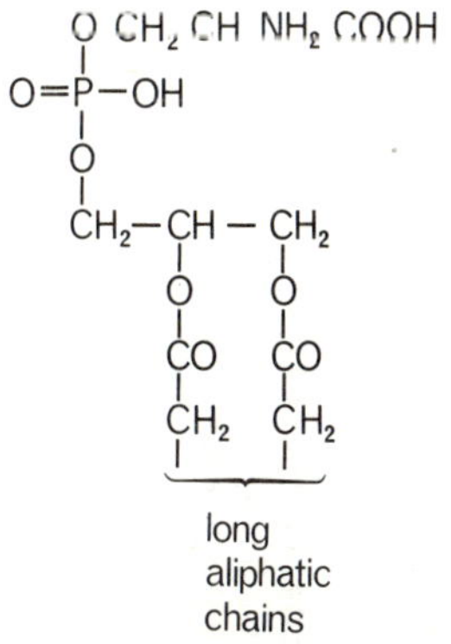

Figure 5.12. Phosphatidylserine (diacyl serine phosphoglyceride).

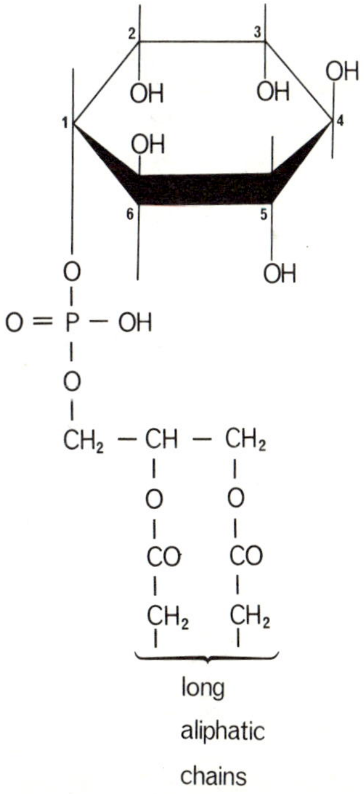

Figure 5.13. Phosphatidylinositol (diacyl inositol phosphoglyceride).

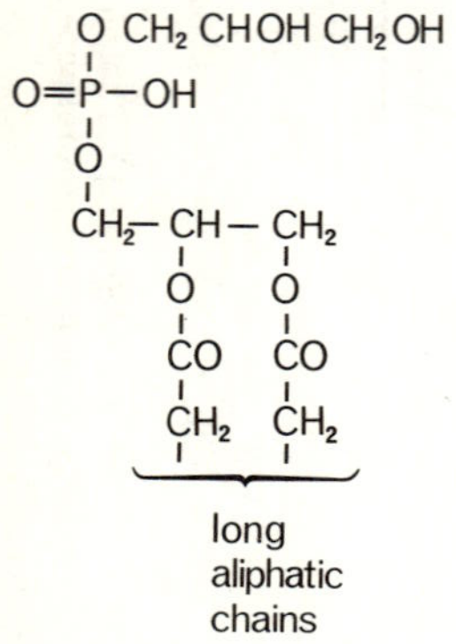

Figure 5.14. Phosphatidylglycerol (diacyl glycerol phosphoglyceride).

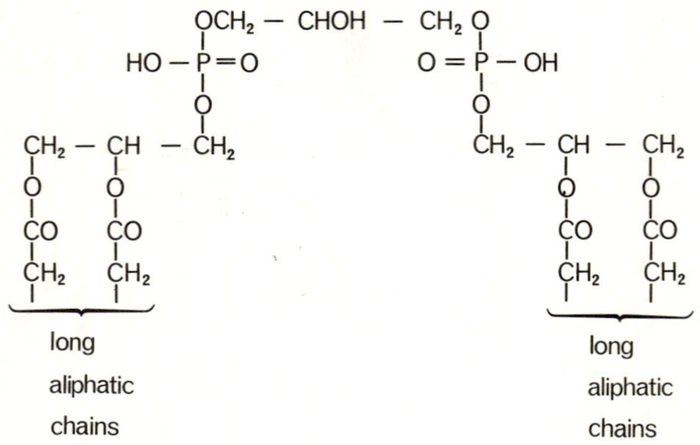

Figure 5.15. Diphosphatidylglycerol (cardiolipin).

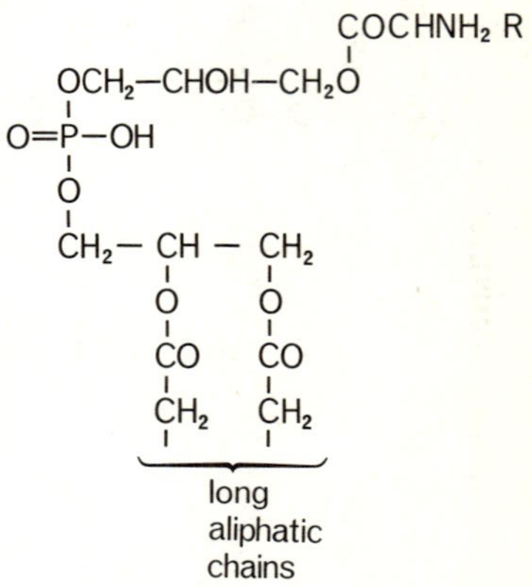

Figure 5.16. Phosphatidyl 3-O-aminoacyl-*sn*-glycerol (diacyl 3-O-aminoacyl-*sn*-glycerol phosphoglyceride).

glyceride (figure 5.14) vary from small amounts in animal membranes (largely mitochondrial) to 20–30% of phospholipids in plant membranes generally (40–60% in chloroplasts). Its content in bacterial membranes is again variable and can constitute as much as 70% of the membrane phospholipid in Gram positive cells. Phosphatidylglycerol is a biosynthetic precursor of diphosphatidylglycerol (cardiolipin) (figure 5.15), and the latter is accordingly also found in mitochondria, chloroplasts and many bacteria. Since the two lipids are difficult to separate, they are often reported as their sum. It has been shown that an inverse relationship often exists in bacteria between phosphatidylglycerol and cardiolipin concentrations which depends upon conditions and phase of growth.

Phosphatidyl 3-O-aminoacyl-*sn*-glycerols (diacyl 3-O-aminoacyl-*sn*-glycerol phosphoglycerides) (figure 5.16) are also derived from phospha-

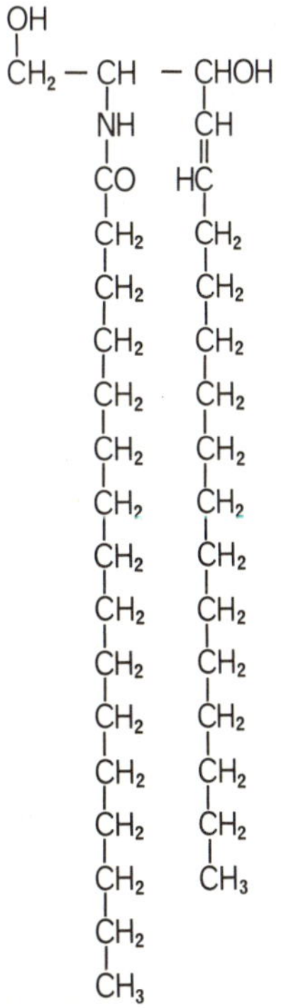

Figure 5.17. Ceramide.

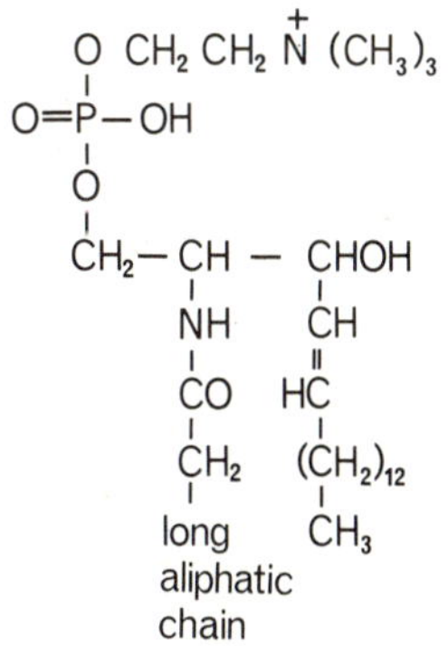

Figure 5.18. Ceramide 1-phosphorylcholine (sphingomyelin).

tidylglycerol and have been largely located in Gram positive bacteria where the L-alanyl, L-lysyl and L-ornithyl esters have been characterized.

The second major class of phospholipids is that of the *phosphosphingolipids*, which are based on the general polar lipid structures shown in figure 5.2 where the hydrophilic head group is a phosphate diester. With recent improvement in separation techniques, the number of sphinganine-type structures characterized has greatly increased. The three main structures are shown in figure 5.2, although the chain lengths may vary. 4-sphingenine (sphingosine) is the major sphinganine derivative of animal phosphosphingolipids, which also often have a low content of sphinganine itself, while the main phosphosphingolipid of plants contains 4-D-hydroxysphinganine. Until recently bacteria were thought not to contain phosphosphingolipids. Such lipids containing sphinganine and some of its less common derivatives have now been isolated from bacteria.

The fatty-acylated sphinganine derivative is referred to as a ceramide. A ceramide based on 4-sphingenine (sphingosine) is shown in figure 5.17. Sphingomyelin (figure 5.18) is accordingly systematically named ceramide 1-phosphorylcholine. Sphingomyelin occurs primarily in animal tissues, being present in appreciable quantities in myelin, blood and kidney, and in lesser amounts (4–10% of total phospholipids) in most other tissue. Sphingomyelin of myelin contains predominantly longer-chain fatty acids [mainly lignoceric (24:0) and nervonic (24:1)] whereas that of grey matter contains largely stearic acid (18:0).

Ceramide 1-phosphorylethanolamine, ceramide 1-phosphorylglycerol and ceramide 1-phosphorylinositol have all been relatively recently characterized in tissue from widely-varying sources.

Space-filling models of a range of phospholipids are shown in figure 5.19.

The phospholipids are the most polar of the lipids. They all carry a phosphate acidic grouping with pK_a 1–2 which has a negative charge at pH 7·0. Choline and ethanolamine additionally have amino groups with pK_a values of 13 and 10 respectively, and are positively charged at neutral pH, giving rise to dipolar zwitterions with no net charge. Serine has one negative and one positive charge at physiological pH, and phospholipids containing serine consequently normally carry a single net negative charge, as do those containing inositol and glycerol. There is, therefore, a considerable range of hydrophilic head groups available among the phospholipids varying in size, shape, polarity and charge. Just as variations in chain length and degree of unsaturation of the

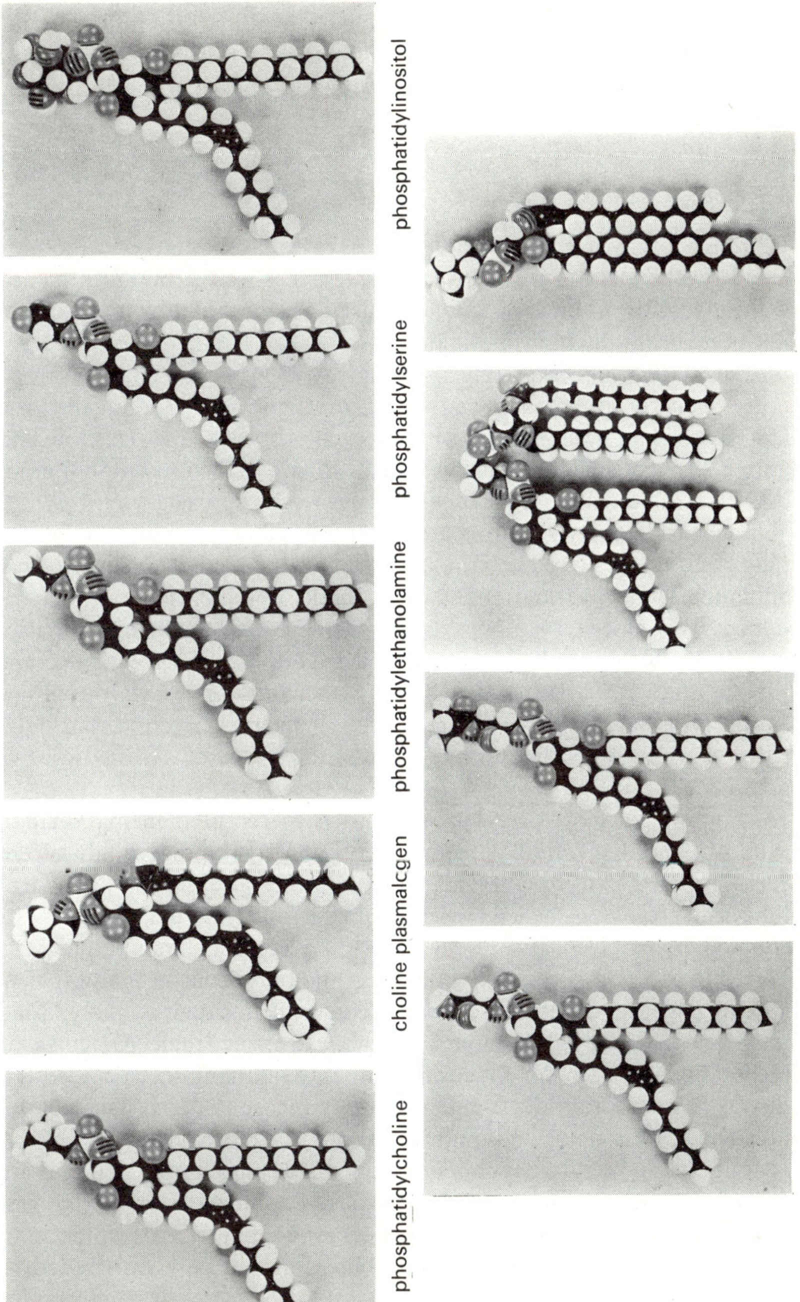

Figure 5.19. Space-filling models of phospholipids.

aliphatic chains of polar lipids might be expected to influence the properties of the lipid bilayers, so might the overall properties of the bilayer differ according to the proportions of the various hydrophilic head groups.

Glycolipids

The range of hydrophilic head groups of polar lipids is further extended by the class of *glycolipids* in which the head group is attached via the glycosidic linkage of a sugar molecule rather than by a phosphate ester bond, as in the phospholipids.

Glycosyl diacylglycerols (glycosyl diglycerides) are glycolipids based on the general polar lipid structure of figure 5.1. Monogalactosyl diacylglycerol is a major glycolipid of chloroplasts and is shown in figure 5.20. A digalactosyl diacylglycerol (figure 5.21) and sulphoquinovosyl diacylglycerol (figure 5.22) also occur in chloroplasts.

Disaccharide diacylglycerols are widely distributed among the glycolipids of Gram positive bacteria, and structures have been characterized containing D-glucose and D-galactose in the combinations α-glucosyl-α-glucosyl, β-glucosyl-β-glucosyl, α-galactosyl-α-glucosyl and β-galactosyl-β-galactosyl in which the α-linked sugars are joined 1–2 and the β-linked units 1–6. α-D-mannosyl (1–3) α-D-mannosyl diacylglycerol has also been demonstrated in Gram positive bacteria. Glycosyl diacylglycerols are not generally found among the lipids of Gram negative bacteria.

Although galactosyl diacylglycerol has been reported in mammalian brain, glycolipids of animal membranes are largely polar lipids of the general types shown in figure 5.2. In these *glycosphingolipids*, the hydrophilic head group is attached to the terminal hydroxymethyl grouping of a ceramide by a glycosidic linkage, and the resulting compounds are referred to as glycosyl ceramides. Such compounds occur in brain, spleen, erythrocytes, kidney and liver, where they are located in the plasma membranes. The glycosyl moiety can vary from a single galactose or glucose unit to complex oligosaccharides containing D-galactose, D-glucose, D-galactosamine, D-glucosamine, L-fucose (6-deoxy-L-galactose) and sialic acid (*N*-acetylneuraminic acid).

Monoglycosyl ceramides contain a single monosaccharide unit and are now often generally termed cerebrosides. Cerebroside originally was applied specifically to monogalactosyl ceramide (figure 5.23) which is an important lipid constituent of brain, but is also widely distributed in mammalian tissue, commonly occurring as sulphatides, in which a sulphate ester is attached to C-3 of the galactose unit. Cerebrosides often contain longer-chain fatty acids, the most abundant of which are lignoceric (24:0), cerebronic (α-hydroxylignoceric) and nervonic (24:1) acids.

β-Galactosyl (1–4) β-glucosyl ceramide (lactosyl ceramide) is shown in

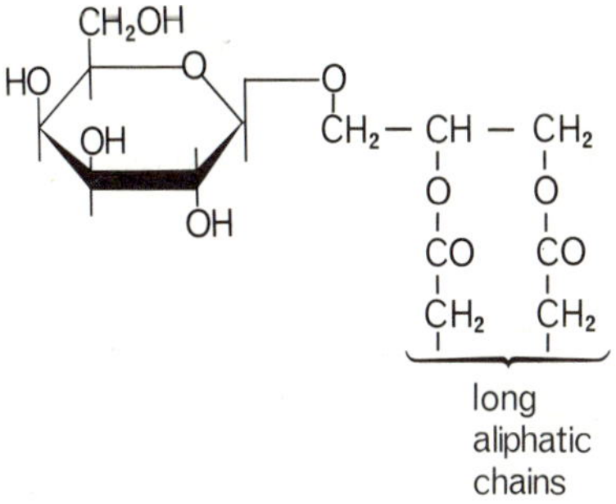

Figure 5.20. Monogalactosyl diacylglycerol (monogalactosyl diglyceride).

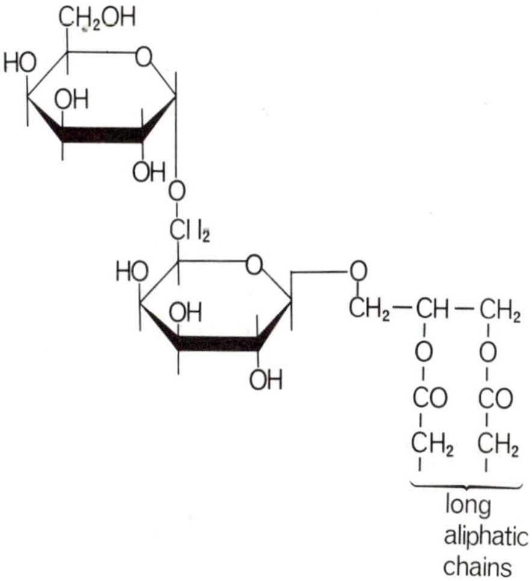

Figure 5.21. α-D-Galactosyl (1 – 6) β-D-galactosyl diacylglycerol (α-D-galactosyl (1 – 6) β-D-galactosyl diglyceride).

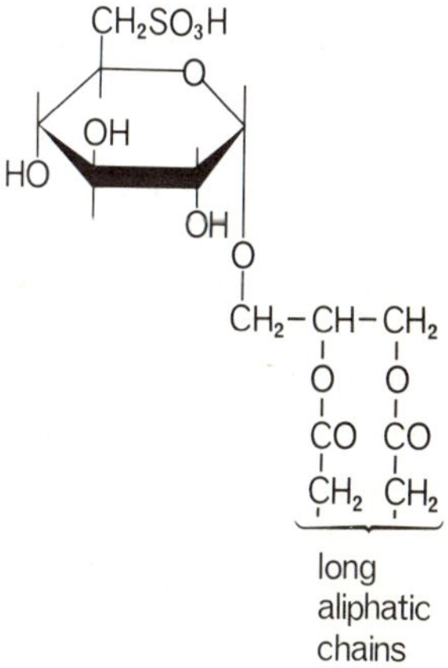

Figure 5.22. 6-Sulpho-α-D-quinovosyl diacylglycerol (6-sulpho-α-D-quinovosyl diglyceride).

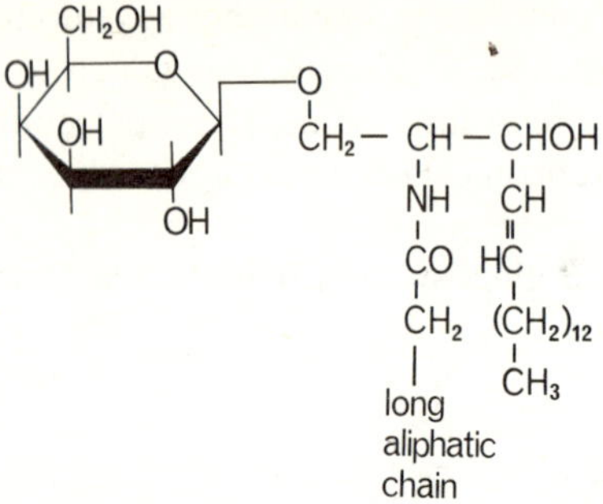

Figure 5.23. Monogalactosyl ceramide.

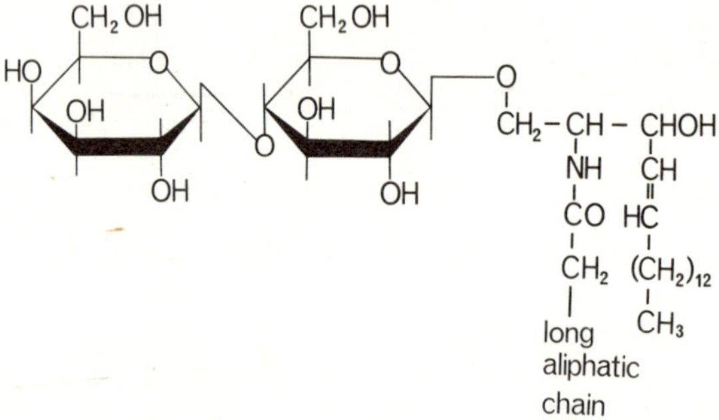

Figure. 5.24. β-D-Galactosyl (1 – 4) β-D-glucosyl ceramide (lactosyl ceramide).

figure 5.24. More complex glycosphingolipids are usually structurally derived from lactosyl ceramide by extension of the carbohydrate head group, and have been classified according to the nature of the carbohydrate backbone. Thus the ganglio series contains gangliotetraose, β-galactosyl (1–3) β-*N*-acetylgalactosaminyl (1–4)-lactose, the globo series contains β-*N*-acetylgalactosaminyl (1–3) β-galactosyl (1–3 or 4) lactose, and the lacto series contains β-galactosyl (1–3 or 4) β-*N*-acetylgalactosaminyl (1–3) lactose. Members of the ganglio series are further substituted by sialic acid, while those of the lacto series can be substituted by sialic acid or fucose. Even more complicated oligosaccharide complexes have recently been characterized.

Gangliosides are generally understood to mean glycosphingolipids containing sialic acid, and are present in the outer membranes of many animal cells, especially nerve cells. A member of the ganglio series is shown in figure 5.25.

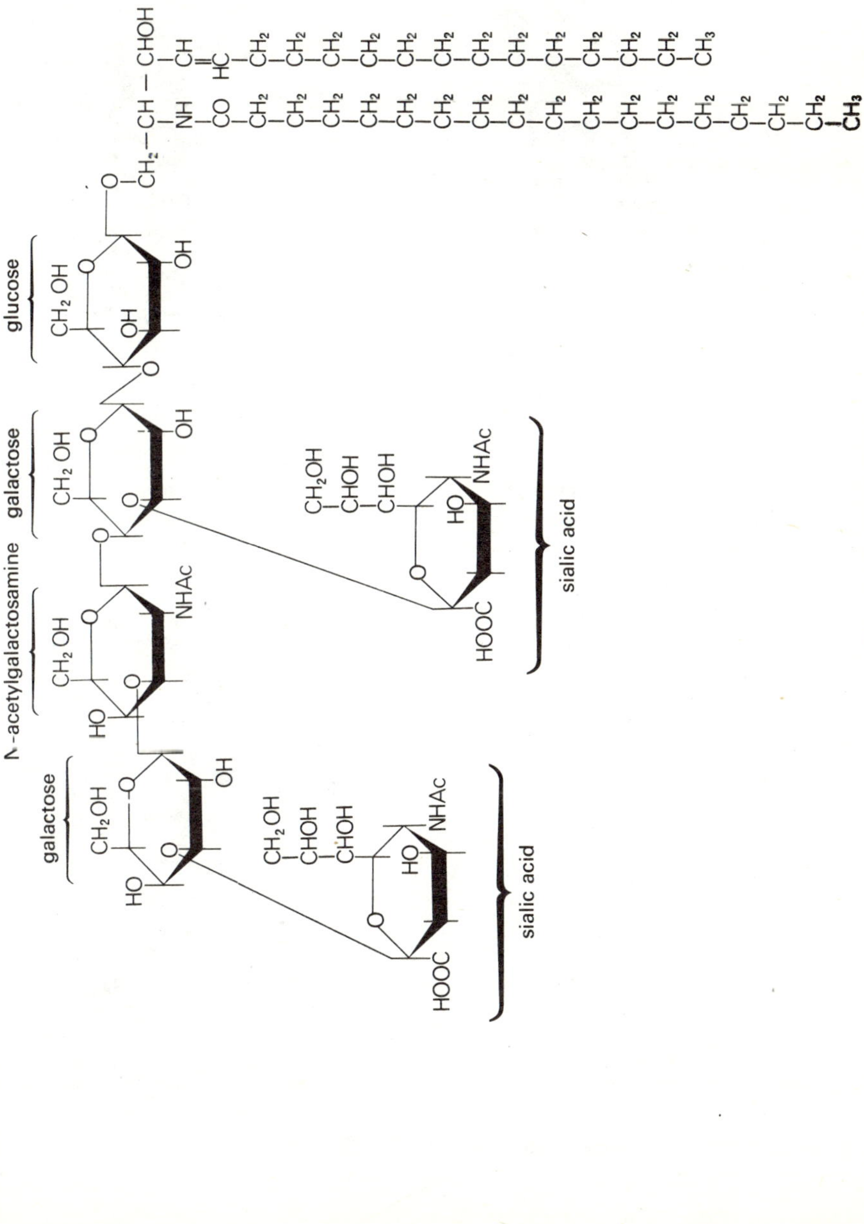

Figure 5.25. A ganglioside.

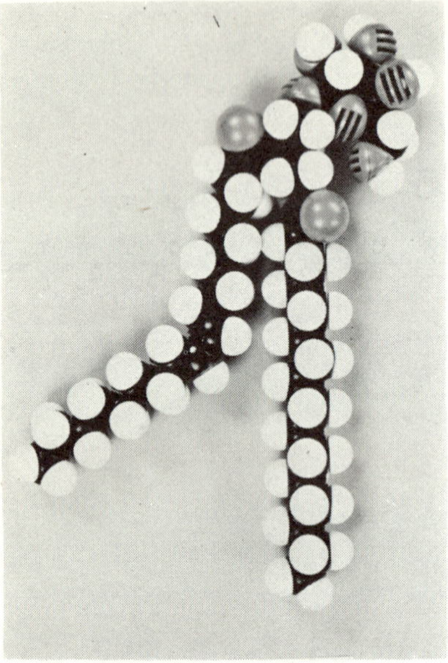

glycosyl diacylglycerol

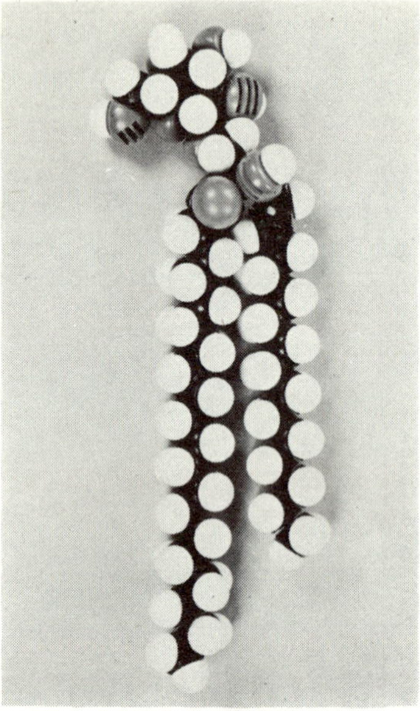

glycosyl ceramide

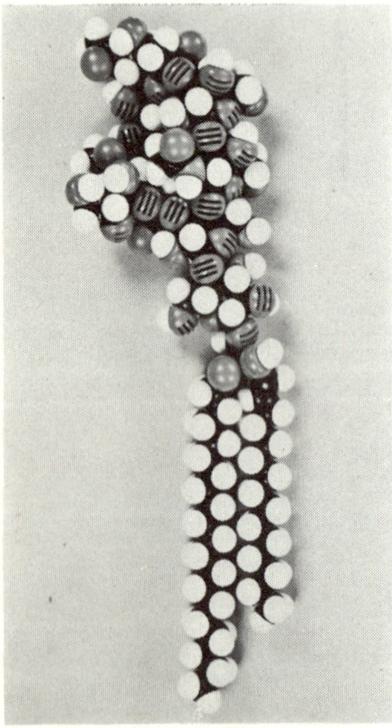

ganglioside

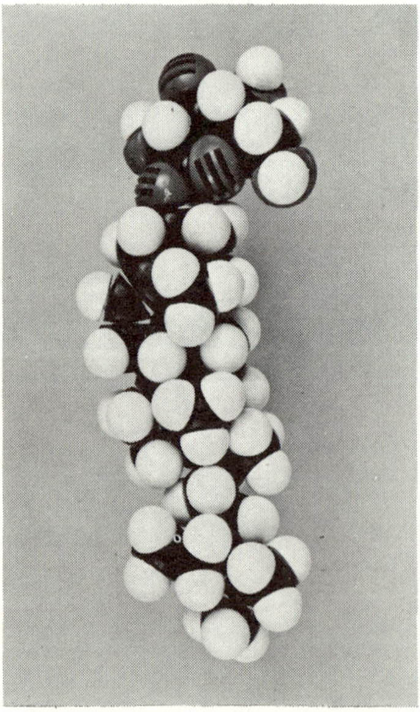

steryl glycoside

Figure 5.26. Space-filling models of glycolipids.

Steryl glycosides in which a monosaccharide molecule is glycosidically linked to the hydroxy group of a sterol (see next section) consitute a further class of glycolipid and are found in plant membranes.

Space-filling models of glycolipids are shown in figure 5.26. It is likely that the sugar residues are exposed on the outer surface of the plasma membranes in which the glycolipids are mostly found. Particularly the more complex oligosaccharide residues of the glycosphingolipids might be expected to contribute to the specific nature of cell surfaces. Blood group specificities, for instance, are known to be associated with glycolipids in the erythrocyte membrane. Cell surface specificity will be further discussed in chapter 7.

Sterols

The sterols constitute a third major class of membrane polar lipids in addition to the phospholipids and glycolipids. The most abundant sterol in animal tissues is cholesterol (figure 5.27) with a polar hydroxy-group at one extreme of a compact hydrophobic molecule (figure 5.28).

Cholesterol is known to cause condensation of phospholipid mono-

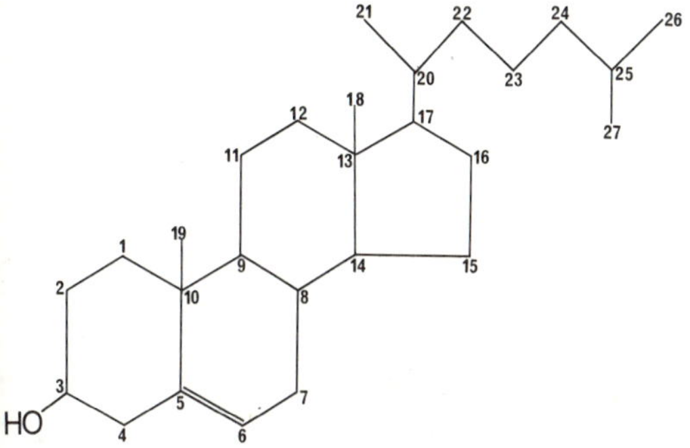

Figure 5.27. Cholesterol.

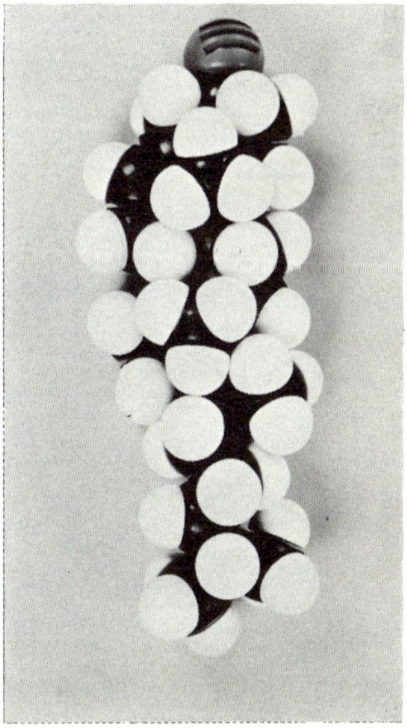

Figure 5.28. Space-filling model of cholesterol.

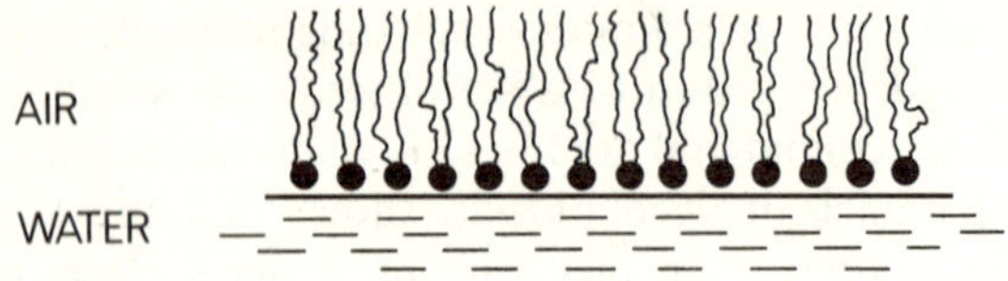

Figure 5.29. Polar lipid monolayer at an air-water interface.

layers (figure 5.29) spread at an air-water interface. It also reduces the permeability of phospholipid bilayers and enhances their stability. The stabilizing effect of cholesterol has been observed in natural membranes, which show increased osmotic fragility following cholesterol depletion. All these effects have been attributed to the demonstrated ability of cholesterol to restrict the molecular mobility of hydrocarbon chains of phospholipids, probably by way of an equimolar complex with phospholipid (chapters 6 and 11).

Cholesterol is usually only a minor sterol component of membranes of higher plants, in which the major sterols are frequently sitosterol (figure 5.30) and stigmasterol (figure 5.31). These molecules show structural features which are widespread among plant sterols (*phytosterols*). Phytosterols commonly have an additional side chain at C-24, which may be methylene, methyl, ethylidene or ethyl and/or a double bond at C-22.

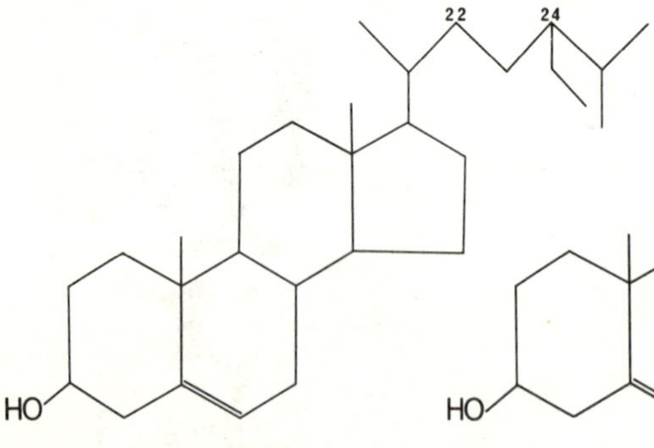

Figure 5.30. Sitosterol.

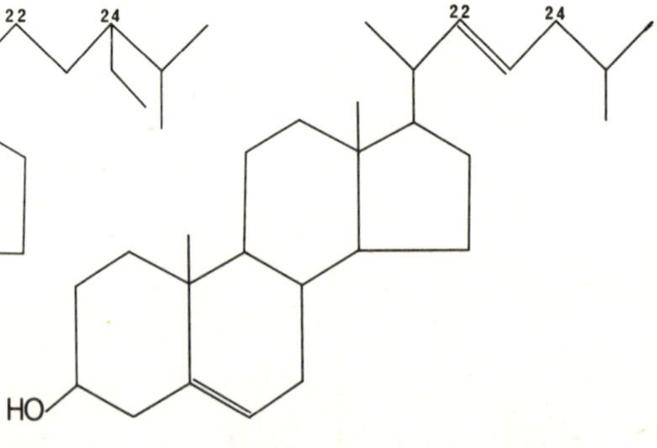

Figure 5.31. Stigmasterol.

Rather more structural variation is seen among the sterols of eukaryotic micro-organisms, in which a double bond may be present at C-7 in addition to, or instead of, the C-5 double bond in the above structures. Thus ergosterol (figure 5.32) is a major sterol of membranes

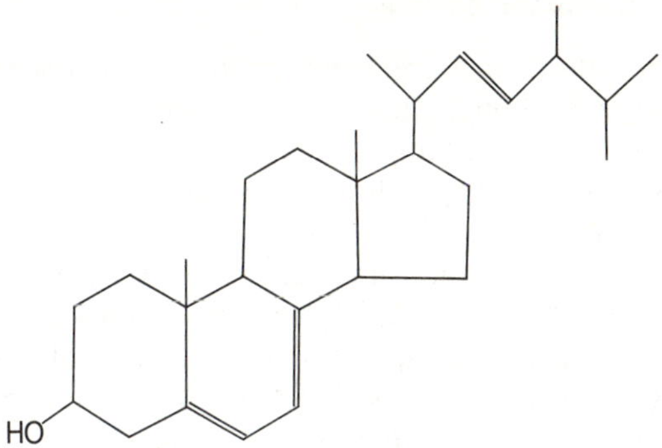

Figure 5.32. Ergosterol.

in such organisms. Ergosterol has been shown to stabilize yeast plasma membranes against osmotic lysis, and similar stabilization can be effected by stigmasterol. Sterols lacking the C-22 double bond are less effective in this respect, and it may be that the rigidity of an unsaturated C-17 alkyl chain is important in the stabilizing mechanisms.

Other polar lipids in membranes

Membrane polar lipids which do not fall into one of the three major classes of phospholipid, glycolipid and sterols are usually minor components. Mono- and diacylglycerols and free fatty acids, for example, all occur in small amounts in animal membranes. Free fatty acids have been shown to be present in small amounts in brain, where they are associated with the synaptic membranes. The level of free fatty acids varies with the functional state of the membrane, and it has been suggested that they may be involved in changes in membrane permeability. Support for this suggestion is given by the discovery of an acylase-deacylase system sensitive to neurotransmitters (chapter 8).

Non-polar lipids

While by far the greater majority of membrane lipids are polar lipids, non-polar lipids such as triacylglycerol, the lipid of depot fat, and steryl esters of long-chain fatty acids are usually found in minor amounts in membranes.

Distribution of membrane lipids

The lipid composition of animal membranes is characteristic for the specific membrane, although the fatty acid content of individual lipid components may vary with temperature or nutritional state. Within the same animal species, corresponding membranes from different organs have different compositions. Moreover, lipid compositions of different subcellular membranes of the same cell also vary. Apart from plasma membranes, which show considerable species variation, corresponding membranes from different vertebrates have remarkably constant lipid composition. Overall lipid compositions for various subcellular membranes of rat liver are shown in figure 5.33.

The components of the phospholipid fraction in the different membranes are shown in figure 5.34.

Plasma membranes, as already mentioned, are subject to considerable compositional variation, both with organ and with species. They generally contain most of the glycolipids of the cell and show the highest content

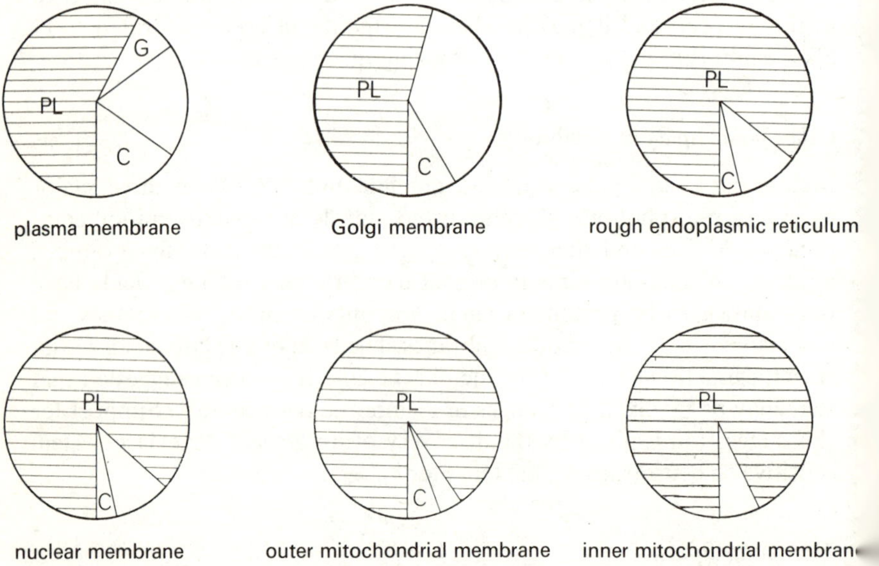

Figure 5.33. Lipid composition by weight of different subcellular membranes of rat liver: PL = phospholipid; C = cholesterol; G = glycolipid; unlabelled = mono-, di- and tri-acylglycerols, free fatty acids and steryl esters. The high neutral lipid content found for Golgi membrane is probably partly attributable to the presence of very-low-density lipoprotein precursor particles in the Golgi fraction.

of cholesterol. The relatively high cholesterol content will tend to reduce the fluidity of the membrane and so stabilize the cell boundary. The same effect may also be brought about by the generally high content of sphingomyelin with its associated long-chain saturated fatty acids in plasma membrane. Inner mitochondrial membrane contains a high proportion of phospholipid and no (or very little) cholesterol, while the content of diphosphatidylglycerol (cardiolipin) is much higher than in other membranes. Comparison of the compositions of rough endoplasmic reticulum, nuclear membrane, and outer mitochondrial membrane, shows many similarities, while that of Golgi membrane is intermediate between rough endoplasmic reticulum on the one hand and plasma membrane on the other. This intermediate composition would accord with the postulate that Golgi membrane is a transitional membrane undergoing differentiation to form new plasma membrane (chapters 4 and 7).

With the exception of chloroplasts, little information is available on the lipid composition of homogeneous preparations of subcellular

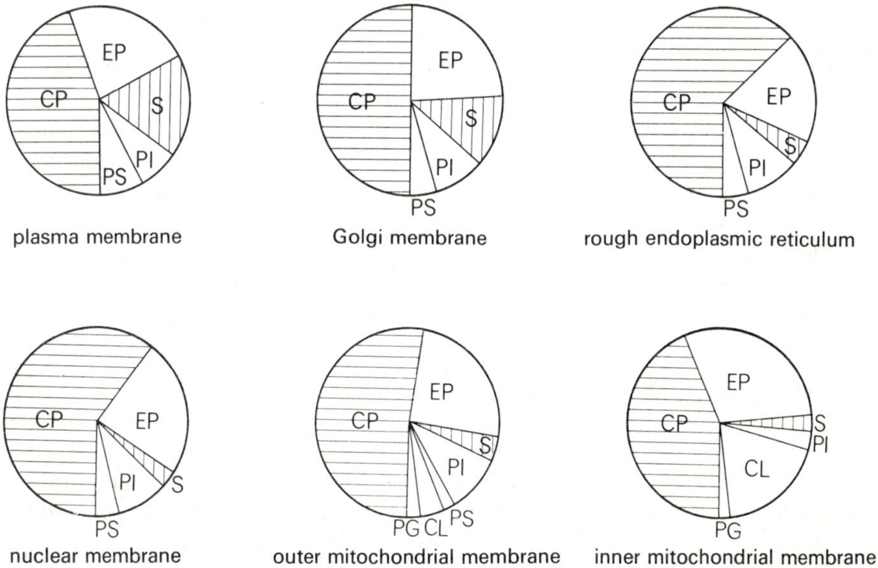

Figure 5.34. Phospholipid composition by weight of different subcellular membranes of rat liver: CP = choline phosphoglycerides; EP = ethanolamine phosphoglycerides; S = sphingomyelin; PS = phosphatidylserine; PI = phosphatidylinositol; CL = cardiolipin (diphosphatidylglycerol).

fractions from plant cells. Glycolipids, especially monogalactosyl diacylglycerol, are the major lipid constituents of chloroplast lamellae, while the lower content of phospholipid is largely made up of phosphatidylglycerol. Plant fatty acids in general are highly unsaturated, and linolenic acid is often a major acyl component. Choline phosphoglycerides occur in plants and eukaryotic micro-organisms, but usually not in prokaryotic membranes where ethanolamine phosphoglycerides and phosphatidylglycerol predominate among the phospholipids of Gram negative and Gram positive bacteria respectively. Gram positive bacteria also have a high content of glycosyl diacylglycerols and contain aminoacyl glycerol phosphoglycerides, which appear to be unique to bacteria. Sterols and sphingolipids are generally absent from bacteria.

Proteins

The protein content of membranes varies considerably with their source. Since many enzymes are known to be associated with membranes, it might be expected that the protein content of a membrane will parallel its range of enzymic activity. This has been found to be true generally. Thus myelin (chapter 3), whose main function is that of an insulator, has only two known enzymic functions and contains only 20% protein by weight. Animal cell plasma membranes with approximately 50% protein, on the other hand, are clearly involved in many enzymic and transport processes, while inner mitochondrial membrane with much higher functional activity contains 75% protein. Not all proteins, however, have been associated with enzymic activity, and it is likely that some of the major proteins will have a structural or surface recognition role within the membrane complex.

Extrinsic and intrinsic proteins

Membrane proteins have been classified in two general categories, extrinsic and intrinsic based on their ease of dissociation from the membrane. *Extrinsic* proteins (also referred to as *peripheral* or *membrane-associated* proteins) are relatively easily dissociated by mild treatment, such as exposure of the membrane to media of very low or very high ionic strength, or of extreme pH. These proteins are released in soluble non-aggregated form and free from contaminating lipid. *Intrinsic* (or *integral*) proteins generally require more drastic treatment, with reagents such as detergents or chaotropic agents (chapter 7), before they can be dissociated from their membranes. Lipids often remain associated with these solubilized proteins, and removal of the lipid can lead to precipitation and aggregation of the protein. Largely because of such difficulties, the separation and characterization of membrane proteins has lagged behind corresponding studies on the lipid components. The introduction of the detergent sodium dodecyl sulphate (SDS) to protein chemistry, however, has simplified many problems. This detergent completely dissociates membranes into single polypeptide chains and lipids, by binding in a constant mass-ratio to the polypeptide chains. Since the charge of the SDS-polypeptide complex is dominated by that of the SDS, electrophoresis of a polypeptide mixture on acrylamide gels in the presence of SDS allows separation as a function of molecular size. A rapid estimate of molecular weight can hence be obtained. Moreover, the polypeptides can be separated preparatively, also on the basis of size, by gel filtration on columns equilibrated with SDS, which can be subsequently removed from the protein fractions by ion-exchange.

The *proteolipids* are a class of intrinsic proteins operationally defined by Folch in 1951 as hydrophobic lipoproteins soluble in chloroform-methanol mixtures but insoluble in water. These lipid-protein complexes occur in a wide range of membranes and usually represent between 1 and 5% of the total membrane protein, though in the case of myelin this figure may rise to 50–60%. The best characterized of the class are the myelin proteolipids (Folch proteolipids) which show no enzymic activity and have a very slow metabolic turnover. It has been suggested that they may have a purely structural role in myelin, possibly helping to maintain the asymmetric distribution of cholesterol in the membrane (chapter 6). Proteolipids with functional activity have been demonstrated in a variety of membranes, including those of insect and vertebrate muscle, mitochondria and erythrocytes. Such proteolipids have been variously reported as acting as receptors, ionophores or carriers—roles for which they are particularly well suited in view of their hydrophobic nature (chapter 8). Purification of proteolipids has been greatly aided by the recent development of hydrophobic gels which allow their fractionation in apolar media. Complete separation of lipid and protein has not, in general, been effected.

It is now clear that considerable diversity is possible among membrane proteins. Plasma membranes of many animal cells, for instance, contain 10–20 different types of proteins. A similar range of proteins has been shown in other membranes, such as endoplasmic reticulum and surface membranes of bacterial cells. Some specialized membranes, on the other hand, may have just one or two protein components. The disc membranes of retinal rods have been shown to contain only one major protein, rhodopsin, which comprises some 50% by weight of the membrane (chapter 8).

Amino acid content of membrane proteins

Currently accepted models of membrane structure (chapter 6) distinguish between the locations of extrinsic and intrinsic membrane proteins. Both are believed to be globular proteins which are positioned relative to the lipid bilayer as shown in figure 5.35. Intrinsic proteins penetrate, and occasionally cross, the hydrophobic interior of the membrane, whereas extrinsic proteins are believed to be associated with the polar head groups of the lipid bilayer. Soluble globular proteins, in general, might be expected to sequester their non-polar side chains within the interior of the molecule, and to expose their polar residues to the aqueous surroundings, in much the same way as do the phospholipids in a bilayer. This also applies to extrinsic membrane proteins, the exterior groups of which will be in contact either with water or with the polar head groups of the lipid bilayer (figure 5.35). Intrinsic proteins, on the other hand, might be expected to have non-polar residues not only within the interior of the protein molecule but also on those external surfaces in contact with the hydrophobic lipid of the membrane (figure 5.35). This suggests a requirement for a higher overall content of non-polar amino acids in intrinsic than in extrinsic or in soluble non-membrane proteins. Many intrinsic membrane proteins have indeed been shown to contain a

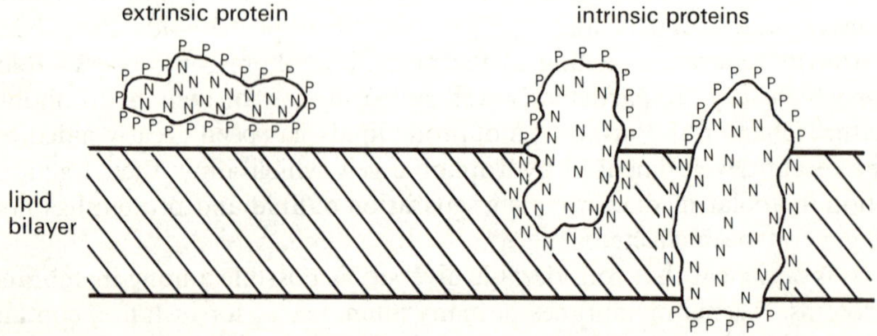

Figure 5.35. Location of extrinsic and intrinsic proteins relative to the lipid bilayer of the membrane. The distribution of polar (P) and non-polar (N) amino acids is schematically illustrated for the two protein types.

relatively high percentage of non-polar amino acids. Comparisons based on such a percentage basis are clearly dependent on the somewhat arbitary classification of individual amino acids as 'polar' or 'non-polar'. A more sophisticated approach is to assign a hydrophobicity index to individual amino acids on the basis of their solubility in solvents of different polarity. The 'average hydrophobicity' of a protein can then be assessed from its amino acid content. Apparent anomalies occur in all analyses based on overall amino acid content, however, and it is probable that demonstration of particular hydrophobic sections in intrinsic proteins is generally more significant.

Proteins of human erythrocyte membrane

The erythrocyte plasma membrane is available in large quantities and can be obtained uncontaminated by other cell organelles and membranes. There is accordingly considerable information concerning the proteins of this membrane, and an outline of such data will serve to give an indication of the types, and particularly locations of membrane proteins in general, although it must be borne in mind that the erythrocyte is not a typical cell. Erythrocytes can be made to swell in distilled water when they become 'leaky', losing their haemoglobin and other cytoplasmic constituents (chapter 4). In this state both internal and external faces of the remaining plasma membrane or *ghost* are accessible to external reagents. It is possible to 'reseal' ghosts in isotonic sodium chloride solution, when the membrane regains the relative impermeability of the original intact erythrocyte. In this state, as in intact erythrocytes, only the external face of the membrane is accessible to subsequently added reagents. It is accordingly possible selectively to modify proteins exposed at both the outer and inner surfaces of the plasma membrane with radiochemical labels or proteolytic enzymes. Subsequent solubilization of treated membranes in SDS, followed by gel electrophoresis, can show which compounds have been modified, and consequently indicate the location of the labelled proteins on the inner or outer surfaces of the membrane.

Erythrocytes contain 7–9 major protein components, ranging in size from 30,000 to over 200,000 daltons, among which are the enzymes glyceraldehyde 3-phosphate dehydrogenase, Na^+, K^+-ATPase and acetylcholinesterase. *Spectrin* or *tektin* constitutes some 30% by weight of the total membrane protein and is located on the inner surface of the membrane. It is composed of two large polypeptides (each greater than

200,000 daltons) which can be readily solubilized along with a smaller polypeptide (approximately 45,000 daltons) by washing membranes with hypotonic buffers. It has been suggested that these polypeptides might be involved in a contractile protein system controlling the mechanical properties of the membrane. A more specific role concerned with the lateral motion of intrinsic proteins within the plane of the membrane has recently been proposed and will be outlined later (chapter 6).

The most abundant single protein of the human erythrocyte membrane migrates as the third major protein band on gel electrophoresis in SDS. This *Band III component* has a molecular weight of 90,000–100,000 daltons and comprises some 20–30% of the total membrane protein. It is a glycoprotein containing approximately 8% by weight of carbohydrate and is believed to span the membrane with portions exposed on both faces. The carbohydrate is localized on the outer surface of the membrane.

Considerably more is known about another intrinsic glycoprotein which spans the erythrocyte membrane. This is the *major sialoglycoprotein or glycophorin*, which comprises a few percent of the total membrane protein and itself contains 40% protein and 60% carbohydrate, including most of the sialic acid of the cell. Estimates of the molecular weight have been complicated because proteins containing more than 20% by weight of carbohydrate behave anomalously on gel electrophoresis in SDS, and values ranging from 31,000 to 55,000 daltons have been quoted. Three major sections of the whole glycoprotein have been distinguished following labelling studies on intact erythrocytes and leaky ghosts. The *N*-terminal end of the polypeptide chain contains largely polar amino acids and protrudes from the outer surface of the membrane. All the carbohydrate of the molecule is contained in oligosaccharide side chains

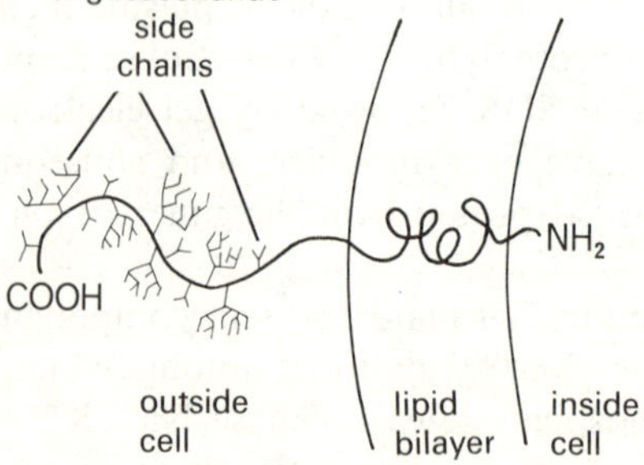

Figure 5.36. Schematic diagram of the major sialoglycoprotein (glycophorin) of erythrocyte membrane.

attached to the polypeptide backbone of this section. The middle section of the peptide chain, containing a high proportion of non-polar amino acids and no carbohydrate, is located within the hydrophobic interior of the membrane and is not accessible at either face. Finally, the *C*-terminal end of the polypeptide, containing no carbohydrate, is believed to extend from the inner surface of the membrane into the cytoplasm. A schematic diagram of the glycoprotein is shown in figure 5.36.

The carbohydrate is made up of the sugars D-galactose, D-mannose N-acetyl-D-glucosamine, *N*-acetyl-D-galactosamine, L-fucose and sialic acid. Because of their involvement in blood group specificity and receptor sites for viruses and lectins (chapter 7), the oligosaccharide side chains have been the subject of considerable structural investigations which will be discussed in chapter 7.

Acetylcholinesterase and glyceraldehyde 3-phosphate dehydrogenase are localized on the outer and inner membrane surfaces respectively of the erythrocyte membrane, while Na^+,K^+-ATPase, as might be expected from its ion transport role (chapter 9) spans the membrane. A schematic model of the erythrocyte membrane showing the location of the proteins discussed above is shown in figure 5.37. Evidence has recently been presented that the two glycoproteins, Band III and the major sialoglycoprotein are combined in a transmembrane oligomeric structure which interacts with the extrinsic protein spectrin on the inner face of the membrane. This will be further discussed in chapter 6.

It has already been mentioned that the erythrocyte is an atypical

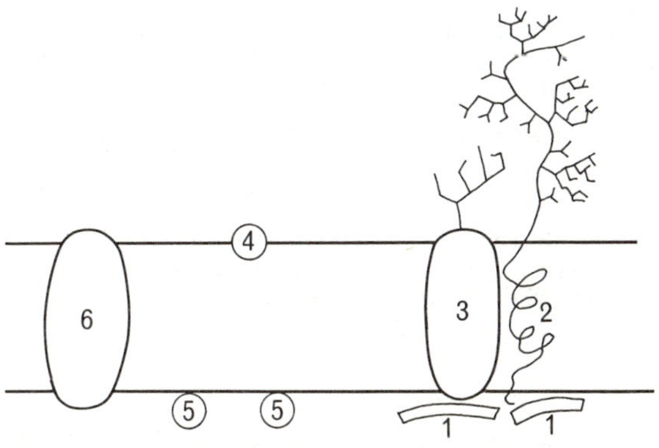

Figure 5.37. Schematic diagram of the major erythrocyte membrane proteins: 1 spectrin, 2 major sialoglycoprotein (glycophorin), 3 Band III glycoprotein, 4 acetylcholinesterase, 5 glyceraldehyde 3-phosphate dehydrogenase, 6 Na^+,K^+-ATPase.

cell, and results found in this sytem cannot necessarily be extrapolated to other membranes. Mitochondrial and chloroplast membranes are certainly more complex, containing 20–40 species of polypeptide chain, with many interrelated enzyme functions. It may be that many erythrocyte membrane proteins will have parallels in other membranes. Glycoproteins, for example, are known to be involved in the outer surfaces of an increasing range of cell membranes (chapter 7), and spectrin-type proteins may well have a general role on the internal surface of plasma membranes. The study of membrane protein is still in its infancy, and an explosive growth of knowledge can be expected in the next few years.

SUMMARY

1. Approximately 40% of the dry weight of membranes is composed of *lipids*, most of which are polar lipids containing hydrophilic and hydrophobic sections linked through a bridging moiety. The bridge may be supplied by a glycerol molecule, a sphinganine derivative, or the body of a steroid molecule. The hydrophobic tails of polar lipids are made up of long aliphatic chains.

2. *Phospholipids* are polar lipids in which the hydrophilic head group consists of one of a range of complex alcohols joined by a phosphodiester linkage to the terminal hydroxy-group of a substituted glycerol or sphinganine-type molecule.

3. The hydrophilic head groups of *glycolipids* consist of mono or oligo-saccharide units glycosidically linked to the terminal hydroxy-group of one of the three types of bridging moiety listed in (1). The hydrophilic section of *sterols* is simply the C-3 hydroxy-group of the steroid molecule.

4. There is more information concerning the *lipid composition* of animal than of microbial or plant membranes. Within the same animal species, corresponding membranes from different organs have different lipid compositions as do different subcellular membranes from the same cell. Corresponding membranes from different vertebrates generally have similar lipid compositions.

5. Some 60% of the dry weight of membranes is made up of *protein*, which is classified as *intrinsic* or *extrinsic* depending on its ease of dissociation from the membrane. Intrinsic proteins are believed to be intercalated in the lipid bilayer of the membrane.

6. Erythrocyte membranes contain 7–9 major protein components, including enzymes and two major glycoproteins. One of the glycoproteins, glycophorin, contains 60% carbohydrate, the structure of which has been extensively studied.

CHAPTER 6

STRUCTURAL ORGANIZATION

IN OUR CONSIDERATIONS OF THE CHEMICAL COMPONENTS OF MEMBRANES we have partially anticipated discussion of their organization in the membrane. Thus, the hydrophilic-hydrophobic nature of membrane lipids was stressed as being compatible with their arrangement as a bilayer (figure 5.3) and in the present chapter we shall be largely concerned with models of membrane structure which incorporate a lipid bilayer as their primary feature.

The Davson-Danielli-Robertson model

Gorter and Grendel in 1925 reported that lipids extracted from erythrocyte membranes spread as a monolayer at an air-water interface (figure 5.29) so as to occupy an area which was approximately twice the total surface area of the intact erythrocytes. They pointed out that this is consistent with the presence in the erythrocyte membrane of a lipid bilayer, in which the hydrocarbon chains all occupy the centre of the bilayer and the polar head groups face outward (cf. figure 5.3). In fact the figures of Gorter and Grendel arose as a result of two errors. Not only were the erythrocyte lipids incompletely extracted, but the erythrocyte surface area was underestimated. These errors partially cancelled each other, and subsequent work has shown that sufficient lipid is indeed available to cover the erythrocyte surface completely as a bilayer, but only if that bilayer is highly expanded.

Apparently independently, Danielli and Davson in 1935 proposed the presence of a lipid bilayer in membranes and, in order to explain what seemed to be anomalously low surface tensions of biological membranes compared with model lipid systems, postulated that the lipid core of natural membranes was sandwiched between two layers of protein. Although this conclusion also was later found to have been based on a misconception, in that phospholipids alone can produce the low surface tensions shown by natural membranes, the Davson-Danielli model dominated discussion of membrane structure for over thirty years. Following the development of electron microscopy, it was found that biological membranes from many sources show a typical three-layered structure (figure 3.1) which can be interpreted in terms of the Davson-Danielli protein-lipid-protein sandwich model. The widespread occurrence of such apparently similar membranes led Robertson in the late 1950s and early 1960s to promote the concept of a universal *unit membrane* based on the Davson-Danielli model. The Davson-Danielli-Robertson model was supported largely by electron microscopic and X-ray diffraction evidence and, as can be seen in figure 6.1, suggested an asymmetric distribution of protein about the lipid core.

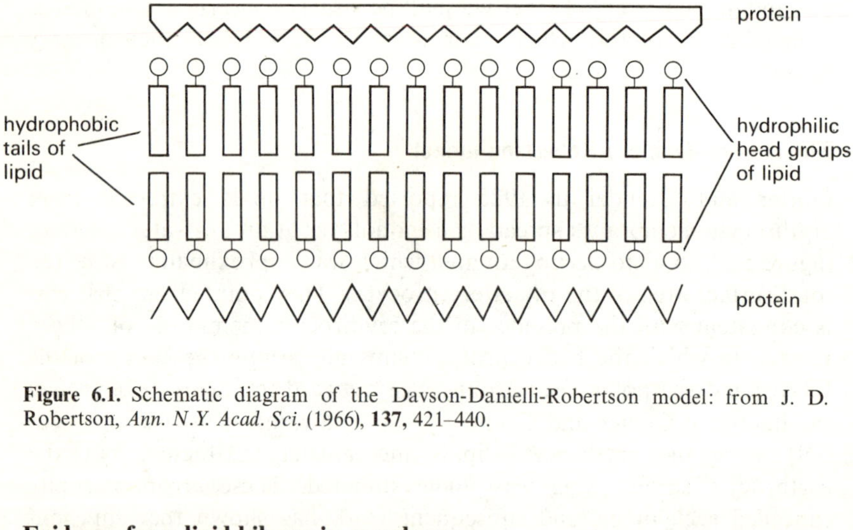

Figure 6.1. Schematic diagram of the Davson-Danielli-Robertson model: from J. D. Robertson, *Ann. N.Y. Acad. Sci.* (1966), **137,** 421–440.

Evidence for a lipid bilayer in membranes

The fact that sufficient lipid is available in membranes to form a continuous, if expanded, lipid bilayer has already been mentioned. It has been known for many years that small molecules with a high oil-water partition coefficient penetrate cell membranes most readily, and this is clearly consistent with the idea that the permeability barrier of the cell is a hydrophobic barrier formed by lipid (chapter 1).

The lipid bilayer is thermodynamically stable and is the major structural unit of phospholipid-water systems. Above the transition

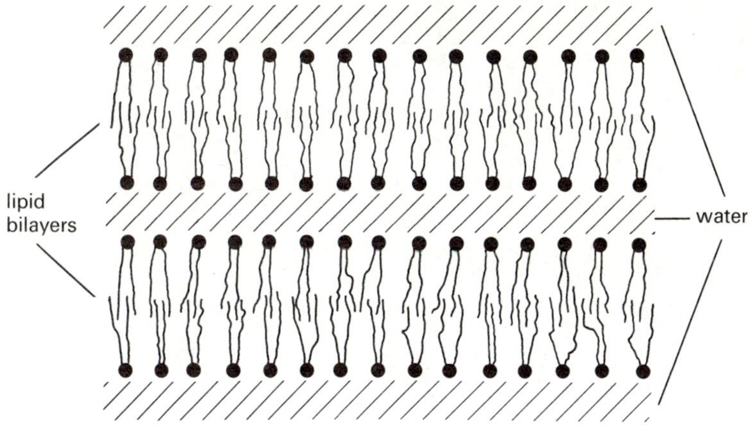

Figure 6.2. Bulk lamellar phase of phosphatidylcholine-water system containing less than 40% water above its transition temperature.

temperature (see p. 110) phosphatidylcholine with low water content exists in a lamellar phase (figure 6.2) consisting of stacked bilayers containing water between the lipid bilayers. As the water content is increased from 0 to 40% (by weight), the width of the aqueous layers increases, and the system remains homogeneous.

Above 40% water a two-phase system results in which maximally-hydrated multilamellar vesicles (*liposomes*) are dispersed in water (figure 6.3). Such vesicles can be produced simply by shaking phosphatidylcholine in water, and tend to precipitate on standing. More stable homogeneous liposome preparations can be obtained by ultrasonication, which promotes formation of single-bilayer-bounded vesicles (figure 6.4) which have been shown by many methods, including nuclear magnetic resonance (n.m.r.) and electron spin resonance (e.s.r.) (chapter 11) to be completely sealed. They accordingly constitute a simple model system for permeability studies of lipid bilayers, particularly as swelling of the vesicles can be followed by measurements of light scattering. The water and small-molecule permeabilities of a number of phospholipid and phospholipid-cholesterol systems have been examined in this way and found to approximate to those of natural membranes. Cholesterol was found to decrease liposome permeability in a manner which parallels its ability to condense phospholipid monolayers (chapter 5).

(*a*)

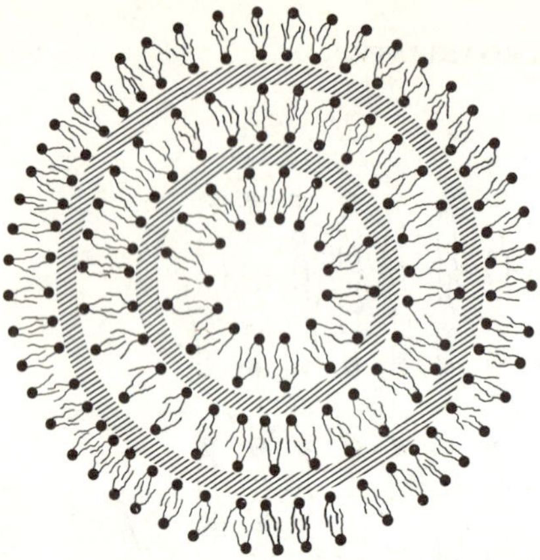

Figure 6.3. Multilamellar vesicles of phosphatidylcholine dispersed in excess water. (*a*) Diagrammatic representation showing only three concentric bilayers. (*b*) Freeze-fracture electron micrograph (see p. 102) showing a number of successive bilayers A: from H. Hauser *et al., J. Mol. Biol.* (1970) **53,** 419–433 by courtesy of Dr. E. G. Finer, Unilever Research, Welwyn.

(*b*)

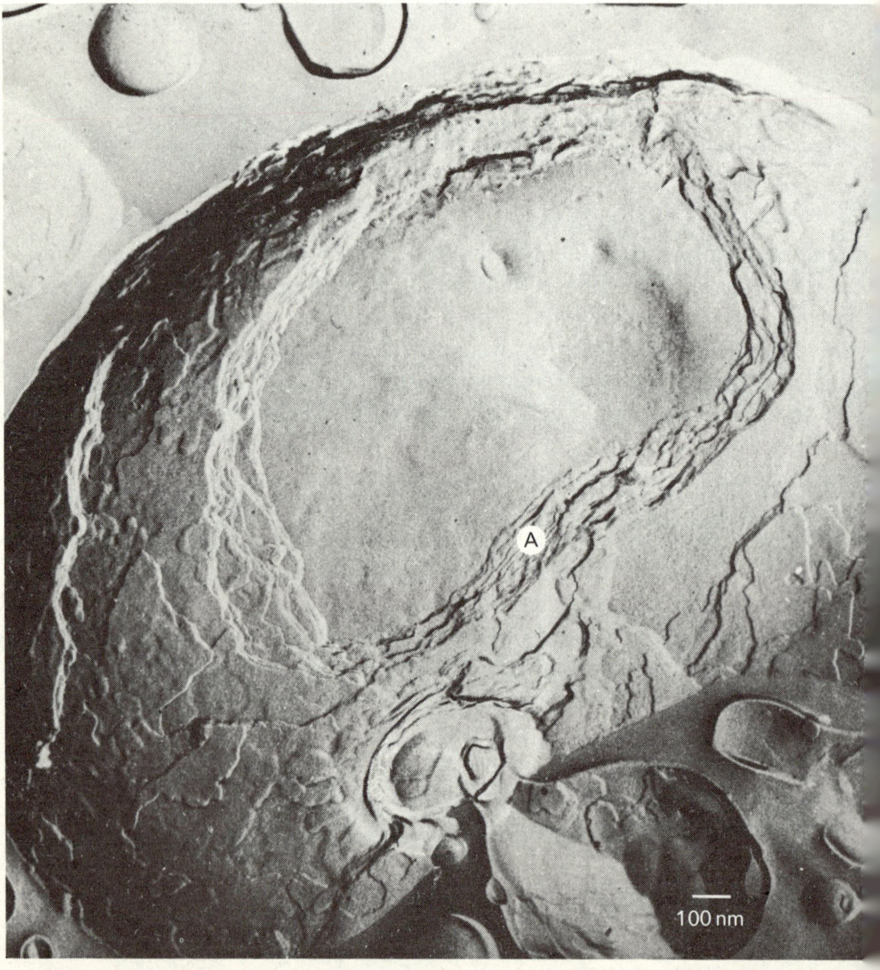

Figure 6.4. Diagrammatic representation of single-bilayer-bounded vesicles obtained by ultrasonication of phosphatidylcholine in water.

A convenient model system for studying the electrical properties of lipid bilayers is the *black lipid film* (figure 6.5). A dilute solution of lipid in a hydrocarbon solvent is applied across a hole (about 2 mm diameter) separating two electrically-insulated compartments filled with electrolyte. Under reflected light and at low magnification, the lipid layer can be observed to thin over a period of about 15 minutes, until it is reduced to bilayer thickness over most of the aperture. At this stage light reflected from the front and back surfaces of the film is very nearly in counter phase, and the film appears to be black. The capacitances and permeabilities of black films of phospholipid and phospholipid-cholesterol mixtures have been measured and found to agree well with

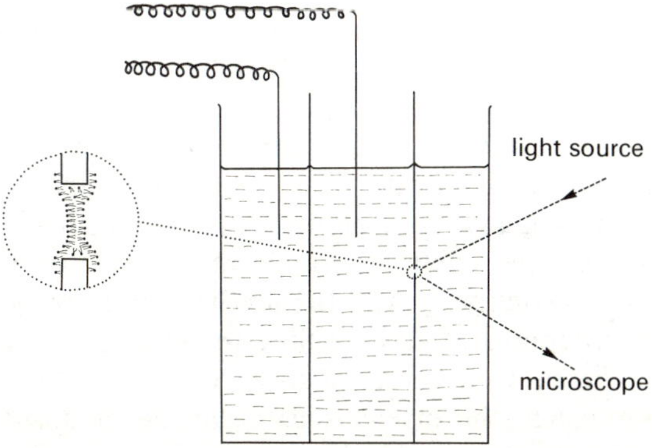

Figure 6.5. Simple apparatus for the study of black lipid films.

values for some biological membranes. Although the electrical resistance of black lipid films is generally very much higher than that of natural membranes, the resistance may be greatly reduced following incorporation of certain proteins into the lipid film (chapter 8). A particularly interesting observation is that cation and anion selectivities can be induced in both black films and natural membranes by addition of certain cyclic polypeptide antibiotics (chapter 10).

Incorporation of cholesterol into black lipid films stabilizes the film and reduces water permeability, consistent with its ability to condense phospholipid monolayers (chapter 5) and to reduce the fluidity of hydrocarbon chains (see p. 112). Cholesterol also reduces the effect of the ion-carrying antibiotics, probably by inhibiting their diffusion in the bilayer.

Distribution of protein in membranes

There is clearly considerable support for the presence of a lipid bilayer in membranes. Evidence for the distribution of protein as depicted in the Davson-Danielli-Robertson model is less convincing. Electron micrographs of a wide variety of membranes show a typical 'tramline' appearance (figure 3.1) which directly suggests the trilaminar structure of the Davson-Danielli-Robertson model. The true significance of the staining patterns observed after $KMnO_4$ or OsO_4 fixation (commonly used in electron microscopy) is not, however, clear. While the three layers seen in electron micrographs could be consistent with the protein-lipid-protein structure, they might well simply reflect the hydrophilic-hydrophobic-hydrophilic sequence across a lipid bilayer. Indeed electron micrographs have been obtained from artificial bilayers which are remarkably similar to those of natural membranes (figure 6.6).

Much of the experimental support for the Davson-Danielli-Robertson model was derived from X-ray diffraction data of myelin. The myelin sheath forms an insulating coat around nerve axons and is produced by a spiral wrapping of many layers of plasma membrane from the Schwann cell (chapter 3). The trilaminar appearance of the Schwann cell membrane and its continuity with the myelin spiral can be clearly seen in electron micrographs of a nerve fibre in the process of myelination (figure 3.13). The electron density distribution across the width of one plasma membrane in the myelin sheath can be obtained from X-ray diffraction patterns, and is made up of two fairly broad maxima separated by a trough (figure 11.25). Such patterns can be explained on

Figure 6.6. Electron micrograph of an artificial bilayer formed from phosphatidylethanolamine in *n*-decane. The bilayer was fixed with $La(NO_3)_3$ and $KMnO_4$ and dehydrated by air-drying at room temperature: from J. M. Palmier and D. O. Hall, *Progr. Biophys. Mol. Biol.* (1972), **24,** 127–176 by courtesy of Professor J. W. Greenawalt, School of Medicine, The Johns Hopkins University, Baltimore.

the basis of the Davson-Danielli-Robertson model, when the electron-dense outer humps would arise largely from the protein layers which are relatively rich in the heavier O and N atoms. The central trough would represent the light C and H atoms of the hydrocarbon chains. Much the same distribution is also given by a simple bilayer of phospholipid (figure 11.24), and the X-ray diffraction patterns of myelin do not tell us much about the protein of the membrane.

The Davson-Danielli-Robertson model envisaged a central lipid bilayer of some 4·0 nm thickness sandwiched between two protein layers, each approximately 2·0 nm thick, so making a total membrane width of about 7·5 nm as determined from electron micrographs of $KMnO_4$-stained membranes. Membrane dimensions vary both with their source and the means of measurement, but the space generally available for protein on the basis of the Davson-Danielli-Robertson model is such that a significant proportion of the membrane protein could be expected to be in the extended β-pleated sheet structure (figure 6.7). This structure has ionic side-chains in contact with both the polar lipid head groups of the bilayer and with the aqueous environment outside the membrane. In such a system the ionic groups at the lipid-protein interface are effectively buried in a non-polar environment, without access to the aqueous medium. Moreover a significant proportion of the non-polar residues in

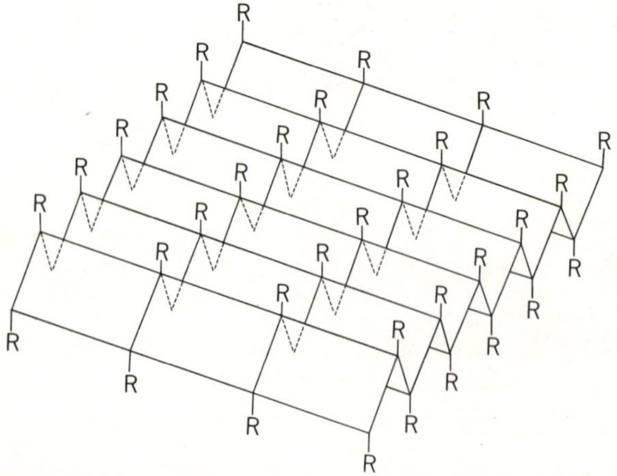

Figure 6.7. β-pleated sheet conformation of proteins. The polypeptide chains are cross-linked by hydrogen bonds. The amino acid side chains (R) project above and below the plane of the pleated sheet.

the protein must be exposed to the aqueous surroundings. A system of much lower free energy would result if the hydrophobic groupings could all be gathered together in a non-polar environment, leaving as many of the polar residues as possible in direct contact with water.

The mosaic model

Such a situation obtains in the *mosaic model*, forms of which were proposed in the mid 1960s by Singer and by Wallach. This model is illustrated in figure 6.8, where it can be seen to involve globular protein embedded in, and even crossing, a lipid bilayer core. In such a structure the polar groups of lipid and protein are in direct contact with the aqueous surroundings, while the non-polar residues of both molecular species are sequestered in the heart of the structure, away from water.

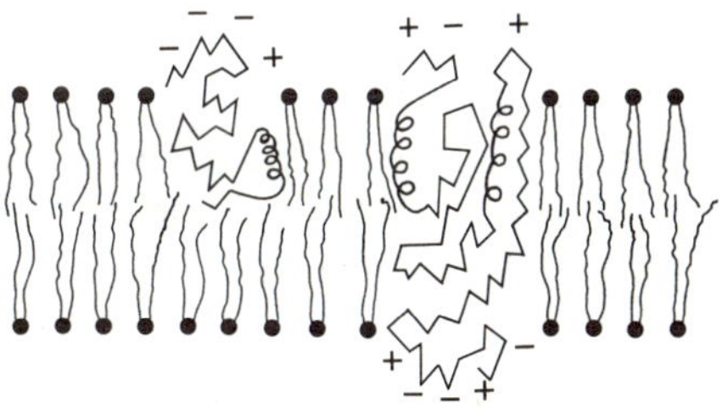

Figure 6.8. The mosaic model of membrane structure. The intrinsic proteins are shown as globular molecules partially embedded in the lipid bilayer. The protruding parts carry the ionic residues of the protein, while the apolar residues are largely in the embedded parts: from S. J. Singer and G. L. Nicholson, *Science* (1972), **175,** 720–731.

Apart from thermodynamic considerations, the mosaic model is attractive in that it offers a potential route through the lipid bilayer barrier by way of the transmembrane protein. No such provision had been made in the original Davson-Danielli concept, although Danielli did modify his model in 1958 to include protein-lined pores which spanned the membrane.

Evidence for the mosaic model

If the mosaic model is conceptually more attractive than that of Davson, Danielli and Robertson, how does it fit experimental facts? Like the earlier model, the mosaic model is based on a lipid bilayer, and many of the data quoted in support of the presence of a lipid bilayer in membranes are relevant to both models. The relationship of the total amount of membrane lipid to the membrane surface area is, in fact, rather better accounted for by the mosaic model. Repeats of Gorter and Grendel's monolayer experiments with erythrocyte membrane lipids indicate that sufficient lipid is available to form a continuous bilayer around the erythrocyte, as in the Davson-Danielli-Robertson model, only if the bilayer is in a highly expanded state. The lipid bilayers of membranes are, however, believed to be compact close-packed structures, and sufficient lipid is not available to cover the erythrocyte surface completely with such a structure. The intercalated protein of the mosaic model effectively decreases the surface area to be covered by lipid, and it can be shown that a relatively close-packed bilayer can be formed in the remaining surface area by the available erythrocyte lipid.

The arrangement of protein in the two models is, of course, completely different. We have already seen that electron microscopic and X-ray diffraction data quoted in support of the protein arrangement of the Davson-Danielli-Robertson model were probably more relevant to the presence of a lipid bilayer than to any particular protein arrangement. So how may the alternative protein locations be distinguished? Membranes are generally thicker than lipid bilayers, and the Davson-Danielli-Robertson model provides two layers of protein to explain this. It might seem that the mosaic model would predict a membrane thickness much closer to that of a lipid bilayer. This is not necessarily the case, since not only may the intercalated proteins project some way from the surface of the lipid bilayer but, as mentioned in chapter 5, globular extrinsic proteins are envisaged as being associated with the polar head groups of the lipid bilayer, so adding to the average membrane thickness.

The association of the extrinsic proteins with the membrane is by means of ionic interactions with the lipid polar head groups, just as postulated for the protein of the Davson-Danielli-Robertson model. The mosaic model differs in that only a fraction of its protein is so bound to the membrane. Such an arrangement is supported by the observation that variations in ionic strength sufficient to disrupt ionic associations do not in general extensively dissociate membrane proteins. Further evidence that the polar lipid head groups are not of major importance in the attachment of most of the protein to the bilayer is provided by the fact that 60–70% of the lipid head groups can be enzymically removed without protein loss.

Some indication of the location of membrane proteins can be obtained from consideration of their structure. Thus calculations based on the total amino acid content (see p. 86) of many intrinsic proteins has indicated that these proteins are relatively hydrophobic, consistent with the immersion of the proteins in a non-polar lipid environment. Moreover certain intrinsic proteins, e.g. glycophorin of erythrocyte membrane (see p. 88), cytochrome b_5 and cytochrome b_5 reductase of endoplasmic reticulum membrane, have been shown to contain sections rich in non-polar amino acids which are intimately associated with the membrane and cannot be removed by proteolytic enzymes. The secondary structures of membrane proteins are also relevant to their location in the membrane. The outer protein sheets of the Davson-Danielli-Robertson model should contain a large proportion of β-pleated sheet (see p. 98), whereas the globular proteins of the mosaic model would be expected to contain a significant amount of α-helical conformation (figure 6.9). Optical rotatory

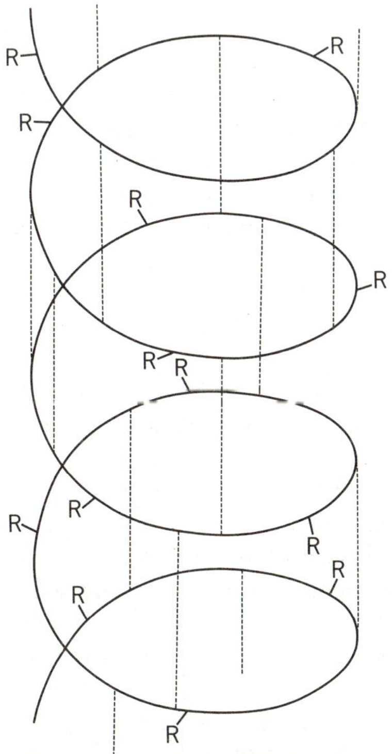

Figure 6.9. α-helical conformation of protein. The amino acid side chains (R) extend outward from the helix. Intrachain hydrogen bonds (------) join peptide bonds in successive turns of the helix.

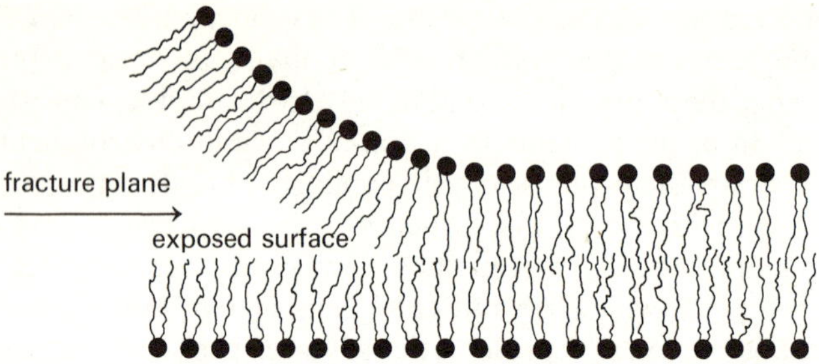

Figure 6.10. Freeze-fracture of a lipid bilayer showing the plane of fracture and the exposed surface.

dispersion and circular dichroism spectra (chapter 11) of a wide range of membranes show that a considerable percentage of the protein is present as α-helix with the remainder largely in the random coil conformation, with generally little β-conformation. This evidence strongly supports the mosaic model of membrane structure.

Perhaps the most dramatic evidence for the existence of globular proteins embedded in the membrane comes from the recently-developed technique of *freeze-etching* or *freeze-fracture electron microscopy*. In this procedure, a fresh membrane specimen is rapidly frozen under vacuum, and fractured with a microtome knife; this is believed to cleave the membrane along its interior hydrophobic face (figure 6.10). Frozen water is then sublimed (etched) from the exposed surface, which is metal shadowed and replicated. Electron microscopy of the surface replica reveals the topography of the interior hydrophobic exposed face. A characteristic feature of the cleaved surface of many membranes studied in this way is a smooth matrix interrupted by a large number of fairly uniform particles (figure 6.11).

This pattern can be most satisfactorily explained by the mosaic model, provided that the matrix particles are protein. Thus, if the fracture line circumvents any intrinsic proteins (e.g. protein A, figure 6.12) which cross the mid-plane of the membrane, such proteins will remain as part of the exposed surface. Intrinsic proteins (proteins B and C, figure 6.12) which do not interrupt the membrane cleavage plane will not appear on the electron micrographs.

Whereas freeze-fracture electron microscopy has the advantage of avoiding problems of conventional thin-sectioning methods, such as possible changes in the specimen resulting from fixation, staining and embedding procedures, it has the disadvantage that the structural features so

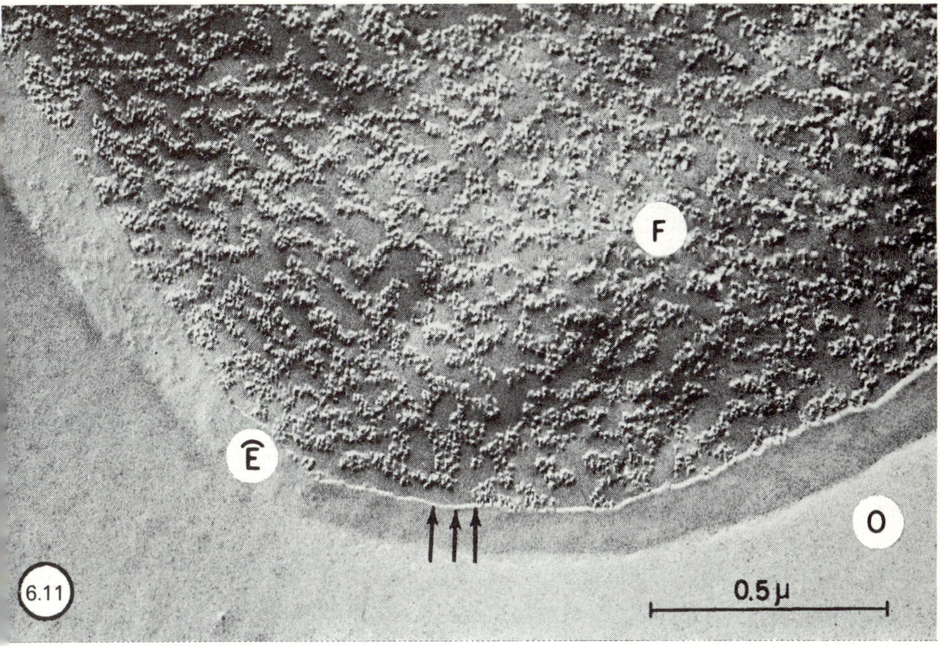

Figure 6.11. Freeze-fracture electron micrograph of an erythrocyte membrane. The fracture plane F is bounded by the arrows and can be seen to be covered with particles of approximate diameter 8·5 nm from P. Pinto da Silva and D. Branton, *J. Cell. Biol.* (1970) **45**, 598–605, by courtesy of Professor D. Branton. The Biological Laboratories, Harvard University.

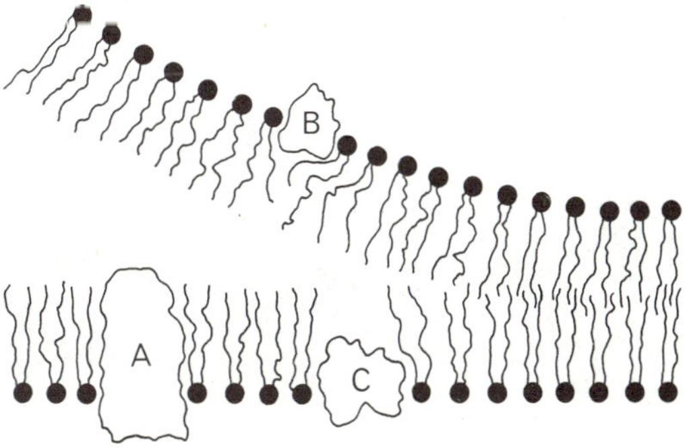

Figure 6.12. Illustration of the exposure of globular intrinsic protein by freeze-fracture of a membrane lipid bilayer. Only protein A, which crosses the mid-plane of the membrane, will be associated with the exposed surface.

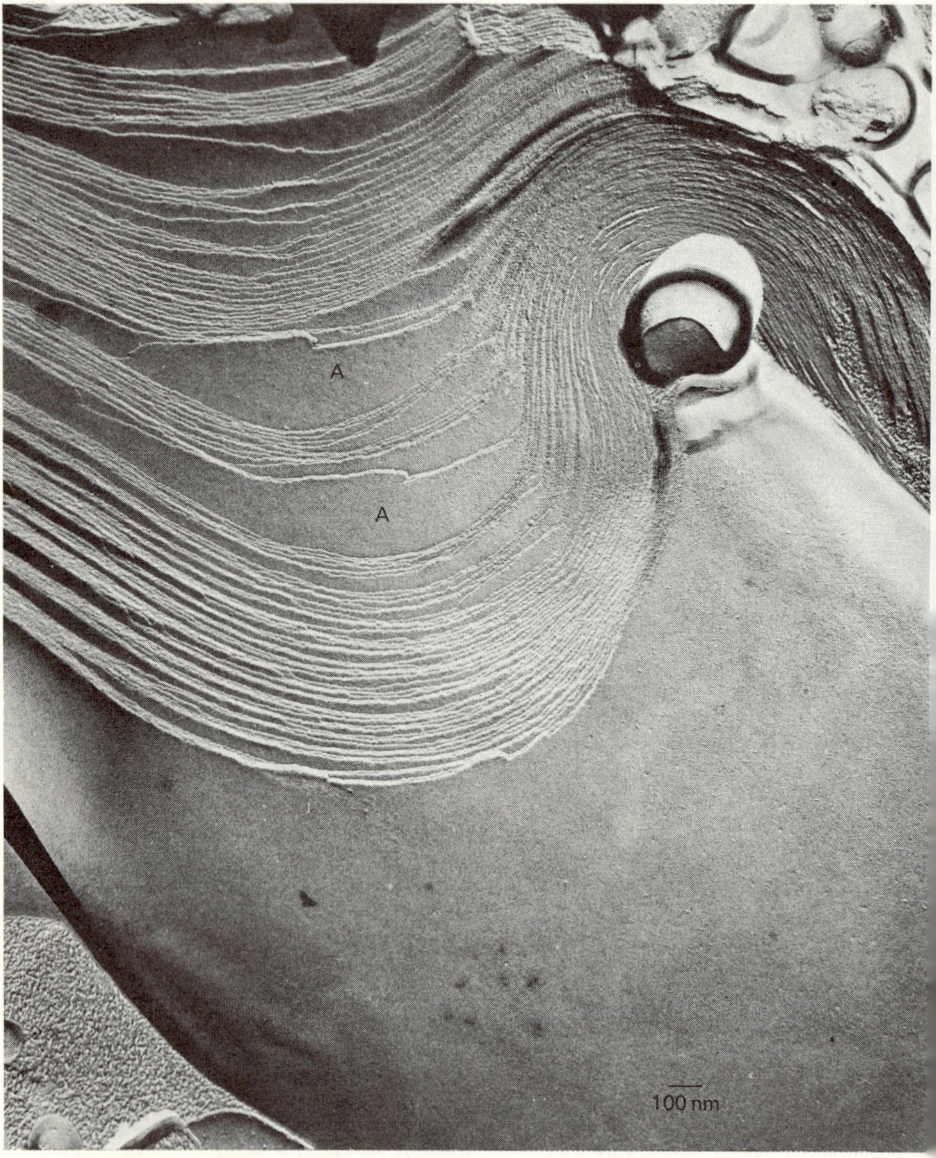

Figure 6.13. Freeze-fracture electron micrograph of rat myelin. The exposed surface of the freeze-fracture faces (A) can be seen to be particle-free: from D. Branton, *Expt. Cell. Res.* (1967), **45,** 703–707 by courtesy of Professor D. Branton, The Biological Laboratories, Harvard University.

strikingly demonstrated in the electron micrographs cannot be chemically identified. Direct characterization of the matrix particles seen in membrane freeze-fracture electron micrographs is accordingly difficult. However, much indirect evidence is consistent with their protein nature. Thus a rough correlation is possible between the functional activity of a membrane and the fractional area of its freeze-fracture surface occupied by particles. Myelin, for example, has little apparent function save that of an insulator surrounding nerve axons, and presents a completely particle-free surface in freeze-fracture electron micrographs (figure 6.13). Protein-free phospholipids also show smooth electron micrographs. Membranes of chloroplast lamellae and retinal rods, on the other hand, are highly functional and show freeze-fracture electron micrographs in which most of the surface area consists of particles (figure 6.14). Since the various activities of membranes are generally associated with proteins, the identity of the latter with the intercalated particles is suggested.

The distribution of particles in the freeze-fracture plane of the erythrocyte has been correlated with the distribution on the outer surface of the membrane of both the major sialoglycoprotein (glycophorin) and the Band III glycoprotein (chapter 5), both of which have been shown to cross the membrane. It has accordingly been suggested that the particles in the freeze-fracture plane are oligomeric structures containing both Band III and glycophorin polypeptides. Such an association would account for both the number and size (8·5 nm diameter) of the particles. The correspondence between the distribution of Band III glycoprotein on the outer surface of the erythrocyte membrane with that of the membrane intercalated particles is shown in the freeze-fracture electron micrograph of figure 6.15.

Other models of membrane structure

There is clearly considerable support for the interrelationship of lipid and protein in membranes along the lines of the mosaic model, which, in its refinement as the *fluid mosaic model* (next section), is now widely accepted as best explaining the accumulated data from a variety of membranes.

Other models, apart from that of Davson, Danielli and Robertson, have been proposed and largely abandoned, although some of their features have been incorporated into the currently accepted theory. Prominent among these other postulated structural arrangements has been the *subunit model* championed by Green and others. The subunit

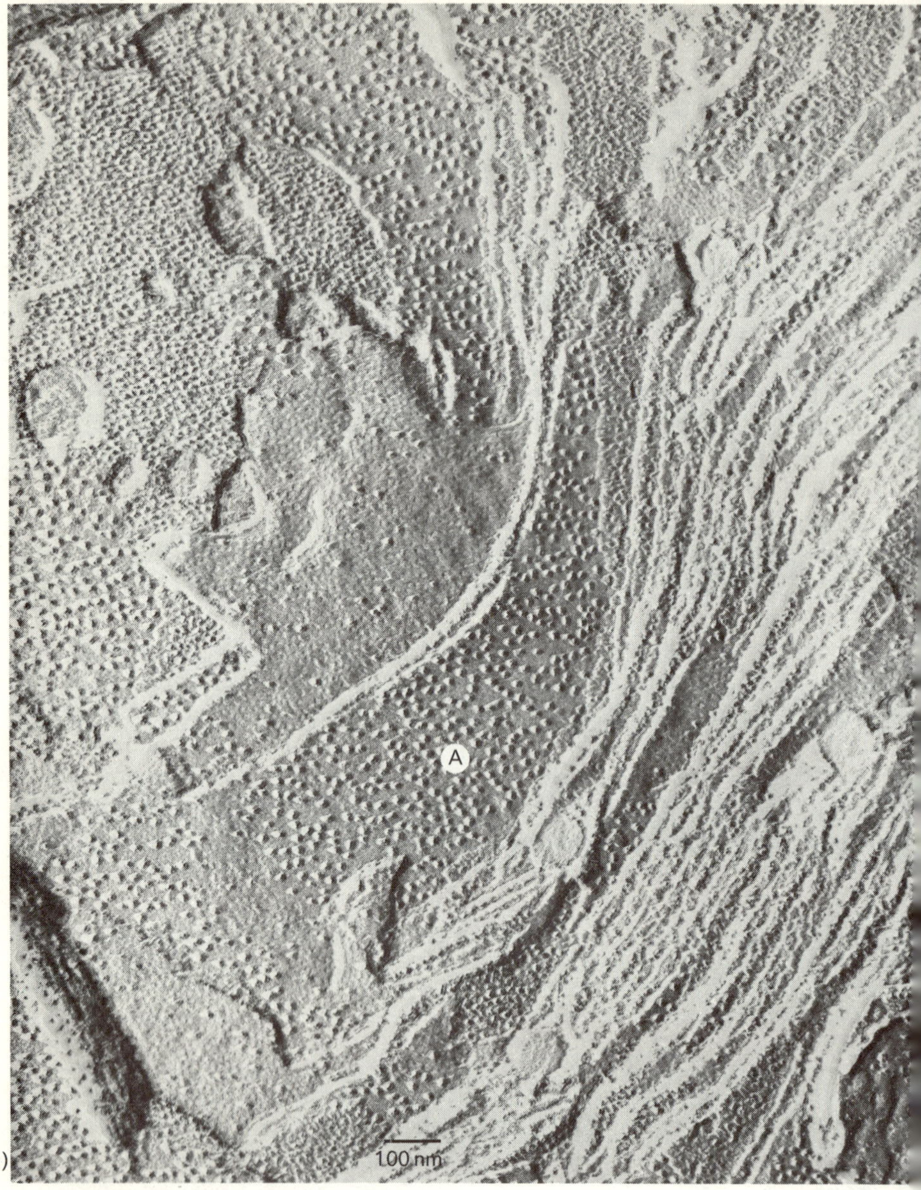

(*a*)

Figure 6.14. Freeze-fracture electron micrographs of (*a*) chloroplast lamellae: from D. Branton and R. B. Park, *J. Ultrastruct. Res.* (1967), **19,** 283–303 and (*b*) retinal rod outer segment: from A. N. Clark and D. Branton, *Z. Zellforsch. Mikrosk. Anat.* (1968), **91,** 586–603. The exposed surfaces of the freeze-fracture faces A are in each case covered with particles. That of chloroplast lamellae (*a*) shows particles 16–20 nm in diameter, while that of retinal rod (*b*) shows a worn cobblestone appearance with irregular 'stones' of the order of 20–25 nm diameter: both micrographs by courtesy of Professor D. Branton, The Biological Laboratories, Harvard University.

(b)

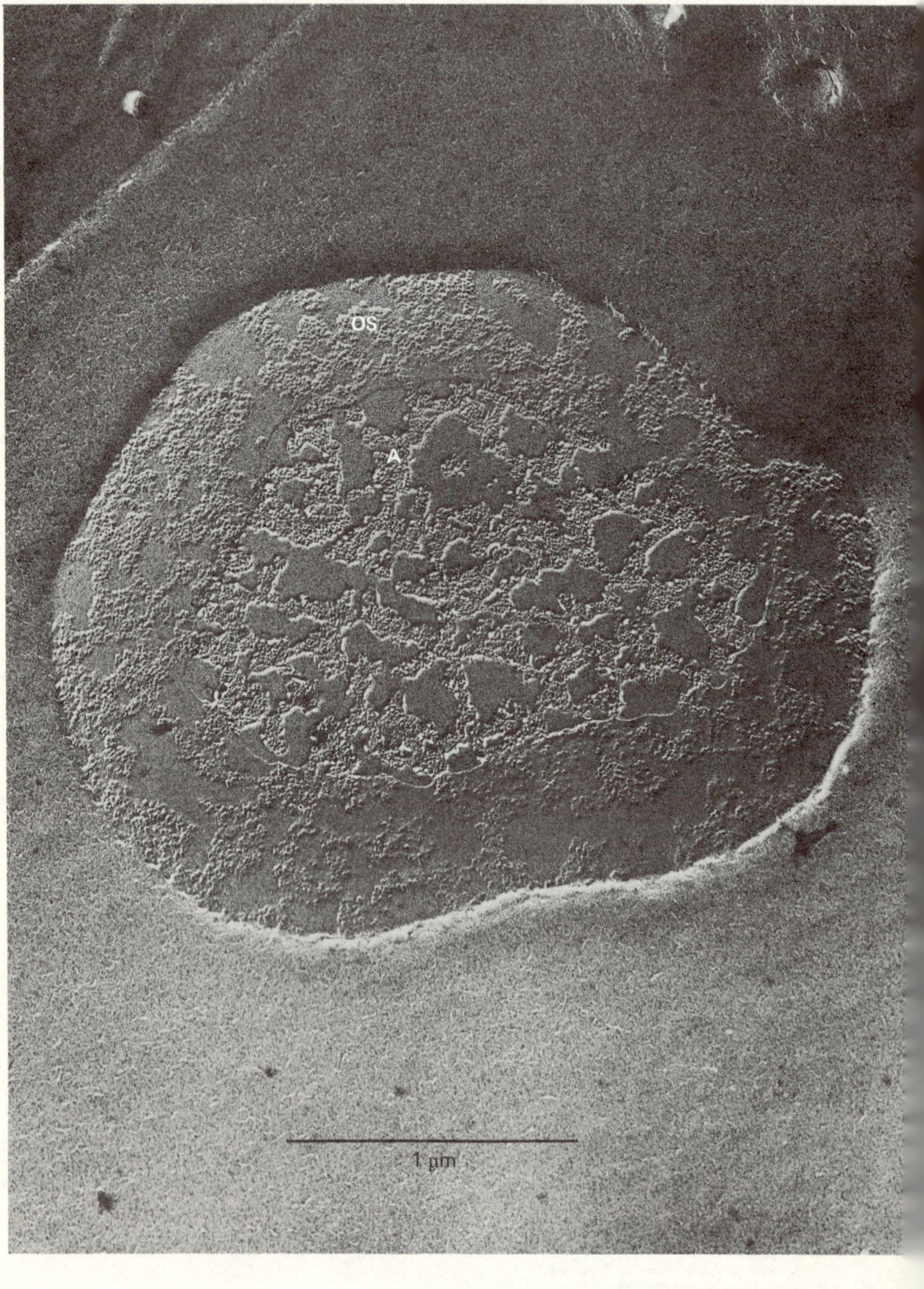
OS
A
1 μm

model pictures membranes as aggregates of a few classes of identical subunits, probably lipoprotein complexes. Most supporting evidence for the model was derived from electron microscopic and biochemical studies on mitochondrial membranes, although it was promoted as a general membrane structure. Mitochondrial inner membrane is metabolically highly active, containing a range of enzymes, many of which may be arranged in complexes (chapter 8) much as envisaged in the subunit theory. Local organization of membrane components in this way can now be regarded rather as a refinement of the mosaic model than as evidence for a separate concept.

The fluid mosaic (Singer-Nicolson) model

The mosaic model was amplified by Singer and Nicolson in 1972 when they stressed the dynamic aspects of membrane structure in describing the *fluid mosaic model.* The refined model is most aptly illustrated by their now classic diagram (figure 6.16) in which globular proteins are shown to resemble 'icebergs' floating in a 'sea' of lipid bilayer. To this picture must be added the globular extrinsic proteins discussed in chapter 5, which are external to the body of the membrane and interact electrostatically with the hydrophilic head groups of the lipid bilayer.

The mobility of the globular proteins in the membrane arises from the fluidity of the lipid bilayer, the hydrocarbon chains of which are largely highly mobile at physiological temperatures. At lower temperatures, hydrated phospholipids exist as *gels* containing crystalline hydrocarbon chain regions (figure 6.17) in which parallel fully-extended hydrocarbon chains tilt away from the perpendicular to the plane of the membrane at an angle which depends on the degree of hydration (chapter 11). Such chains are largely in the trans-planar conformation (figure 5.4*a*) and undergo only slight torsional oscillations.

Figure 6.15. Freeze-fracture electron micrograph of human erythrocyte membrane labelled on its outer surface with ferritin-concanavalin A. The ghosts were first incubated in the presence of Ca^{++} to aggregate the membrane intercalated particles. Incubation with ferritin-concanavalin A (chapter 7) then specifically labelled the Band III glycoprotein on the outer membrane surface (glycophorin interaction with concanavalin A is known to be negligible). Freeze-fracture, etching and metal-shadowing gave rise to the above electron micrograph in which it can be seen that the pattern of aggregation of the label on the outer surface (OS) closely resembles the random network of aggregated membrane intercalated particles on the freeze-fracture face (A). The pattern of distribution of the ferritin-concanavalin A is continuous and contiguous with that of the membrane intercalated particles: From P. Pinto da Silva and G. Nicolson, *Biochim. Biophys. Acta* (1974), **363,** 311–319 by courtesy of Dr. P. Pinto da Silva, The Salk Institute for Biological Sciences, San Diego.

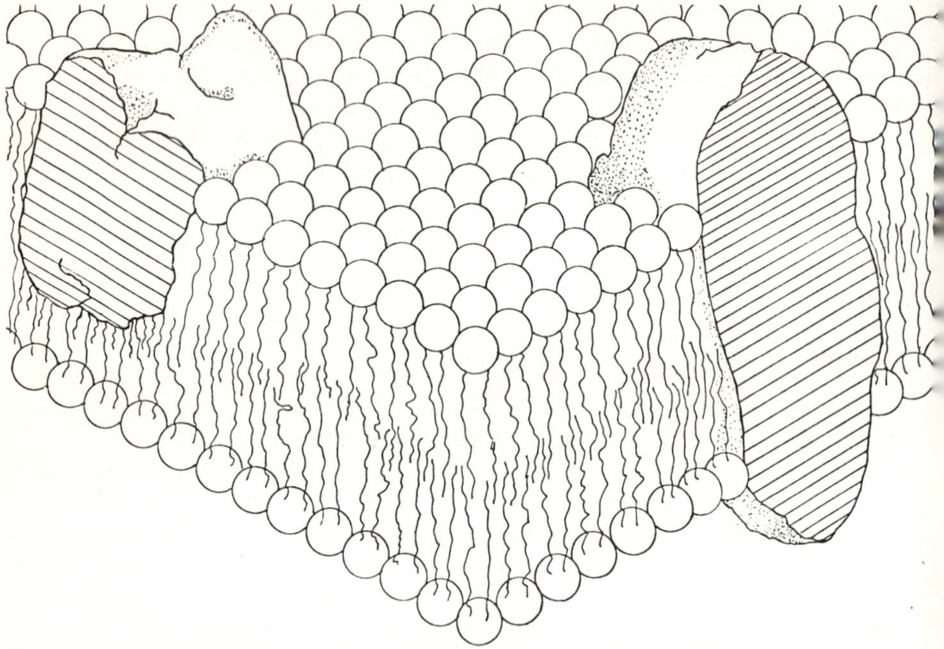

Figure 6.16. The fluid mosaic model. The globular proteins are shown as immersed in and occasionally crossing a lipid bilayer matrix: from S. J. Singer and G. L. Nicolson, *Science* (1972), **175,** 720–731.

As the temperature is raised, molecular motion of the hydrocarbon chains gradually increases until, at a characteristic transition temperature, a sharp rise in heat absorption occurs and the mobility of the hydrocarbon chains abruptly increases, giving rise to the liquid crystalline state. This gel-to-liquid crystalline phase transition can be followed by a number of physical techniques (chapter 11). The transition temperature of a given lipid varies with length and degree of unsaturation of the hydrocarbon chains. Mixtures of phospholipids show different thermal behaviour, depending on the similarity between the components of the mixture, while addition of cholesterol to phospholipid bilayers tends to smooth out, or even abolish, the abrupt changes in heat flow and molecular motion which characterize the transition temperature of pure phospholipid-water systems (chapter 11).

The molecular motions of the hydrocarbon chains of phospholipid bilayer-water systems have been examined in some detail by n.m.r. and e.s.r. (chapter 11). As the temperature of the system is raised through

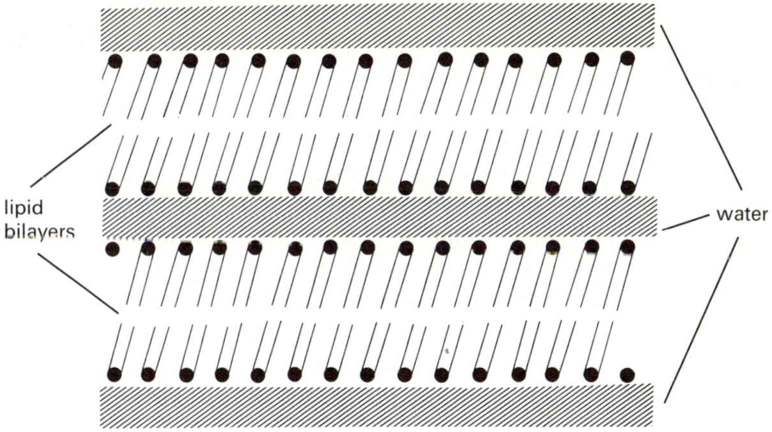

Figure 6.17. Gel phase of hydrated phospholipid below its transition temperature.

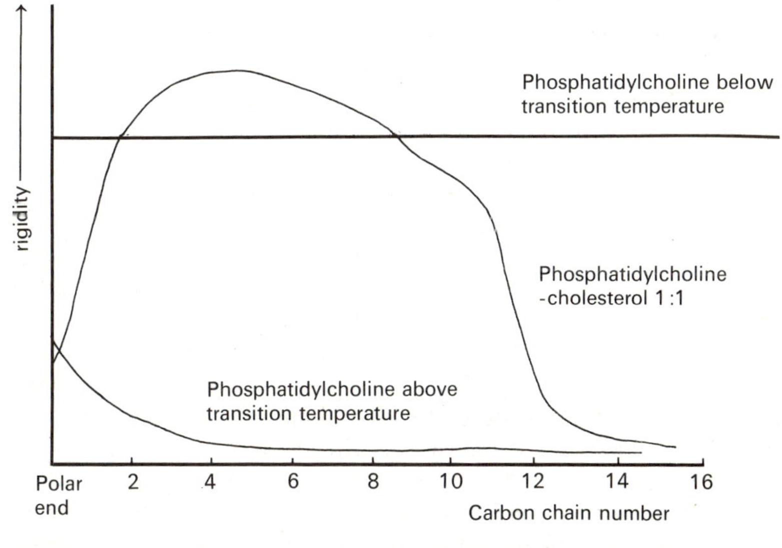

Figure 6.18. Diagrammatic representation of fluidity along phosphatidylcholine hydrocarbon chains in phosphatidylcholine and phosphatidylcholine-cholesterol dispersions. The vertical scale is derived from widths of wide lines in n.m.r. spectra: from A. Darke *et al.*, *J. Mol. Biol.* (1972), **63,** 265–279.

that of the phase transition, the hydrocarbon chains rapidly change from the trans-planar conformation of the gel phase to a mobile state involving considerable flexing and twisting, resulting from carbon-carbon bond rotation. In the mobile liquid crystalline state, a flexibility gradient exists down the chain. The mobility of successive methylene groups increases with their separation from the glycerol backbone and is maximal at the terminal methyl group in the hydrophobic centre of the bilayer (chapter 11). A diagrammatic representation of the mobility gradient for phosphatidylcholine dispersions is shown in figure 6.18 in which values of 'rigidity' are derived from wide-line n.m.r. studies (chapter 11). Also shown in figure 6.18 is the effect of adding cholesterol to phosphatidylcholine dispersions above their transition temperature. The rigidity of all methylene groups is increased, but rigidity of carbons C-2–C-10 is particularly high, in some cases even higher than that in the gel phase of a pure phosphatidylcholine-water system. This behaviour can be explained by the formation of equimolar complexes between cholesterol and phospholipid molecules. Molecular models show that if the cholesterol hydroxy-group is located next to the phosphate group of phosphatidylcholine, the remainder of the sterol molecule reaches to about the tenth carbon along the phospholipid hydrocarbon chain. It has been suggested that the two molecules are held together by hydrophobic interactions, and that the interacting sections are thereby immobilized. The condensation caused by addition of cholesterol to phospholipid monolayers (chapter 5) is consistent with the action of cholesterol in reducing hydrocarbon chain mobility via complex formation.

Natural membranes contain a complex mixture of phospholipids and many have a high content of cholesterol. It is not surprising, therefore, that their phase transitions are generally less clear-cut than those of synthetic phospholipid systems, and often cannot be detected at all. The hydrocarbon chains in natural membranes are, however, generally in a fluid state (but see p. 243) and, as in the case of phospholipid dispersions, e.s.r. and n.m.r. (chapter 11) have been used to demonstrate increasing methylene group mobility along the hydrocarbon chains towards the centre of the bilayer. As with the model systems it is likely that some phospholipids in natural membranes are associated in complexes with sterol molecules, and consequently have less freedom of motion than uncomplexed phospholipids. There is evidence that protein also can influence the mobility of neighbouring lipid molecules. Recent spin label experiments (chapter 11) have indicated that the intrinsic protein molecules of some membrane-bound enzymes are surrounded by an immobilized coat of *boundary lipid* which is essential for maximal enzyme activity. The content of immobilized boundary lipid in a membrane matrix will depend on the number of intrinsic proteins in that membrane. Inner mitochondrial membrane, for instance, might be expected to have a considerable content of lipid which is intimately associated with its many membrane-bound enzymes (chapter 8).

Since much of the membrane lipid is in a fluid state, the intrinsic proteins, lipoprotein complexes and individual lipids may all be expected to show some freedom of lateral motion. Movement of phospholipids in the plane of a phospholipid bilayer has been shown to be remarkably fast, with an estimated neighbour-exchange rate of the order of 10^7 per second. In contrast, translation of lipid molecules from one side of the phospholipid bilayer to the other, in a so-called 'flip-flop' motion, is extremely slow. Spin-labelling studies indicate that neighbour-exchange across the bilayer is some 10^{10} times slower than lateral exchange (chapter 11). Such a situation is thermodynamically reasonable, since considerable energy would be required to force the hydrophilic head groups of a polar lipid down through the hydrophobic interior of the membrane and out to the opposite side.

Similar considerations might be expected to govern the motion of protein molecules. The lateral motion of intrinsic membrane proteins was first demonstrated by Frye and Edidin in 1970. These workers labelled antigenic intrinsic proteins of human and mouse cells in culture with different fluorescent antibodies. Fusion of the two cell types was then induced by virus to give compound 'super-cells'. Shortly after fusion, the human and mouse antigenic components were largely segregated in different halves of the fused cell membrane. After incubation at 37 °C for 40 minutes the components were essentially completely intermixed. The mixing process was shown to be independent of chemical energy in the form of ATP, and was attributed to lateral diffusion of the protein molecules in the lipid bilayer (estimated diffusion coefficient 2×10^{-10} cm^2/sec). The lateral diffusion of protein has been examined in other membrane systems and found to be generally slower than that of phospholipids (diffusion coefficient approximately 2×10^{-8} cm^2/sec in bilayers) as might be expected from considerations of size. There is considerable variation in the diffusion coefficients reported for protein in different membranes. The diffusion coefficient of rhodopsin in frog retinal rod membranes (chapter 8) has been assessed at 4×10^{-9} cm^2/sec, whereas that of Band III glycoprotein (chapter 5) in erythrocytes has been estimated to have an upper limit of 3×10^{-12} cm^2/sec. The apparently very slow lateral diffusion of Band III glycoprotein could be partially explained by the relatively high viscosity of erythrocyte lipids. A more important factor may well be its association with other proteins in the erythrocyte membrane. There is evidence, for instance, that Band III glycoprotein and the integral sialoglycoprotein (glycophorin) are linked, and also that glycophorin is associated with the extrinsic protein spectrin. When spectrin, which is located on the inner surface of the erythrocyte membrane, is caused to aggregate by means of added antibody, glycophorin also aggregates. It is possible, therefore, that spectrin, glycophorin and Band III glycoprotein are all associated in a supramolecular complex which controls and limits mobility of the individual protein components. It is clear that lateral movement of protein in the plane of the membrane must be subject to control in many instances. Intestinal epithelial cells, for example, contain their glycoprotein and Na^+,K^+-ATPase at opposite ends of the cell. Moreover, many membranes, particularly inner mitochondrial membrane (chapter 8) contain multienzyme sequences in which the product of one enzymic reaction becomes the substrate for the next, and maintenance of correct spatial relationships between enzymes is clearly important. In some extreme cases, e.g. *Torpedo* electroplax membrane and the purple membrane of *Halobacterium halobium* (chapter 8), extensive protein lattices have been demonstrated in the membrane. The general nature of membrane protein interrelationships remains obscure and is currently an area of intense research activity.

Unanswered questions

The current picture which we have of the biological membrane, based on the fluid mosaic model, is incomplete in respects other than those directly concerning protein associations. There is, for instance, evidence that the phospholipids of erythrocyte membrane are asymmetrically distributed, with phosphatidylcholine and sphingomyelin on the outside, and phosphatidylserine and phosphatidylethanolamine on the inside of the bilayer. Moreover, X-ray diffraction data indicate that cholesterol is asymmetrically located in myelin (figure 11.25). Although 'flip-flop' motion is slow, it is not slow enough to explain the maintenance of such unequal distribution in membranes. It has recently been suggested that the explanation may lie in interaction of specific lipids with asymmetrically distributed protein in the membrane. A possible steric explanation is discussed in chapter 11.

Other apparently important factors which have been largely ignored in membrane models are the roles played by inorganic cations and water. Removal of either can lead to disruption of the membrane, and yet membrane models in general assign no clear structural function to either within the membrane complex. It should also be stressed that although intrinsic membrane proteins are generally believed to be implicated in transport of material through the membrane, the exact molecular basis for the operation of most postulated transport mechanisms (chapter 9) remains obscure.

Finally, the important question of the mechanism of membrane biosynthesis is still largely unclarified. It is believed that both growing and non-growing cells continuously synthesize fresh membrane, and that this is either used to supply new membrane in the growing cell or involved in membrane turnover in a non-growing cell. It seems likely that membrane is synthesized by a multistep process, possibly by sequential addition of protein components to an initially formed lipid bilayer. An interesting theory involving such an assembly-line process of synthesis of membrane glycoprotein is outlined in chapter 7. The alternative to multistep synthesis would be simultaneous formation of lipid, protein and carbohydrate, and assembly together into a membrane complex, possibly by way of initially-formed 'building blocks'. The idea of such a mechanism appealed to proponents of the subunit model of membrane structure, but is not generally supported by radioactive incorporation studies, and is not so attractive a concept in the context of the fluid mosaic model.

SUMMARY

1. The Davson-Danielli-Robertson model of membrane structure proposed a unit membrane based on a lipid bilayer sandwiched between two layers of protein.
2. There is good evidence, particularly from model systems, for the presence of a lipid bilayer in natural membranes. Support for the distribution of protein as in the Davson-Danielli-Robertson model is less convincing.
3. The mosaic model of membrane structure involves intercalation of protein molecules in the lipid bilayer. It is preferable to the earlier model on thermodynamic grounds and is well supported by experimental data.
4. The dynamic aspects of the mosaic model are stressed in the fluid mosaic model of Singer and Nicolson, in which proteins and lipoprotein complexes are largely mobile within the plane of the membrane. Considerable knowledge concerning the fluidity of lipid bilayers has been obtained from the use of physical techniques in phospholipid model systems.
5. Many points of membrane structure and biosynthesis remain unexplained.

CHAPTER 7

MEMBRANE CARBOHYDRATE AND CELL SURFACE SPECIFICITY

MAMMALIAN PLASMA MEMBRANES CONTAIN BOTH GLYCOPROTEIN AND glycolipid, and there is currently a great deal of interest in the possible involvement of such surface carbohydrate in cellular recognition, contact and other social phenomena. Less is known of the carbohydrate content of non-mammalian plasma membranes. Whereas glycolipids have been found in plasma membranes from a wide range of cell types, there are practical problems in demonstrating the presence of glycoprotein in plasma membranes of bacteria, fungi and higher plants in which the outer membrane is surrounded by a carbohydrate-containing cell wall. It is often difficult to establish that carbohydrate demonstrated in a plasma membrane preparation from such cells does not derive from contaminating cell wall fragments. There is, however, good evidence for the presence of glycoproteins in some bacterial membranes, and future work may well show that glycoprotein is a constituent of plasma membranes from all sources.

Whereas mammalian cell membranes interact directly with the external environment, any extracellular relationships of the plasma membranes of walled organisms are complicated by the presence of the intervening cell wall. The present chapter will be primarily concerned with the role of membrane carbohydrate in the relationship of the cell with its surroundings, and will accordingly concentrate on the mammalian cell plasma membrane which has been most extensively studied in this connection. For similar reasons, intracellular membranes, which have been shown to contain both glycolipid and glycoprotein, will not be discussed.

Evidence for the presence of carbohydrate on the surface of plasma membranes

The isolation of plasma membranes uncontaminated by intracellular membranes and organelles is difficult (chapter 4). Plasma membrane preparations have, however, now been obtained from a range of cells and found to contain 1–10% of their total weight as carbohydrate of glycolipid or glycoprotein. Such gross chemical analysis gives no indication of the localization of carbohydrate within the membrane, and this has largely been obtained from microscopic, electrokinetic and immunochemical methods.

Microscopy

Visualization of plasma membrane carbohydrate in both light and electron microscopy has depended upon histochemical reagents believed to be specific for carbohydrate, and it is worth while to describe briefly some of these reagents and their supposed specificity.

Periodic acid oxidatively cleaves the carbon-carbon bond of vicinal secondary hydroxy groups to give a dialdehyde (figure 7.1).

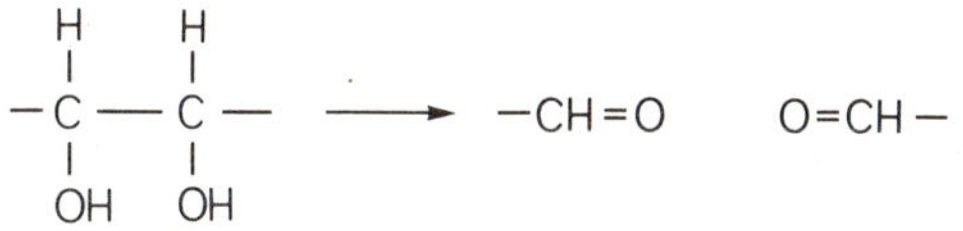

Figure 7.1. Periodate cleavage of vicinal secondary hydroxy-groups.

If the dialdehyde is allowed to react with leuco-fuchsin, a Schiff's Base results which can be readily detected in the light microscope as a purple stain. As vicinal diol groupings are common in carbohydrates, the periodic acid-Schiff (PAS) reaction gives a fairly specific carbohydrate stain, although prolonged periodic acid oxidation can elicit a false positive PAS reaction from hydroxyamino acids. Periodic acid oxidation is also used to visualize carbohydrate in electron microscopy, when the dialdehyde oxidation product is allowed to react with silver methenamine to give an electron-dense silver precipitate.

Membrane carbohydrate commonly contains sialic acid and occasionally sulphate anions. A number of microscopic procedures have accordingly been developed which depend upon the presence of acidic groupings. In the Hale stain, colloidal iron is attracted to the acidic groups where it is allowed to react with potassium ferrocyanide, giving Prussian blue, detectable by both light and electron microscopy. Other cationic stains include the use of colloidal thorium and of ruthenium red. Ruthenium red has the proposed structural formula $[(NH_3)_5Ru—O—Ru(NH_3)_4—O—Ru(NH_3)_5]^{6+}$. It undergoes a complex reaction with acidic carbohydrate and has been widely used, both alone with the light microscope and in combination with osmium tetroxide in electron microscopy. Although the bulk of available evidence suggests that ruthenium red has an affinity for acidic polysaccharide, it has been shown to bind to lipid, and could possibly react with polyanions in general.

An electron micrograph showing the surface of an erythrocyte membrane stained with ruthenium red-osmium tetroxide is shown in figure 7.2. The densely-stained surface layer is believed to be the site of the carbohydrate portion of membrane glycoprotein. Similar evidence has been obtained, from the use of ruthenium red and other staining methods, that the plasma membranes of a wide range of both normal and malignant cells contain carbohydrate asymmetrically located on their outer surfaces.

More specific techniques for visualization of carbohydrate have recently resulted from the use of *lectins*. Lectins are proteins, usually derived from plants, which can bind to cell surfaces, causing agglutination. A number of lectins have been purified and found to be specific for different carbohydrate receptors on the cell surface. Thus concanavalin A, from Jack beans, is specific for α-D-glucopyranosyl and α-D-mannopyranosyl residues, while wheat germ agglutinin binds specifically to *N*-acetylglucosamine units. Other lectins require more complex carbohydrate receptors and will be discussed further later in this chapter. Both concanavalin A and wheat germ agglutinin have been tagged with fluorescein

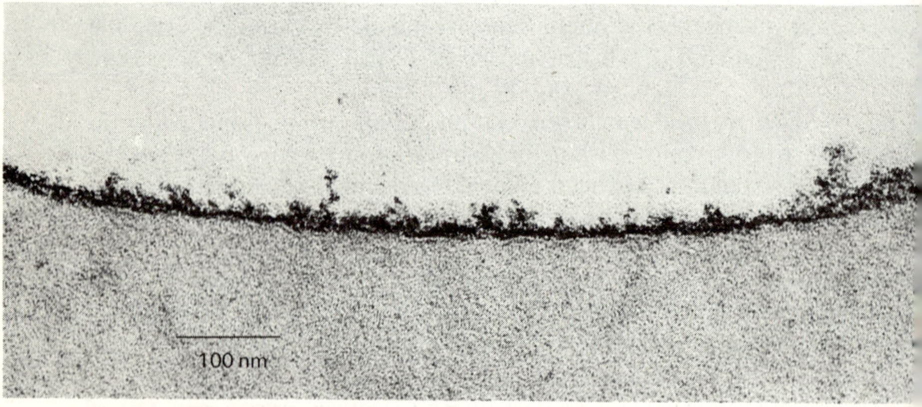

Figure 7.2. Electron micrograph of a section of human erythrocyte membrane stained with ruthenium red-osmium tetroxide. The very densely stained layer is believed to be the site of the carbohydrate portion of membrane glycoprotein: from G. M. W. Cook and R. W. Stoddart, *Surface Carbohydrate of the Eukaryotic Cell* (1973), London, Academic Press, p. 74, by courtesy of Dr. G. M. W. Cook, Strangeways Research Laboratory, Cambridge.

isothiocyanate, following which the labelled lectin is allowed to bind to a cell membrane, where it is detected by fluorescence microscopy. The binding of lectins to cell membranes has also been detected by electron microscopy by coupling electron-dense material to the lectin, both before and after attachment to the cell.

Cell-bound lectins have been visualized by making use of the fact that lectins have more than one binding site. Horseradish peroxidase, a glycoprotein, is allowed to bind to the unoccupied sites of lectins already attached to a cell surface. The catalytic activity of the lectin-bound peroxidase is then utilized to produce an electron-dense product by reaction with diaminobenzidine. A similar but rather more direct procedure involves attachment of haemocyanin via its carbohydrate residues to membrane-bound lectin, and stabilization of the complex with glutaraldehyde. Haemocyanin is a large molecule of distinctive shape which can be seen directly in shadow-cast replicas (figure 7.3).

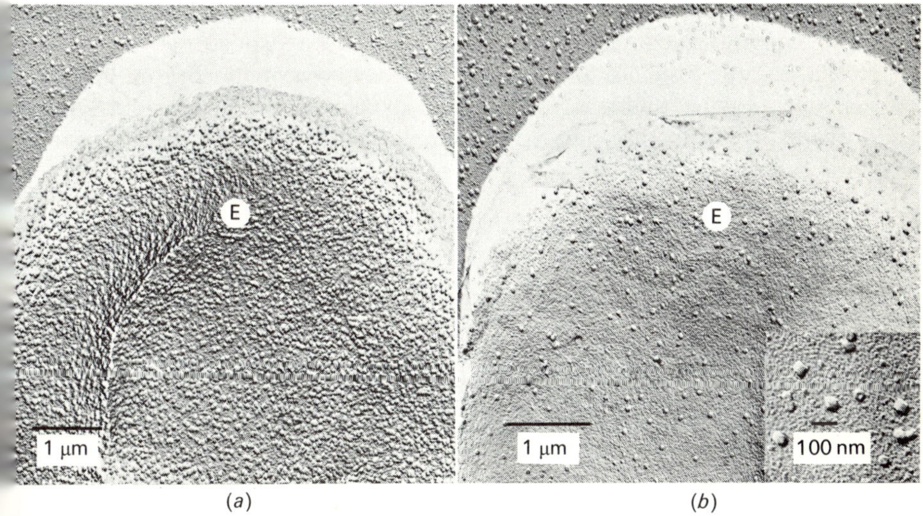

Figure 7.3. (*a*) Rat erythrocyte (E) treated with concanavalin A followed by haemocyanin. The haemocyanin molecules are distributed evenly over the surface of the cell.
(*b*) Rat erythrocyte (E) treated with concanavalin A plus methyl α-D-glucoside, then haemocyanin. This is the control to figure (*a*). Methyl α-D-glucoside inhibits concanavalin A binding, so that very few haemocyanin molecules are seen on the cell. The amount of haemocyanin seen in the background on the glass is unchanged. The inset is a higher magnification showing that the haemocyanin molecules can be clearly recognized. Since they are cylindrical, the molecules seen from the side appear rectangular and seen end on circular. Representatives of these two views have been circled: from S. B. Smith and J. P. Revel, *Developmental Biology* (1972), **27,** 434–441, by courtesy of Dr. S. Smith Brown, Division of Biology, California Institute of Technology.

Alternatively, electron-dense molecules can be covalently bound to lectins before attachment of the conjugate to the cell membrane. Cytochrome peroxidase has been coupled to concanavalin A using glutaraldehyde, and the conjugates allowed to bind to mouse thymocytes, where they were visualized in both light and electron microscopy by the diaminobenzidine reaction. Ferritin has also been linked to lectins using glutaraldehyde before attachment to the cell membrane (figure 6.15). Ferritin, like haemocyanin, is directly visible in the electron microscope, and lectin conjugates of both compounds have been used to produce maps of lectin binding sites on the cell surface.

The presence of carbohydrate material on the outer surface of plasma membranes has been demonstrated by a variety of such specific labelling techniques. Combination of these techniques with protease and neuraminidase (which cleaves off sialic acid) treatment of the membrane has indicated, further, that the carbohydrate is largely contributed by glycoprotein, often containing sialic acid. Plasma membranes also contain glycolipids which are likely to be exposed at the cell surface. Little evidence for their presence has been obtained from histochemical studies, and it is possible that glycolipids, which are soluble in organic solvents, are largely removed from tissues in histological processing.

Cell electrophoresis

The mobility of cells suspended in an electrolyte solution and subjected to an electric field reflects the cell surface potential. All mammalian cells have been found to migrate toward the positive electrode at physiological pH, indicating a net negative charge at the cell surface. Some indication of the nature of the ionogenic groups at the cell surface can be obtained from a study of the variation of the electrophoretic mobility of cells with the pH of the suspending medium. Use of this fact is made in the technique of *cell electrophoresis* or *microelectrophoresis*, in which migration of individual cells in a known potential gradient is directly observed through a microscope. A simple microelectrophoresis apparatus is shown in figure 7.4.

The first mammalian cell to be studied in detail by cell electrophoresis was the erythrocyte, the pH-mobility profile for which is shown in figure 7.5 (upper curve). The increase in negative mobility (i.e. mobility toward the anode) with increase in pH corresponds to progressive ionization of an acidic group at the membrane surface. The pK of an

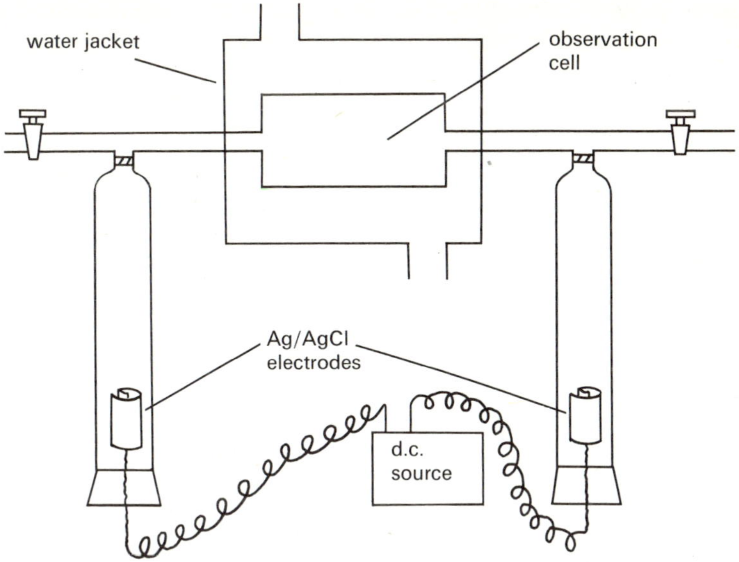

Figure 7.4. Schematic outline of a simple microelectrophoresis apparatus.

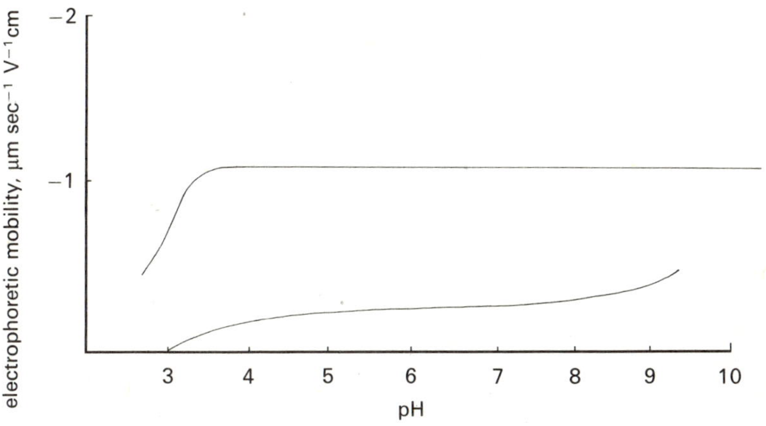

Figure 7.5. pH-electrophoretic mobility relationships for human erythrocytes before (upper curve) and after (lower curve) neuraminidase treatment: from G. M. W. Cook *et al.*, *Nature* (1961), **191,** 44–47.

ionogenic group is characteristic for that group at constant ionic strength, and may be defined in practical terms as that pH at which one half of those particular groups are ionized. The upper curve of figure 7.5 accordingly depicts the ionization of acidic groups on the erythrocyte surface with pK of approximately 2·5. These groups have been shown to be largely sialic acid (pK 2·6) by treatment of erythrocytes with neuraminidase, which releases sialic acid into the medium and causes a fall in electrophoretic mobility of the treated cells to that of the lower curve (figure 7.5). The electrophoretic mobility of erythrocytes is also reduced by treatment with trypsin, which releases sialic acid-containing glycopeptides into the medium, indicating that sialoglycoprotein makes a major contribution to membrane surface charge. The negative mobility (figure 7.5, lower curve) remaining after neuraminidase treatment could be attributed to the presence of ionized glycolipid sialic acids (not always susceptible to neuraminidase) or to acidic groupings of higher pK, such as the carboxylic side chains of protein glutamic acid or aspartic acid residues.

pH-electrophoretic mobility curves which have additional features to those of erythrocytes have been determined for other cell types. The profile for human lymphocytes shown in figure 7.6*a* has a region of cathodic mobility consistent with a preponderance of the positively charged amino groups of basic amino acids at the cell surface. When these amino groups are blocked by aldehyde treatment, the positive region is eliminated, and a negative curve remains which shows a gradual increase over the range pH2–5 (figure 7.6*b*, upper curve) indicating ionization of more than one ionogenic group. When aldehyde-blocked lymphocytes are subsequently treated with neuraminidase, sialic acid is released, and the negative electrophoretic mobility is reduced (figure 7.6*b*, lower curve). The resulting curve shows the presence of remaining acidic groups with a pK of 4–5 which could correspond to the ionization of protein carboxyl groups.

The cell electrophoretic studies of lymphocytes accordingly indicate that protein, as well as sialic acid, makes a significant contribution to the cell surface potential. Features of this sialic acid-protein pattern have been shown in pH-electrophoretic mobility profiles of blood platelets, milk fat globules (chapter 4), Ehrlich ascites tumour cells, and a variety of other normal and malignant cells. Cell electrophoresis has the advantage that the cell surface can be directly observed without the need for prior modification by fixing or staining procedures, and the initial demonstrations of the presence of sialic acid on the erythrocyte surface by these methods did much to stimulate interest in the presence of carbohydrate generally in plasma membranes.

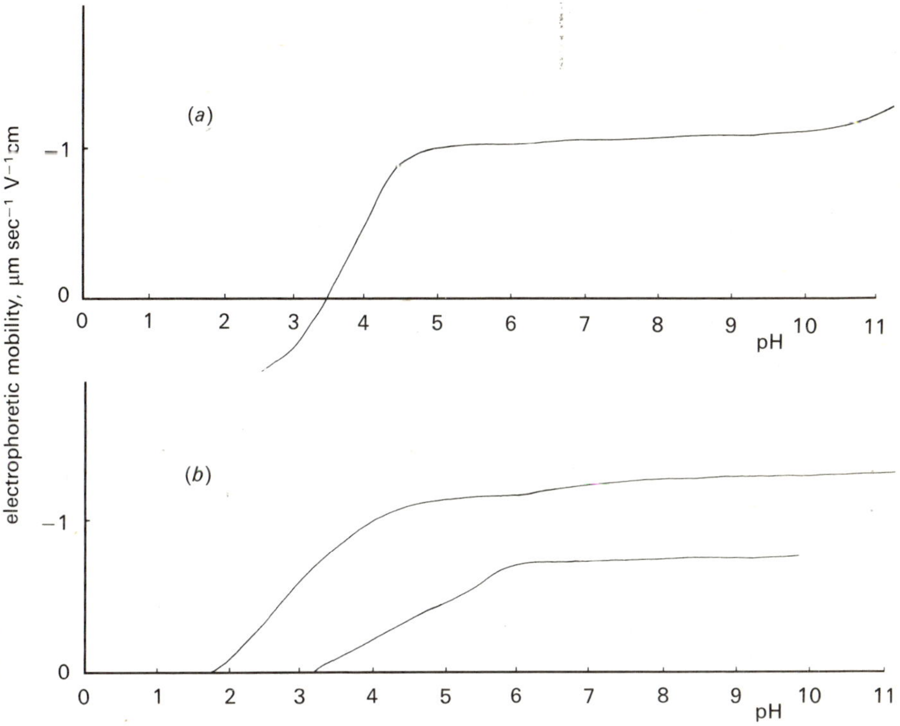

Figure 7.6. pH-electrophoretic mobility relationships for lymphocytes (*a*); glutaraldehyde-fixed lymphocytes (*b*, upper curve) and glutaraldehyde-fixed neuraminidase-treated lymphocytes (*b*, lower curve): from P. S. Vassar *et al*., *Biochim. Biophys. Acta* (1973), **291**, 107–115.

Immunochemistry

The presence on the surface of human erythrocytes of antigens which determine blood group specificity has been recognized for very many years. The carbohydrate nature of these antigens was demonstrated over twenty years ago by Morgan and Watkins, who showed that certain monosaccharides could inhibit the agglutination of red cells by specific antisera. In such *hapten inhibition* studies it is believed that the inhibitor acts by combining with the site on the antibody which is normally occupied by the antigen. This implies a close relationship between the structures of the inhibitor and antigen.

The cell agglutination properties of lectins have already been mentioned. It has been known for a long time that lectin binding to cell surfaces and subsequent agglutination can be inhibited by specific monosaccharides, showing that the cell surface receptors are themselves carbohydrates.

The nature of cell surface antigens and receptor sites will be discussed in more detail later in the present chapter. It is merely wished to emphasize at this stage that immunochemical techniques have played a part in demonstrating the presence and importance of carbohydrates on cell plasma membranes.

Isolation and purification of membrane glycolipids and glycoproteins

Lipids are commonly extracted in chloroform-methanol mixtures which also tend to dissolve some sugars, amino acids and peptides. Addition of aqueous salt solutions causes phase separation and polar contaminants partition in the upper layer of aqueous methanol. Glycolipids are polar lipids (chapter 5) with hydrophilic head groups which can be particularly large, containing several monosaccharide units, and consequently can appear in both organic and aqueous phases, even following several phase separations. Because of such problems, other solvents such as pyridine and its derivatives or tetrahydrofuran are often used to extract glycolipids. Following extraction, glycolipids can be separated by the conventional techniques of lipid chemistry, such as chromatography, particularly thin-layer, on silica.

Membrane glycoproteins are generally intrinsic rather than extrinsic proteins (chapter 5) and as such are difficult to solubilize in a form free from solubilizing agent without denaturation or aggregation. Most experimental data are available for the major sialoglycoprotein of erythrocyte membrane, glycophorin. Glycophorin has been extracted using aqueous mixtures of organic solvents (e.g. chloroform-methanol-water-EDTA, phenol-water, ethanol-water, pyridine-water) when the membrane glycoprotein can be obtained in a water-soluble form. Non-ionic (Triton), cationic (cetyltrimethylammonium bromide), and anionic (sodium dodecyl sulphate) detergents have also been used in solubilization of membrane glycoproteins, and particular interest has recently been expressed in the use of lithium diiodosalicylate (LIS) for this purpose. LIS is both a detergent and a *chaotropic agent*. Such agents act by 'destructuring' water, hence reducing the unfavourable entropy effects of an apolar residue in structured water, and so tending to disrupt hydrophobic associations (chapter 5) in membranes. Chaotropic agents can be organic molecules (e.g. guanidine hydrochloride, urea) or inorganic ions with large hydration shells (e.g. Li^+, Cl^-, SCN^-).

Glycoproteins which can be extracted into true aqueous solution may be purified by the standard techniques of protein chemistry. In many cases, however, removal of the solubilizing agent from intrinsic membrane proteins leads to aggregation of the protein, and fractionation must be carried out in the presence of the solubilizer. As the solubilizing agents are often charged, separations based on the charge of the protein itself are not possible, but gel filtration and electrophoresis are to some extent still possible in the presence of organic solvents, detergents and chaotropic agents.

A powerful technique for the purification of soluble glycoproteins has resulted from the development of *affinity chromatography* using columns packed with lectins bound to insoluble supports such as agarose. Glycoproteins which act as receptors for bound lectins are selectively retarded on such columns, and may be subsequently eluted by solutions of monosaccharides which are specific for the lectin. The technique, summarized in figure 7.7, is applicable in principle to purification not only of lectin receptors but of any molecule able to bind specifically.

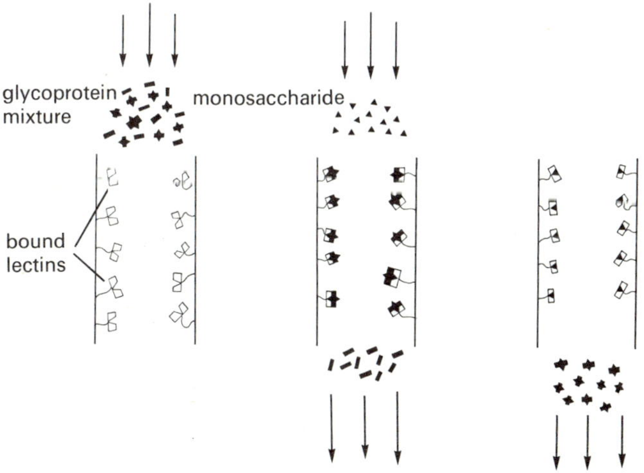

Figure 7.7. Schematic diagram showing the principle of affinity chromatography as applied to the purification of glycoproteins. Lectin bound to the insoluble support on the column retards glycoprotein molecules carrying carbohydrate receptors for which the lectin is specific. Subsequent elution with the receptor itself (often a monosaccharide) displaces the glycoprotein from the lectin, and hence from the column.

The term *purification* is usually subject to qualification when applied to molecules as complex as glycoproteins. Membrane glycoproteins can be purified with respect to a given function, e.g. their specific activity as receptors, as judged by a suitable assay, can be maximized. Alternatively, they can be defined as pure when no further separation can be achieved by any fractionation technique. In either case it is unlikely that the product will contain identical chemically-defined molecules. It is becoming increasingly apparent that, unlike proteins, in which a specific amino-acid sequence results from a particular base sequence of DNA, the carbohydrate in a given glycoprotein may show a range of related structures. Such *microheterogeneity* has been demonstrated in many soluble glycoproteins in which a range of oligosaccharide side-chains has been found representing minor modifications and various stages of 'completion' of a theoretical 'complete' unit. It is likely that the addition of sugar residues to a growing oligosaccharide side-chain by glycosyl transferases is not absolutely specific, and that within certain limits a family of variable structures will result.

Structure of membrane glycolipids and glycoproteins

Structural analysis of purified glycolipids and glycoproteins is based on standard procedures of lipid, protein and carbohydrate chemistry. Examination of the carbohydrate fraction of glycoproteins usually involves the separation of oligosaccharides from the bulk of the protein in one of two ways. In the first, solubilized membrane glycoprotein is subjected to extensive proteolytic degradation, leaving a glycopeptide. Alternatively, use is made of the fact that membrane carbohydrate is generally located towards the end of a protein chain which protrudes from the outer surface of the cell. Treatment of the intact cell with proteolytic enzymes accordingly results in release of most of the glycoprotein carbohydrate as glycopeptides. Glycopeptides obtained by either method are usually water-soluble and may be further purified by gel filtration, ion exchange chromatography, etc. The detailed structure of the oligosaccharides can then be examined by conventional carbohydrate techniques, such as periodate oxidation, methylation and enzymic cleavage procedures, coupled with gas chromatographic analysis of released monosaccharide units.

The structures of membrane glycolipids have been outlined in chapter 5. Although detailed carbohydrate structural studies have only been carried out on the major sialoglycoprotein of human erythrocytes (see

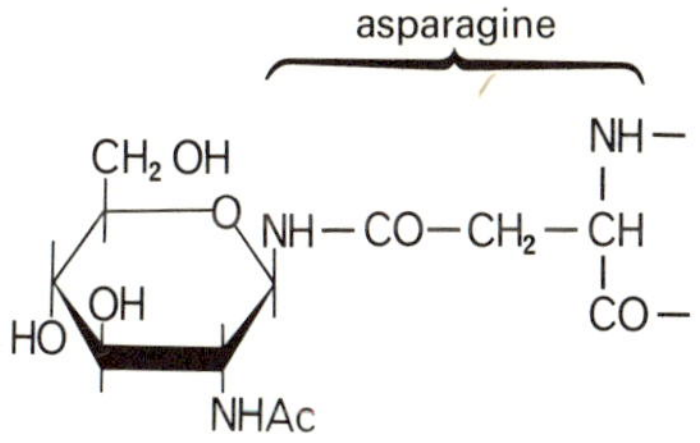

Figure 7.8. Alkali-stable glycopeptide bond involving an N-glycosidic linkage between asparagine and N-acetylglucosamine.

p. 135), the structures of membrane glycoproteins are believed to fall into a general pattern. The carbohydrate portion is made up of some or all of a group of just six monosaccharides: D-galactose, D-mannose, L-fucose, N-acetyl-D-glucosamine, N-acetyl-D-galactosamine and sialic acid (acylated neuraminic acids, commonly N-acetylneuraminic acid or N-glycolyl-neuraminic acid) arranged in oligosaccharide side chains of varying sizes which are glycosidically linked to a polypeptide backbone. Carbohydrate-peptide linkages are of two major types, both of which may occur together within the same glycoprotein. One linkage involves an N-glycosidic bond from N-acetylglucosamine to the amide nitrogen of asparagine (figure 7.8) and is relatively stable to hydrolysis by strong alkali.

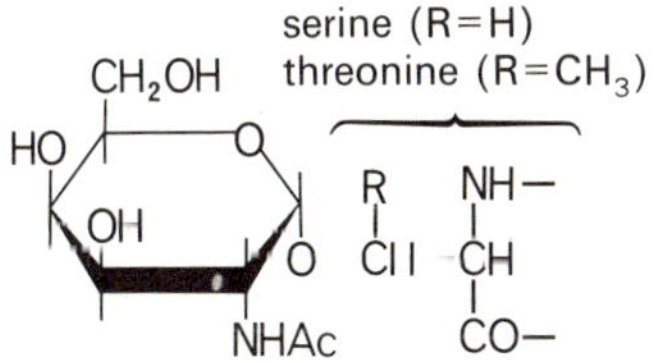

Figure 7.9. Alkali-labile glycopeptide bond involving an O-glycosidic linkage between serine or threonine and N-acetylgalactosamine.

The second type of linkage contains an O-glycosidic bond from N-acetylgalactosamine to the hydroxy-group of serine or threonine (figure 7.9) and is cleaved by mild alkaline treatment. Alkaline cleavage involves β-elimination of the glycosidically-linked sugar moieties as shown in figure 7.10, leaving a double-bonded amino-acid residue in the peptide chain. Structural investigations of glycoprotein carbohydrate have usually involved separation of alkali-stable and alkali-labile carbohydrate. Treatment with alkaline borohydride is often preferred to simple alkali,

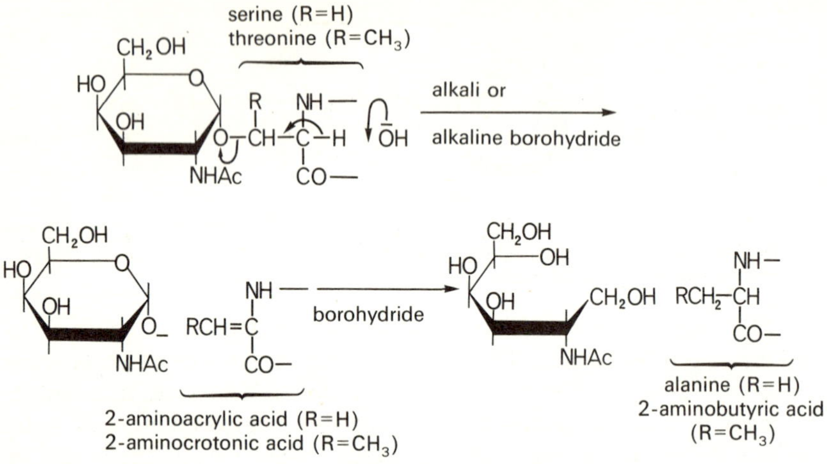

Figure 7.10. Alkali-induced *β*-elimination of N-acetylgalactosamine from serine or threonine, and subsequent reduction of the cleavage products by borohydride.

as the released N-acetylgalactosamine is protected from alkaline degradation by reduction to N-acetylgalactosaminitol. Moreover, the double-bonded amino acids 2-aminoacrylic acid (from serine) and 2-aminocrotonic acid (from threonine) are reduced to the more stable alanine and 2-aminobutyric acids respectively.

In the few membrane glycoproteins examined, it appears that the alkali-labile oligosaccharide side chain is relatively simple, containing only three or four sugar units, while the alkali-stable side chains are considerably more complex. It may be that future studies will show this to be a general rule.

Biosynthesis of membrane carbohydrate

The mechanism of biosynthesis of glycoproteins is not completely understood. It appears that the polypeptide backbone is first synthesized in the usual manner on the polyribosomes, and then migrates via the cisternae of the rough endoplasmic reticulum to the smooth endoplasmic reticulum. It is possible that initial attachment of carbohydrate takes place while the polypeptide is associated with the rough endoplasmic reticulum. Current evidence indicates that the bulk of the sugar residues are added, particularly in the case of membrane glycoprotein, in the smooth endoplasmic reticulum and especially in the Golgi apparatus, which contains a battery of glycosyl transferases. Each glycosyl transferase transfers a given monosaccharide residue from its nucleotide to an acceptor, which may be either a partially completed oligosaccharide chain or an amino acid residue in the polypeptide backbone. The transferases are specific, both for the sugar nucleotide and for the acceptor molecule, thus allowing a defined structure to be synthesized (but see p. 126). It has been observed, for example, that the amino acid sequence containing a glycosylated asparagine residue always has the form:

```
                 sugar
                   |
———X—asparagine—Y—serine (threonine)
```

where X and Y may be varying amino acid residues, suggesting that the relevant glycosyl transferase is specific for this sequence. The signal for termination of an oligosaccharide chain may well come from the presence of a sialic acid or a fucose residue, both of which are found at the ends of sugar chains.

The oligosaccharide chains of glycolipids are believed to be synthesized in the same manner as those of glycopeptides, probably by similar enzymes at the same intracellular site.

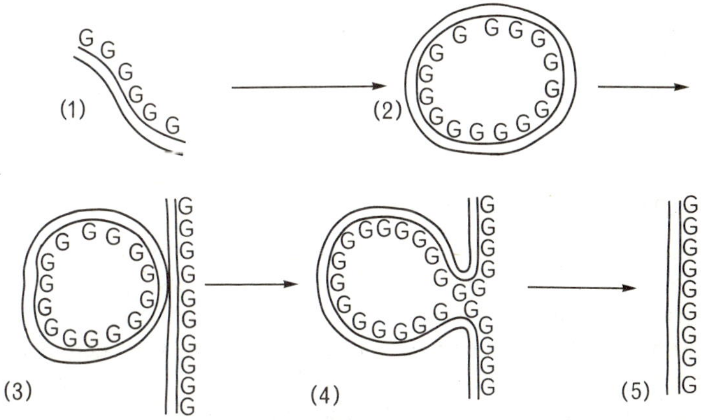

Figure 7.11. Schematic mechanism for the incorporation of glycoprotein into the plasma membrane of eukaryotic cells. Golgi membrane (1) containing glycoprotein (G) on its internal surface forms into vesicles (2) which migrate to the cytoplasmic surface of the plasma membrane (3). The vesicle fuses with the plasma membrane (4) and the glycoprotein is thereby incorporated into its outer surface (5): adapted from Hirano *et al.*, *Proc. Natl. Acad. Sci. US* (1972), **69,** 2945–2949.

The transfer of completed glycolipid and glycoprotein to the plasma membrane is still a subject for speculation. An attractive transfer mechanism has recently been proposed by Singer and co-workers. On the basis of microscopic evidence, these workers proposed that Golgi membranes, containing complete or nearly complete glycoproteins on their internal surface, form into vesicles which migrate to, and fuse with, the plasma membrane. This scheme, partially outlined in figure 7.11, very neatly explains the transport of glycoprotein from the inside of the Golgi membrane to the outside of the plasma membrane, and further supporting evidence for such a mechanism would be of great interest. Figure 7.11 suggests that the glycoprotein is complete before incorporation into the plasma membrane. It is possible that some terminal carbohydrate residues (e.g. sialic acid) could be added after incorporation. Indeed sialyl transferases have been demonstrated as plasma membrane constituents.

Functions of cell surface carbohydrate

In view of the demonstrated presence of complex glycoprotein and glycolipid molecules at the outer surface of mammalian cells, it is not surprising that these molecules should be involved in the interaction of the cells with their surroundings. Since highly variable structures can be achieved in the outer oligosaccharide complexes, such structures are likely to be major determinants of cell surface specificity. A number of roles have been attributed to cell surface carbohydrate in recent years, and the more important of these will be discussed in the remainder of the present chapter.

Blood group specific antigens

The classical ABO blood group system was discovered in 1900 by Landsteiner. Since that time, blood group characters have been demonstrated to be inherited according to Mendelian laws, and many independent blood group systems have been discovered. The chemical nature of the antigens determining ABO and the related Lewis (Le^a and Le^b) specificities is now established, and information concerning antigens of the MN system is available. Little is known about the molecular basis of other blood group antigens, including those of the clinically important Rhesus system.

Classification of the *ABO blood group system* is based on the occurrence of antigens on the red cells, and the relationship of these antigens to the

Table 7.1. Antigen and antibody characteristics of the ABO blood group system

Blood group	*Antigen on red cell*	*Antibody in serum*
A	A	Anti-B
B	B	Anti-A
AB	A and B	—
O	—*	Anti-A and Anti-B

* Red cells of group O carry an H antigen for which antibodies are present in some non-human species.

presence of specific antibodies in the blood serum is shown in Table 7.1.

Specific ABO characters are found not only on erythrocytes but also on cells of many other tissues and as soluble forms in various tissues and secretions. Whereas the antigenic determinants on the erythrocyte surface are mainly glycolipid, those of soluble blood group substances are glycoproteins and, because of the difficulties of isolating large quantities of erythrocyte membrane glycolipid, the chemical basis of the ABO and Lewis systems has been worked out using blood group specific glycoproteins of ovarian cyst fluid, which are available in quantity. Relationships worked out in this sytem have been extrapolated to the glycolipid

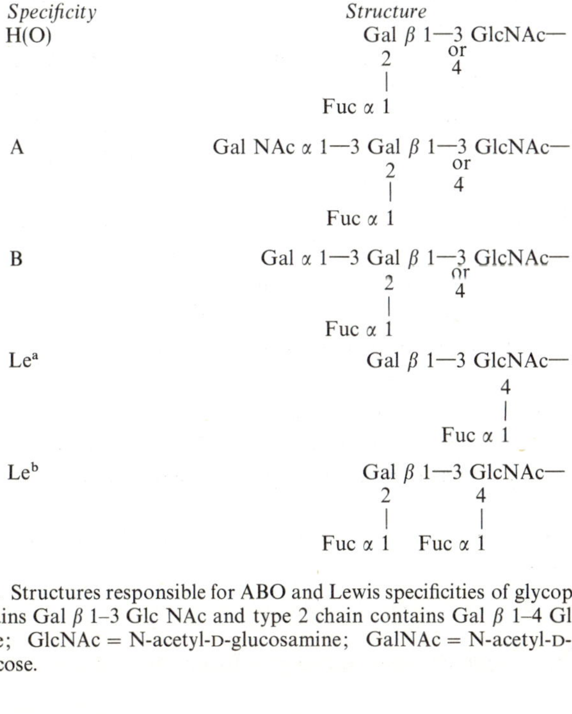

Figure 7.12. Structures responsible for ABO and Lewis specificities of glycoproteins. Type 1 chain contains Gal β 1–3 Glc NAc and type 2 chain contains Gal β 1–4 GlcNAc. Gal = D-galactose; GlcNAc = N-acetyl-D-glucosamine; GalNAc = N-acetyl-D-galactosamine; Fuc = L-fucose.

antigens of the red cell. The blood group activities of the soluble glycoproteins are assessed by their ability to inhibit agglutination of red blood cells by specific antisera and also by direct precipitation by antisera. The blood group specificity of the glycoproteins was found to be determined by certain combinations of monosaccharide units located at the non-reducing ends of oligosaccharide chains, which could be of two structural types (type 1 and type 2) (figure 7.12).

Inheritance of ABO and Lewis characteristics is controlled by the action of genes at four independent loci, ABO, Lele, Hh and Sese. It is believed that the A, B, Le and H genes produce glycosyl transferases which attach the relevant immunodominant sugar to a specific precursor. Production of the different characteristics from one (type 1) of the two possible chain endings in a precursor oligosaccharide is shown in figure 7.13.

The Le gene and H gene each produce a fucosyl transferase which attaches fucose to a specific sugar of the precursor structure giving respectively Le^a and H structures. Expression of both the Le and H genes causes addition of two fucose residues producing the Le^b structure. The A and B genes produce N-acetylgalactosaminyl transferase and galactosyl transferase respectively, which can only act on the H structure. If the H gene is absent, neither A nor B structures can occur, even though the relevant genes may be present. Providing the H gene is present, however, the A gene gives rise to the A antigen, and the B gene to the B antigen. When both A and B genes are present together, both A and B structures arise whereas, when both are absent, the H structure remains unaltered and the blood group is termed O.

These relationships have been worked out using soluble glycoproteins. In fact the appearance of soluble blood group substances with A, B or H specificity is dependent on the presence of the Se gene. About 80% of the population (so called *secretors*) possess the Se gene which controls the expression of the H gene in secretions. In 'non-secretors' the Se gene is absent and the H gene cannot be expressed in secretions, which consequently (see figure 7.13) cannot carry A, B, H or Le^b blood group activities. Non-secretors may have secretions with Le^a activity, since this does not depend upon the H gene and can show A, B or H antigens on the erythrocyte surface.

A similar sequence of structures results from the alternative precursor chain ending (type 2):

Gal 1—4 Glc NAc—

except that the 4 fucosyl transferase produced by the Le gene cannot act on this precursor and the Lewis antigens do not occur with type 2 chains.

The structures of the glycolipid blood group antigens of the erythrocyte itself have not yet been fully characterized. Glycosphingolipids of blood

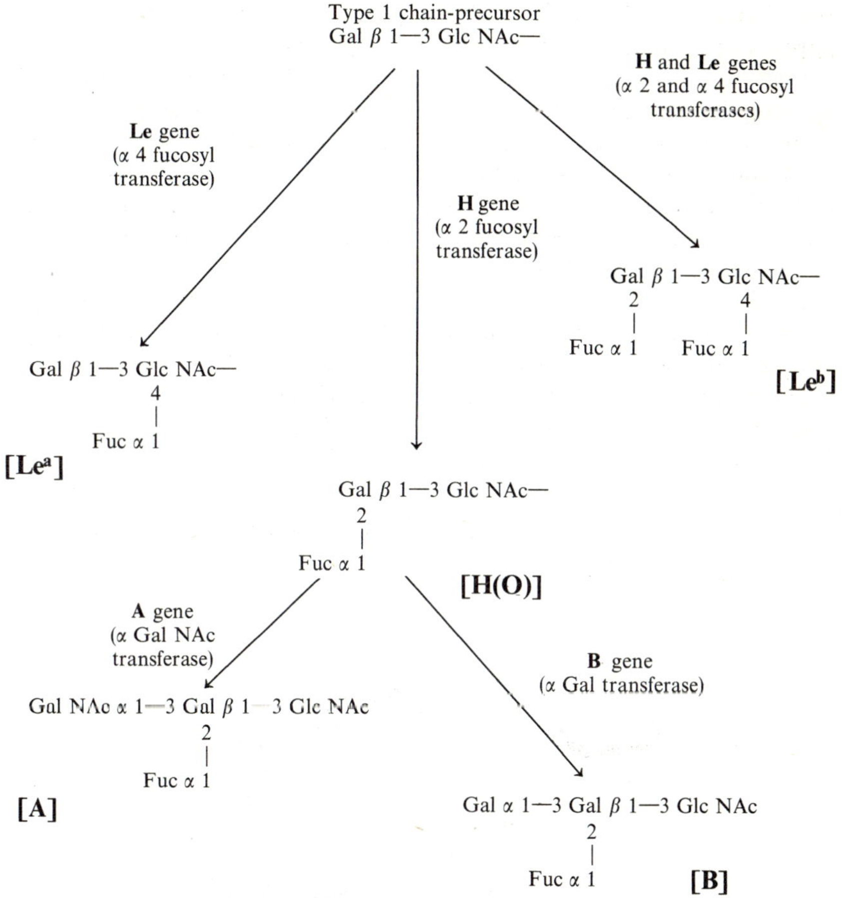

Figure 7.13. Biochemical pathways for the conversion of type 1 chain endings in precursor glycoprotein into Le^a, Le^b, A and B active structures. [ ] specific activity of structures; ( ) specificity of enzymes. Gal = D-galactose; GlcNAc = N-acetyl-D-glucosamine; GalNac = N-acetyl-D-galactosamine; Fuc = L-fucose: adapted from W. M. Watkins in *Glycoproteins. Their Composition, Structure and Function*, Part B, Amsterdam, Elsevier (1972), pp. 830–891.

groups A, B, H, Le^a and Le^b have been isolated from human erythrocytes and partially characterized as having a common backbone:

Gal—GlcNAc—Gal—Glc—ceramide

which has the terminal Gal—GlcNAc structure shown by type 1 and type 2 (figure 7.12) chains of glycoprotein blood group substances. It appears likely that the erythrocyte glycolipid ABO and Lewis antigens will all be found to have structures based on the above structure and carrying the same immunodominant sugar residues as the soluble blood group-active glycoproteins. There is some evidence that the erythrocyte A, B and H antigens of secretors (having the Se gene) are associated with glycoprotein as well as glycolipid. Lewis blood group activity, on the other hand, is believed to be always determined by glycolipid.

The second human blood group system, the *MN system;* was discovered by Landsteiner and Levine in 1928 using antisera from rabbits injected with human red blood cells. As the corresponding antibodies appear infrequently in man, the MN system does not cause major problems in blood transfusion. The system has been the subject of considerable study as a research tool since its discovery. Three genotypes MM, MN and NN are controlled by two allelic genes M and N, which

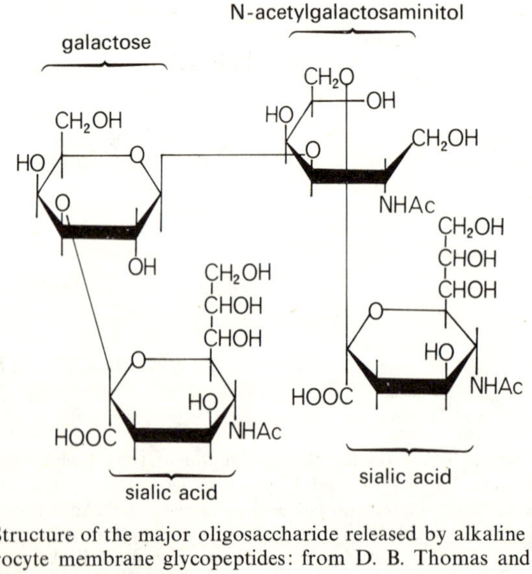

Figure 7.14. Structure of the major oligosaccharide released by alkaline borohydride from human erythrocyte membrane glycopeptides: from D. B. Thomas and R. J. Winzler, *J. Biol. Chem.* (1969), **244,** 5943–5946.

are independent of other blood group systems. The MN antigens are associated with the major sialoglycoprotein of the erythrocyte membrane which also contains the receptor sites for influenza virus and for various lectins (see below).

The major erythrocyte sialoglycoprotein carries most of the sialic acid of the membrane and contains 60% by weight of carbohydrate which is concentrated at the N-terminal end of the molecule and extends from the outer surface of the cell membrane (see chapter 5, figure 5.36). Details of the carbohydrate portion of the glycoprotein have been obtained from studies of glycopeptides obtained following proteolytic cleavage of the N-terminal end of the polypeptide chain, either from isolated glycoprotein or from intact erythrocytes. Treatment of a glycopeptide fraction with alkaline borohydride released 30–40% by weight of the carbohydrate as small oligosaccharides which were separated. The most abundant oligosaccharide was shown to be a tetrasaccharide with the structure shown in figure 7.14.

The presence of *N*-acetylgalactosaminitol indicated that *N*-acetylgalactose had been involved in a glycopeptide linkage, and the presence of 2-aminobutyric acid together with an increased alanine content in the peptide after cleavage showed that both threonine and serine had been the amino acids involved (see p. 128).

The alkali-stable glycopeptide remaining after the alkaline borohydride treatment is rather more complex, and when treated with the proteolytic enzyme Pronase yields a mixture of glycopeptides which is difficult to separate. A partial structure has been suggested for the carbohydrate portion of one of these smaller glycopeptides and is shown in figure 7.15. A similar alkali-stable glycopeptide has been characterized by other

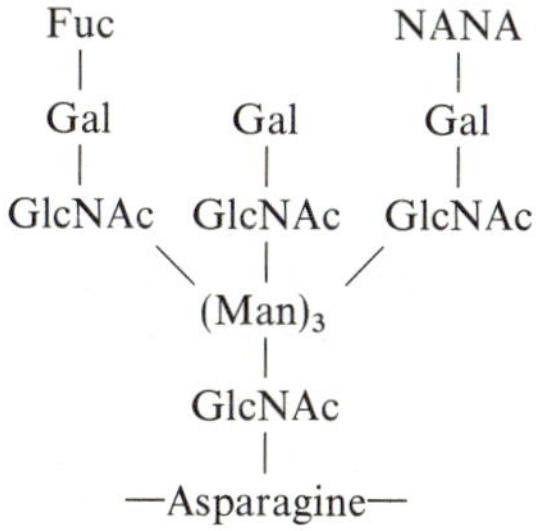

Figure 7.15. Suggested partial structure of a glycopeptide released by Pronase digestion of an alkaline borohydride-treated erythrocyte membrane glycoprotein. Gal = D-galactose; GlcNAc = N-acetyl-D-glucosamine; Man = D-mannose; NANA = N-acetylneuraminic acid (sialic acid); from D. B. Thomas and R. J. Winzler, *Biochem. J.* (1971), **124,** 55–59.

workers studying lectin receptor sites on the erythrocyte membrane (see p. 138).

The major sialoglycoprotein of the erythrocyte membrane carries both M and N antigens, and this activity is retained in sialoglycopeptides released by proteolytic digestion, although activity falls with decreasing size. The chemical basis of antigenicity is, however, not clear. M and N specificities are both destroyed by alkaline treatment of the glycopeptides, when inactive oligosaccharides of identical structure are released from type MM and from type NN erythrocytes. M and N activities of erythrocytes or of isolated glycoprotein are destroyed by neuraminidase, suggesting that sialic acid is directly involved in the determinant group of both antigens. There is also evidence that branched structures with a terminal β-D-galactose and a sialic acid residue are required for the N-antigen, which may be a precursor for M structure. It appears likely that full expression of M or N antigenic activity is dependent upon a rather complex structure involving not only carbohydrate but also protein. The involvement of the free amino-groups of protein side chains in M and N activity has been demonstrated.

Receptor sites for viruses

An important early step in the attack of a virus is its attachment to the surface of the host cell. Such attachment takes place at specific receptor sites which are located on the cell wall in the case of bacterial host cells, and on the plasma membrane itself in the case of mammalian cells. Following attachment, the bacterial virus discharges viral nucleic acid into the host cell, whereas the mammalian virus is generally completely engulfed by its host. Much of our knowledge concerning the effects of viruses in mammalian systems is derived from studies of the *myxoviruses* [enveloped viruses (chapter 4) containing RNA] such as influenza virus. An influenza virus particle will bind to receptor sites on a number of different erythrocytes, so causing bridging and haemagglutination. The erythrocyte is not a permissive host cell, however, and attachment is not followed in this case by engulfment of the virus particle. Nevertheless the virus receptor sites of the erythrocyte membrane have been extensively studied. The site of viral attachment is the major sialoglycoprotein of the erythrocyte membrane (glycophorin), and the terminal sialic acid residues themselves have been shown to be essential for receptor activity. It is known from hapten inhibition studies (cf. p. 123) that other structural features of the glycoprotein apart from its sialic acid are involved in virus binding, but their precise nature is unclear. Less is known about influenza virus receptors on other mammalian host cells, but it is probable that these will involve membrane sialoglycoproteins.

Erythrocytes are also agglutinated by *reoviruses* (non-enveloped viruses containing RNA). In this case *N*-acetylglucosamine, rather than sialic acid, appears to be of major importance at the host cell membrane receptor site.

There clearly must be structures on the surface of the virus particle which recognize the receptor sites on the membranes of host cells. In *non-enveloped viruses* the recognition sites are believed to be located on tail fibres of the virus, and generally involve structural protein. In the case of *enveloped viruses* the recognition sites are on the limiting membrane which often carries an outer layer of spikes or projections. The spikes of the influenza virus are associated with haemagglutinating and also neuraminidase activity. Neuraminidase appears to be required in order that the virus may be released from its sialic acid-mediated attachment to the host cell membrane. The haemagglutinin and neuraminidase are separate glycoproteins which may be released by proteolytic enzymes and are attached to the lipid bilayer of the membrane by short stalks containing hydrophobic amino acids. Although both glycoproteins have been isolated from SDS-disrupted virus particles, rather more is known about the haemagglutinin, which has been shown to contain *N*-acetylglucosamine, fucose, mannose and galactose. In contrast to influenza virus, *parainfluenza viruses* have been shown to have both haemagglutinin and neuraminidase activity associated with a single viral membrane glycoprotein species.

Lectin receptor sites

Proteins which can agglutinate erythrocytes and other cell types have been found in a wide range of plants, particularly in the seeds of legumes, and are often referred to as *phytohaemagglutinins.* Agglutinins have also been extracted from snails, crabs and fish, and the term *lectin* has been applied to protein agglutinins from all sources, and will be used in that sense here. In addition to their agglutinating properties, some lectins, such as that from the red kidney bean *Phaseolus vulgaris*, known as PHA, are mitogenic in that they stimulate the conversion of resting lymphocytes into growing and dividing blast cells. This property has been used in the study of the biochemistry of cell division.

Lectin molecules are multivalent and bring about agglutination by simultaneous binding to receptor sites on more than one cell. It has already been mentioned that lectins bind to carbohydrate receptor sites and are often very specific. Some lectins, for example, will only agglutinate human erythrocytes of a certain blood group and have found a limited use in blood typing. The nature of the cell surface receptor can be examined using the *hapten inhibition technique* in which specific inhibition of lectin-induced cell agglutination by a certain molecule is taken to imply that this molecule bears a close structural relationship to part of the cell surface receptor site. Hapten inhibition studies of lectin receptor sites have been carried out with inhibitors ranging in complexity from simple monosaccharides to large branched glycopeptides. In some cases simple monosaccharide haptens are inhibitors equally as potent as complex oligosaccharides, indicating simple structural requirements in the receptor site. For instance, the blood group A-active haemagglutinin from the snail *Helix pomatia* is inhibited to a greater extent by methyl *N*-acetyl-α-D-galactosaminide than by an A-active pentasaccharide. Also, concanavalin A from Jack beans is generally regarded as being specific for single α-D-mannopyranoside and α-D-glucopyranoside units although there is some evidence that di- and tri-mannosides are more powerful haptenic inhibitors than the monosaccharides. On the other hand, the receptors for some lectins are certainly complex, and haemagglutination by the lectin PHA (*Phaseolus vulgaris*) is inhibited approximately 3,000 times better by the erythrocyte membrane glycopeptide discussed below than by any constituent sugar.

A different approach to the characterization of lectin receptor sites is to solubilize the receptor from the membrane and determine its structure.

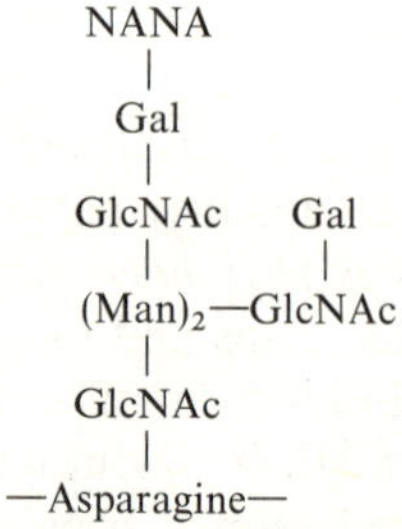

Figure 7.16. Proposed partial structure of a glycopeptide from human erythrocyte membrane which inhibits haemagglutination activity of the lectin PHA from *Phaseolus vulgaris*. Gal = D-galactose; GlcNAc = N-acetyl-D-glucosamine; Man = D-mannose; NANA = N-acetylneuraminic acid: from R. Kornfeld and S. Kornfeld, *J. Biol. Chem.* (1970), **245,** 2536–2545.

Solubilized glycoprotein receptors have been released from membranes and purified by gel-filtration, ion-exchange chromatography, and affinity chromatography on Sepharose-bound lectins. Purification is monitored by the ability of the fraction to inhibit the agglutinating or mitogenic activity of the corresponding lectin. In this way lectin receptors have been isolated from a number of cells, including erythrocytes, lymphocytes and tumour cells, but few have been studied in detail. Trypsin treatment of intact human erythrocytes released a number of glycopeptides which inhibited agglutination of red cells by the lectin PHA. Treatment of these glycopeptides with alkaline borohydride left alkali-stable glycopeptides which retained all the PHA inhibitory activity. After further proteolysis and purification, a low molecular weight glycopeptide was obtained which was a potent inhibitor of PHA-induced haemagglutination. Sequential glycosidase degradation indicated that the glycopeptide had the structure shown in figure 7.16.

The inhibitory activity of this glycopeptide indicates that it is derived from the PHA receptor site on the erythrocyte. Its structure is very similar to that suggested for the alkali-stable glycopeptide shown in figure 7.15 which was also isolated from human erythrocytes. In contrast to MN and influenza virus receptor activity, PHA inhibition was found to be independent of the presence of sialic acid groups in the glycopeptide but did depend on the presence of galactose units, and to a lesser extent on the mannose of the molecule. The PHA receptor glycopeptide is also a potent inhibitor of a lectin from the common lentil (*Lens culinaris*). In this case the dominant sugar appears to be *N*-acetylglucosamine not galactose. It is likely that the same glycopeptide on the surface of the erythrocyte carries receptor sites for both lectins. Indeed it is possible that both this glycopeptide and the MN-active glycopeptide are derived from the same membrane sialoglycoprotein, which could carry many other specific receptor sites. There is some evidence that receptors for a given lectin on the surfaces of different cells are very similar, but proof of this must await actual isolation of receptors from cells other than the erythrocyte.

Transplantation (histocompatability) antigens

Rejection of transplanted tissue or organs is now an important and well-publicized medical problem. While transplants can normally be carried out between genetically similar individuals, transplants from genetically different donors are regularly rejected by the host. The immune response of the host, which leads to rejection, is clearly triggered by recognition of foreign material, and it is now believed that this recognition depends on the presence of specific antigens on the surface of the implanted cells. Such histocompatability antigens are genetically coded for at a number of independent loci. Rapid rejection of foreign tissue is determined by histoincompatability at just one locus, in mice the H-2 locus and in man the HL-A locus. Incompatability at other loci gives rise to a slower rejection of the transplanted tissue.

The antigenic specificities are determined by plasma membrane glycoproteins, some of which have been released from the membrane by controlled proteolysis. Glycopeptides carrying mouse H-2 or human HL-A antigens have been cleaved from suitable cells and found in both cases to fall into two types: Class I (molecular weight 55,000 daltons) and Class II (molecular weight 35,000 daltons) carrying mutually exclusive antigenic sites. Both classes of glycopeptide with H-2 activity contained 10–15% carbohydrate, consisting largely of sialic acid, fucose, mannose and galactose, and no differences were apparent in the carbohydrate composition of the two peptides. In view of this similarity, and because small differences were observed in the protein structures, it has been suggested that it is protein and not carbohydrate which carries the antigenic specificity. It is, however, quite possible that small structural differences in the carbohydrate portion of the two antigenically different glycopeptides could have been missed. The current position, based on this and related evidence, is that while it is reasonably certain that plasma membrane glycoproteins carry the histocompatability antigens, the question as to whether these are determined by the carbohydrate or the protein, or both, remains open.

Cell-cell recognition and adhesion

There clearly must be mechanisms by which cells recognize each other during normal processes of cell migration, morphogenesis, etc., and membrane carbohydrate has been implicated in these mechanisms. It has been shown, for example, that the morphology and growth behaviour of mammalian cells in culture can be changed by addition of certain monosaccharides to the medium. This behaviour would be consistent with the involvement of cell surface carbohydrate in cell-cell contact and growth control mechanisms. The added monosaccharides could act as haptens in combining with carbohydrate-receptor sites at the cell surface, and so interfere with cell-cell contact and possible transfer of information concerning growth. Evidence that amino sugars are involved in aggregation of animal cells has been obtained from studies relating aggregation to nutrient requirements. Single cells of a mouse teratoma suspended in a glucose-balanced salt solution were shown to aggregate only if L-glutamine, D-glucosamine or D-mannosamine were added to the medium. As L-glutamine is required for the biosynthesis of amino sugars, it was concluded that the latter are necessary components of the surface macromolecules involved in cell adhesion.

In view of the contribution of sialic acid to the surface charge of mammalian cells (see p. 122), it would seem possible that this amino sugar could be involved in cell adhesion. In this case it might be expected that removal of surface sialic acid, by neuraminidase for instance, would increase cell adhesiveness by lowering electrostatic repulsion between cells. However, both decreased and increased cell adhesiveness have

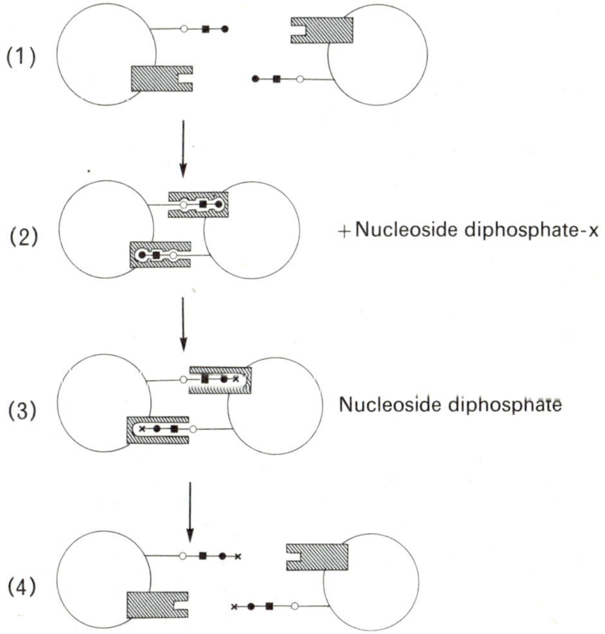

Figure 7.17. Proposed role of glycosyl transferases in cellular adhesion: adapted from S. Roseman, *Chem. Phys. Lipids* (1970), **5**, 270–297. Cells carrying both glycosyl transferases and their oligosaccharide acceptor molecules (—○—■—●) on their outer surfaces (1) come together allowing formation of an enzyme-substrate complex (2). Addition of a further monosaccharide residue (–x) (3) brings about dissociation of the enzyme-product complex and the modified cells part (4).

been reported following neuraminidase treatment, and no such simple role can be postulated for sialic acid in cell adhesion.

An attractive theory of cellular recognition and adhesion has recently been postulated by Roseman (figure 7.17). In this mechanism, cell surfaces contain both glycosyl transferases and their oligosaccharide substrates. Binding of a glycosyl transferase on one cell with its specific carbohydrate receptor molecule on a neighbouring cell would result in intercellular adhesion dependent on a highly specific enzyme-substrate reaction. It is suggested that, following transfer of a sugar residue to the acceptor molecule, the enzyme-product complex dissociates and the cells separate. The cell surface is accordingly modified as a result of cell-cell contact, and a role for such a mechanism could be found in phenomena such as contact inhibition of growth (see later). Glycosyl transferases have been shown to be present in mammalian cell plasma membranes (see p. 129), and other supporting evidence for the Roseman theory has been reported. It must be stressed at this stage that the above mechanism of cell adhesion is still highly speculative.

A phenomenon which is closely related to cell-cell recognition is the *homing of lymphocytes.* Lymphocytes leave the blood stream and enter the lymphatic tissues, after which they return to the blood stream via the lymphatic system. The elegant experiments of Gesner and his co-workers have provided evidence that the homing of lymphocytes to lymphatic tissue is dependent on the presence of specific carbohydrate residues on the lymphocyte plasma membrane. Thoracic duct lymphocytes were labelled with ^{32}P and reinjected into rats, when they rapidly accumulated in the spleen and lymph nodes. If, however, the cells were treated with a mixture of glycosidases from *Clostridium perfringens* prior to intravenous injection, they went mainly to the liver. L-fucose and *N*-acetylgalactosamine were found to inhibit the effects of the glycosidase mixture, suggesting that these monosaccharides are important in determining the course of the homing process. The importance of sialic acid also was shown by the fact that neuraminidase treatment resulted in accumulation of treated lymphocytes in the liver. Trypsin treatment of lymphocytes brought about a similar effect, suggesting that the carbohydrate determinants on the lymphocyte surface which control homing are glycoprotein components. Some enzyme-treated cells which had migrated directly to the liver were found to return to the lymph nodes after a period of some 24 hours, indicating that regeneration of the relevant cell membrane determinants had taken place in the intervening time.

An observation made in connection with these experiments is that *glucose is generally absent from mammalian cell surface carbohydrate.* This is consistent with the role proposed for such carbohydrate in cell recognition processes, since, if glucose were to be involved as a primary determinant of a recognition site, its effect would be continually nullified by the interference of D-glucose, present in body fluids, acting as a haptenic inhibitor.

Tumour cell membranes

Tumour cells are characterized by radically changed social interactions, and changes in the cell surface might well be expected to accompany, or possibly even initiate, the transformation from a normal to a malignant cell. Specific properties of cancer cells which can be related to alterations in the plasma membrane include:

1. *Cellular adhesion.* Tumour cells grown on solid media usually adhere to each other less than do normal cells. However, the situation is not clear cut, and examples of both increased and decreased 'adhesiveness' following malignant transformation have been reported.
2. *Contact inhibition of growth and movement.* Normal cells in culture grow until a confluent monolayer is achieved, when both movement and growth are apparently inhibited by contact with neighbouring cells. Malignant cells under comparable conditions generally continue to grow beyond this stage, giving multilayered associations.
3. *Electrical communication.* Electrical connections can occur between individual cells, and it has been reported that such connections are defective in some cancer cells.
4. *Surface charge.* Comparisons of surface charge have been made between malignant and corresponding normal cells in a number of cases using microelectrophoresis. The anodic mobility, indicative of negative surface charge is commonly, but not always, higher than that of the normal counterpart.
5. *Membrane transport.* Dramatic increases in sugar uptake have been shown to occur in some virus-transformed cells. Although the transport mechanisms of macromolecules are not clear, it is convenient to mention under this heading that tumour cells are often 'leaky' to intracellular enzymes. Thus lysosomal peptidases and hydrolases are released from intact tumour cells into the surrounding interstitial fluid.
6. *Membrane antigens.* Plasma membranes of tumour cells generally carry new antigens not present in the normal cell. In contrast to normal histocompatibility antigens, tumour antigens can induce an immune response against themselves in genetically similar hosts. Under favourable circumstances, such a response in the primary host can lead to elimination of the cancer cells. Whereas antigens on tumours induced by chemical carcinogens or ionizing radiation are tumour specific, those of virus-transformed cells are characteristic of the virus rather than the tumour.

   As well as new antigens, tumour cells can carry unexpected known antigens. Thus antigens normally only occurring in embryonic but not adult cells have been found on malignant cells. A further example is the discovery on tumour cells of blood group antigens of a group different from that of the host.

In view of the involvement of membrane carbohydrate in cell surface effects, considerable effort has been expended in attempts to correlate the above-mentioned surface peculiarities of tumour cells with specific changes in cell membrane carbohydrates.

An increase in surface carbohydrate of transformed cells, compared with normal controls, has been indicated by histochemical and electron microscope studies in which an accumulation of ruthenium red-staining material was found on cancer cells. While the ruthenium red stain is generally regarded as showing the presence of acidic oligosaccharides (see p. 117), it is not clear whether this is mucopolysaccharide, glycoprotein or glycolipid. Moreover, no consistent differences in carbohydrate amount or composition have been found by chemical analysis of total membrane material from transformed and normal cells.

The abnormally high anodic electrophoretic mobility (see p. 143) of many cancer cells has been correlated with high membrane sialic acid content. It has been postulated that an outer coat of sialic acid-containing carbohydrate shields the surface antigens of invading tumour cells from immunological surveillance in the host, and so hinders their rejection. There is some evidence of reduced transplantability of tumour cells following neuraminidase treatment, but immunological results concerning such a role of sialic acid are conflicting, and the protection hypothesis has been strongly challenged. It is not even possible to correlate completely either high anodic mobility or increased sialic acid content with malignancy, and instances of both lower anodic mobility and decreased sialic content of tumour cells compared with normal cells have been reported.

Comparisons of glycoproteins and glycopeptides from plasma membranes of transformed cells and of controls have shown slight differences, although there are problems in obtaining sufficient quantities of purified material for structural studies. The isolation of a fucose-containing glycoprotein in increased quantities from virus-transformed hamster cells has aroused some interest. Few details of either the structure or the biological activity of this glycoprotein have been reported, however, and its possible relevance to cancer is not known.

Changes in levels of certain membrane glycolipids have also been observed following malignant transformation. In general the tendency is towards increased content of the simpler molecules. Thus the major membrane glycolipid of virus-transformed hamster fibroblasts was found to be lactosylceramide (chapter 5), while the more complex *N*-acetylneuraminyllactosylceramide and L-galactosyllactosylceramide predominated in normal cells. These effects have been correlated with blocked synthesis of the more complicated glycolipids caused by repressed activity of specific glycosyl transferases.

Considerable excitement has been generated by the finding that virus-transformed cells are agglutinated by lectins at concentrations which do not affect normal cells. Similar agglutinability by lectins can also be induced in normal cells following mild trypsin treatment, and it was originally proposed that malignant transformation or trypsin both expose agglutinin receptor sites normally present in a hidden form on the surface of animal cells. It was subsequently found, however, that normal, transformed, and trypsin-treated cells all bind approximately the same amounts of lectin. The different agglutinability of the cell types cannot therefore be attributed to exposure of different numbers of lectin receptor sites, and alternative explanations have been offered. Examination of the surfaces of cells treated with labelled concanavalin A (see p. 119) shows that cells which are susceptible to agglutination show a patchy distribution of receptors. Non-agglutinable cells, on the other hand, show a random or uniform distribution of receptor sites. It was accordingly suggested that the agglutinability of the cell was determined by the distribution of the lectin receptor sites on the cell membrane. Further work has indicated that the clustered lectin receptor sites found in agglutinable cells might indeed have been grouped together by the action of the multivalent lectin itself. When lectin receptor sites of agglutinable cells were immobilized in the plane of the membrane by glutaraldehyde treatment prior to lectin addition, a random distribution of sites was observed. It may be that increased mobility of the receptor sites in the membranes of transformed and trypsinized cells, compared with normal cells, leads to 'patching' of receptor sites under the influence of lectins, and consequently to increased agglutinability. The difference between normal and transformed cell membranes would then lie in the increased fluidity of the latter.

A characteristic of malignant cells which has already been mentioned is the lack of *contact inhibition of growth.* A connection between contact inhibition and lectin receptor sites on cell membranes has been demonstrated by Burger and Noonan. These workers treated concanavalin A with trypsin, and obtained a cleaved monovalent molecule. Treatment of virus-transformed mouse fibroblasts, which showed no contact inhibition of growth, with the trypsinized lectin restored normal growth behaviour to the cells. It was suggested that exposure of the lectin-binding sites on the surface of transformed cells led to loss of contact inhibition, and that simple covering of these exposed areas with plant protein was sufficient to bring about normal growth characteristics. Whatever the explanation, it is rather remarkable that the growth behaviour of malignant mouse cells can be so dramatically restored to normal by patching their membranes with plant protein.

A general problem in comparative studies of transformed and normal cells is the choice of the normal cell control. Changes in cell surfaces occur, depending on conditions of growth, state of cells and phase of cell cycle. Moreover, variations can occur within clones of either normal or malignant cells. Some of the inconsistencies of the findings concerning membrane composition of transformed cells may possibly be attributed to these problems. It seems clear that real differences do exist following transformation, and further work may clarify whether these differences in membranes are a primary or a secondary effect of malignancy.

SUMMARY

1. Plasma membranes of mammalian cells contain 1–10% of their total weight as carbohydrate, which has been shown by microscopic, electrokinetic and immunochemical techniques to be largely located on their outer surface.
2. Glycolipids can be solubilized from membranes using polar organic solvents and purified by standard techniques of lipid chemistry. Membrane glycoproteins are generally intrinsic proteins, and accordingly require organic solvents, detergents or chaotropic agents for solubilization. Purification of glycoproteins is complicated by their microheterogeneity.
3. The carbohydrate of membrane glycoproteins is contained in oligosaccharide side chains attached to a polypeptide backbone by one of two major linkage types.
4. Biosynthesis of glycolipid and glycoprotein is believed to involve enzymic attachment of carbohydrate to preformed lipid or protein molecules embedded in Golgi membrane, after which the Golgi membrane and the newly synthesized molecules are incorporated into the plasma membrane.
5. ABO and Lewis blood group activities are specified by terminal carbohydrate residues of plasma membrane glycolipid, and their relationships have been worked out using soluble blood-group active glycoproteins.
6. The major sialoglycoprotein of erythrocyte membrane carries M and N blood group determinants and receptor sites for certain viruses and lectins.
7. Membrane carbohydrate has been shown to be involved in histocompatibility antigens and in a variety of cell recognition and adhesion phenomena.
8. The behaviour of tumour cells differs from that of normal cells in a number of ways, many of which can be attributed to changes in the plasma membrane. Despite considerable effort, however, few consistent differences have been detected in the membrane carbohydrate of normal and transformed cells.

CHAPTER 8

MEMBRANE-MEDIATED PROCESSES

CHAPTER TWO DESCRIBED BRIEFLY SEVERAL OF THE WAYS IN WHICH membranes influence the activities of cells. Metabolism occurs within discrete compartments between which communication can occur only via the boundary membranes. In addition to their role as selectively permeable barriers (see chapter 9), the membranes may also participate directly in the events occurring within the metabolic compartment. Thus many of the enzymes of a metabolic sequence may be membrane-bound, and as such their activities can be regulated by the membrane.

In multicellular organisms the integration of the metabolic activities of the various organs into an overall pattern characteristic of the organism calls for a well-developed control system. In its most highly developed form, such control is achieved by the closely co-ordinated activities of the nervous and endocrine systems. Both convey information to the cells of other organs by means of chemical messengers which interact with specific receptors on the plasma membrane of the target cells. The transfer of information from the exterior to the interior of the cell is mediated by the plasma membrane.

Membranes must be considered as being more than simply protective barriers; rather they should be seen as complex dynamic structures whose activities contribute greatly to the characteristic metabolic patterns of the cell and the organism. In the present chapter we will examine a selected range of membrane activities which touch upon a wide range of cellular functions.

Mitochondrial membranes and oxidative phosphorylation

In chapter 2 attention was drawn to the vectorial nature which can be assumed by membrane-associated metabolic reactions. Probably the most sophisticated development of vectorial metabolism is the process of oxidative phosphorylation which we will now examine in detail.

The basic function of mitochondria is to carry out the process of respiration, and to convert the energy released into a usable form. The first stage involves the breakdown of pyruvate, keto acids or acetyl CoA by the enzymes of the citric acid cycle. This gives rise to carbon dioxide and reduced co-enzymes. The reduced co-enzymes are then oxidized by molecular oxygen, yielding water and energy. The oxidation process is carried out by the respiratory chain, which consists of a series of components of decreasing redox potential. Electrons from the reduced co-enzymes pass down the chain, resulting in sequential reduction of each component until the terminal constituent, cytochrome a, in its reduced form, is oxidized by molecular oxygen. The process is accompanied by a decrease in free energy, almost half of which is utilized for ATP synthesis. This is the process of *oxidative phosphorylation.*

The two mitochondrial membrane systems differ in their ultrastructure (chapter 3), enzymic activities (chapter 4), and chemical composition (chapter 5). It might be expected, accordingly, that their cellular functions would differ, and the question arises as to the role played by the two membranes in the events described above. An examination of Table 4.2 reveals that the outer membrane has associated with it a variety of enzymes, none of which is closely associated with either respiration or oxidative phosphorylation. The inner membrane contains most of the enzymes necessary for these two processes. The matrix is found to contain the enzymes of the citric acid cycle; thus the inner membrane and matrix together form the respiratory unit. This arrangement demands that all respiratory substrates must pass through the outer and inner membranes. Permeability studies of the two membrane systems reveal marked differences. Most substances, with the exception of uncharged molecules of molecular weight less than 100 daltons will not pass through the inner membrane by simple diffusion, and a range of specific transport systems exists to control the entry of respiratory substrates. The outer membrane shows little discrimination to the passive diffusion of substances below a molecular weight of about 10,000 daltons. Thus metabolites can pass freely between the cytoplasm and the inter-membrane space. An interesting enzyme is found in the space. This is adenylate kinase which catalyses the formation of two molecules of ADP from one molecule of ATP and one of AMP. AMP is formed in the cytoplasm but cannot be phosphorylated by oxidative phosphorylation. The ADP formed in the inter-membrane space, however, can be readily transported through the inner membrane and then phosphorylated.

The precise mechanism of the process of oxidative phosphorylation is still unknown, but it is quite clear that the structural organization of the inner membrane is of fundamental importance in any hypothesis. The spatial orientation of the components of the inner membrane has been determined largely by the use of specific redox reagents of limited permeability. Thus, for example, ferricyanide does not penetrate the membrane at all, but can be shown to interact with cytochromes c and c_1, which must therefore be at the membrane's outer surface. The mitochondrial ATPase has been identified with the knobs seen on the inner surface of the membrane (see figure 3.4) and is usually referred to as F_1. Figure 8.1 shows the currently accepted orientation of the electron transport chain in the membrane.

Two main hypotheses of oxidative phosphorylation have been advanced, the *chemical theory* and the *chemiosmotic theory*. The chemical theory of oxidative phosphorylation is modelled on the general biochemical mechanism of substrate-linked phosphorylation, in which energy

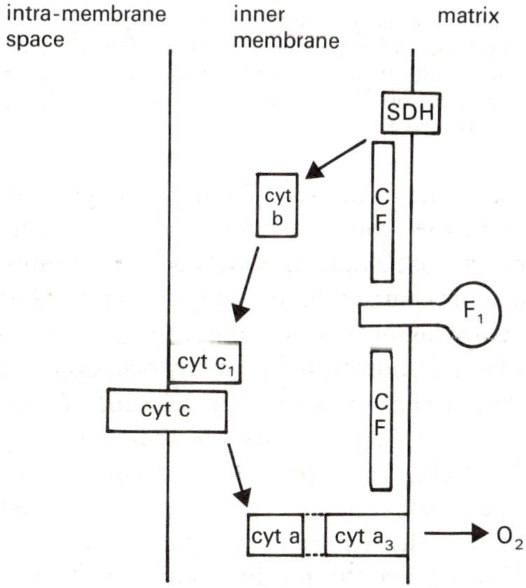

Figure 8.1. The orientation of the electron transport chain within the inner mitochondrial membrane: Succinate dehydrogenase, SDH, is at the inner surface of the membrane. The ATPase, F_1 and cytochrome a_3 are also located at this site. Cytochrome c is readily accessible from the intra-membrane space and is thought to be located at the outer surface of the membrane. Cytochromes b, c, and a are located within the membrane structure. The coupling factors CF are thought to provide a functional link between the ATPase, F_1 and the electron transport chain.

is conserved in an 'energy-rich bond'. In addition to the established constituents of the electron transport chain, the chemical theory demands the presence of two further components, usually designated X and I, which are members of a hypothetical energy conserving system. Energy is conserved by the formation of 'high-energy' intermediates involving X, I and electron carriers as outlined in figure 8.2.

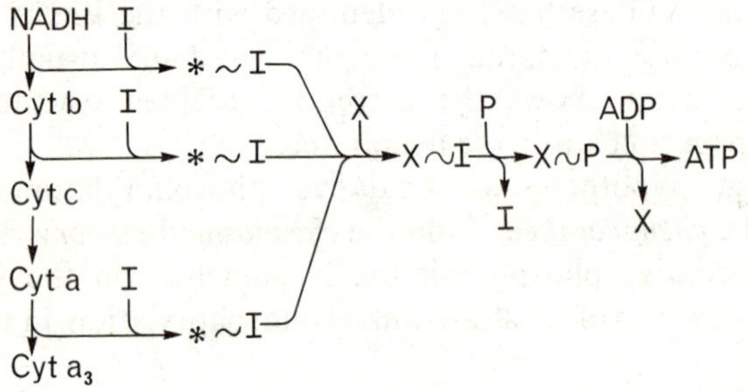

Figure 8.2. The coupling of phosphorylation to the electron transport chain: Coupling is thought to occur at three discrete sites and involves the formation of a 'high-energy' complex between a chain constituent and I, a member of the hypothetical energy conserving system. The energy is utilized for ATP synthesis, the transfer being mediated by the 'high-energy' compounds X-I and X-P.

The scheme involves the formation of a 'high-energy' phosphate which phosphorylates ADP, the reaction being catalyzed by the F_1 ATPase. The theory demands a close association between the various components of the electron transport chain and the energy conserving system. Further, it requires a close coupling of these systems with the F_1 ATPase. Racker and his colleagues have demonstrated on many occasions the dependence of the phosphorylation step on a full complement of membrane components. Racker's group has also shown that not only is there a requirement for the electron transport chain and F_1, but that a series of specific proteins, the *coupling factors* (see figure 8.1) are required, which appear to link functionally F_1 to the chain. More than 20 years of intensive research has failed to produce any direct evidence for the existence of the X-I 'high-energy' intermediates. We might conclude from this that X and I and their various derivatives do not exist, and that an alternative mechanism should be sought.

In the early 1960s Mitchell put forward the chemiosmotic theory of oxidative phosphorylation. In 1939 H. Lundergardh proposed that the electron transport chain was arranged anisotropically across the membrane, protons being utilized on one side and released at the other. He suggested that the resultant charge separation could be used to accumulate salts against a concentration gradient. Mitchell took the basic concept of coupling the potential energy of a trans-membrane charge gradient to an energy-requiring process, and applied it to the problem of oxidative phosphorylation. In simple terms, Mitchell proposed that the energy for ATP synthesis derives from a trans-membrane proton gradient produced by the oxidation-reduction reactions of the electron transport chain. The theory depends on an anisotropic orientation of the chain in the membrane, but requires no hypothetical intermediates nor any close coupling of F_1 to the chain. From this point of view the chemiosmotic theory is more attractive than its chemical counterpart.

Mitchell proposed that the electron carriers are so arranged that they effectively transport protons from the inside to the outside of the membrane (see figure 8.3).

The respiratory chain, as shown in figure 8.3, generates a trans-

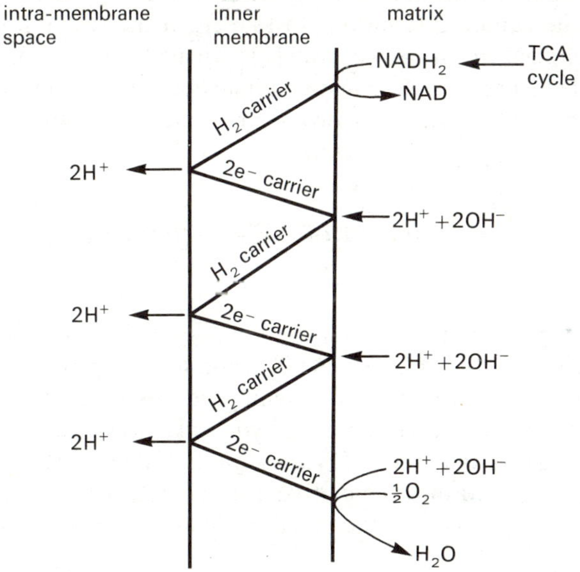

Figure 8.3. The transport of protons by the electron transport chain: The components of the chain are arranged as an alternating series of H_2 carriers, NAD, flavoprotein and ubiquinone, and electron carriers, non-haemiron, cytochrome b and cytochromes c and a. The operation of the chain establishes a trans-membrane proton gradient.

membrane proton gradient. This can be verified experimentally when, at the outset of respiration, the pH of the incubation medium is seen to fall while the intramitochondrial pH rises. Mitchell has shown that the inner membrane is very impermeable to protons, and can therefore maintain a high concentration gradient across it. According to Mitchell the free energy loss incurred by electrons passing down the electron transport chain is conserved in the form of a trans-membrane proton gradient. The next stage involves utilizing the potential energy of the proton gradient, termed by Mitchell *proticity*, for ATP synthesis.

The reaction catalysed by the F_1 ATPase is usually written

$$ADP + P_i \rightleftharpoons ATP \tag{1}$$

However more correctly equation (1) should be written

$$ADP^{3-} + HO-\overset{\overset{\displaystyle O}{\|}}{\underset{\underset{\displaystyle O^-}{|}}{P}}-OH \rightleftharpoons ATP^{4-} + H_2O \tag{2}$$

Under normal circumstances the reaction will not proceed from left to right, i.e. the equilibrium lies far to the left. If the reaction occurred in an environment from which water is virtually excluded, then ATP synthesis becomes feasible. Furthermore, suppose the ATPase is able to separate the proton and the hydroxyl anion derived from the phosphate moiety so that equation (2) becomes

$$ADP^{3-} + HO-\overset{\overset{\displaystyle O}{\|}}{\underset{\underset{\displaystyle O^-}{|}}{P}}-OH \rightleftharpoons ATP^{4-} + [H^+] + [OH^-] \tag{3}$$

then, so long as the proton and the hydroxyl anion are removed from the active site of the ATPase, ATP synthesis will proceed. Figure 8.3 showed that the electron transport chain produces a proton excess outside the membrane, with a corresponding hydroxyl anion excess in the matrix. Mitchell suggests that the ATPase is markedly anisotropic, such that protons are expelled into the matrix, and the hydroxyl anion is expelled through the membrane to the exterior. Thus the overall reaction now becomes

$$ADP + HO-\overset{\overset{\displaystyle O}{\|}}{\underset{\underset{\displaystyle O^-}{|}}{P}}-O^- \rightleftharpoons ATP + \underset{\substack{\text{Inside} \\ (OH^-\text{ excess})}}{\underset{\downarrow}{[H^+]}} + \underset{\substack{\text{Outside} \\ (H^+\text{ excess})}}{\underset{\downarrow}{[OH^-]}} \tag{4}$$

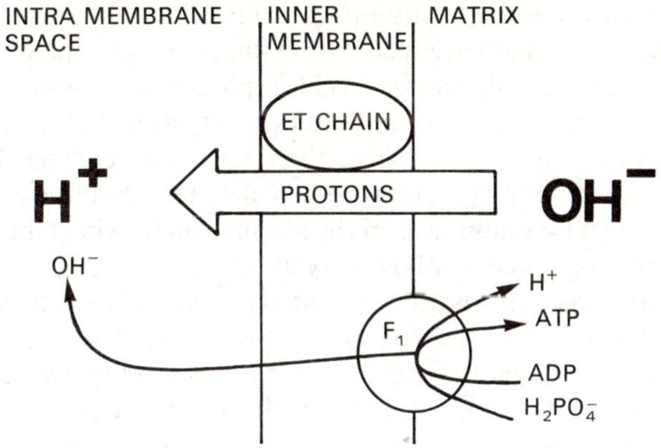

Figure 8.4. The chemiosmotic model of oxidative phosphorylation (ET chain = electron transport chain).

The proticity of the membrane provides the driving force for the removal of the proton and the hydroxyl anion from the ATPase active site, and thus allows the reaction to proceed from left to right. Provided the proticity is maintained, and provided the active site of the ATPase is in a hydrophobic environment, ATP synthesis will continue. The scheme is summarized in figure 8.4.

There is much experimental support for Mitchell's hypothesis. There is ample evidence, for instance, that membrane proteins can have very hydrophobic areas either on their surfaces or as 'pockets' within a predominantly hydrophilic exterior; thus the requirement that water be excluded from the active site could readily be met. An examination of figure 8.4 reveals that a trans-membrane electrical potential such that the matrix is negative will also favour ATP synthesis, and the matrix is, in fact, up to 200 millivolts negative relative to the exterior. The membrane potential arises as a result of its limited permeability to ions, and there is direct experimental evidence that ATP synthesis can be driven by either a pH gradient or by a membrane potential in mitochondria *in vitro*. In the mitochondrion *in vivo* it seems likely that both components contribute to the net osmotic energy of the membrane, and hence to ATP synthesis.

Photosynthetic phosphorylation

In chapter 3 the ultrastructure of the chloroplast was outlined, and some similarities between chloroplasts and mitochondria noted. It is the role of the chloroplast to effect the *transduction* into chemical energy of the light energy which is initially trapped by the photosynthetic pigments, mainly chlorophyll a and, in higher plants, chlorophyll b. Light absorption results in the formation of pigment molecules in an excited state, in which an electron is shifted to a higher energy level (see chapter 11, p. 229). Photosynthesis involves the utilization of the energy of the excited pigment molecules for ATP synthesis, and the mechanism by which this is achieved parallels that of oxidative phosphorylation.

The activated electrons derived from the excited pigments pass through a series of electron carriers reminiscent of the electron transport chain of the inner mitochondrial membrane. Two types of molecules are found in the lamellae of the chloroplast, which together constitute an electron transport chain. These are the hydrogen carriers, which undergo sequential reduction and oxidation by the acquisition and loss of hydrogen atoms, and the electron carriers which are similarly reduced and oxidized, but by the addition and loss of electrons. Mitchell has proposed that the electron transport chain is arranged within the chloroplast membrane in an analogous manner to that in mitochondria; i.e. passage of electrons down the chain results in the build-up of a trans-membrane proton gradient. The arrangement of the chloroplast system, however, results in protons being transported *into* the chloroplast. Experimental evidence for such a process is readily obtained by incubating chloroplasts in an unbuffered medium, when illumination results in a rise in the pH of the medium. Further, the synthesis of ATP in chloroplasts kept in the dark can be promoted by rapidly raising the pH of the incubating medium. The *proticity* of the chloroplast membrane is coupled to ATP synthesis in the same way as in mitochondria, and the membrane-bound ATPase of the chloroplast bears many resemblances to its mitochondrial counterpart.

Both oxidative and photosynthetic phosphorylation call for the fully integrated co-operation of a very heterogeneous group of membrane constituents. Let us now consider a membrane-mediated process which involves only a single protein species.

The retinal disc membrane and light reception

The arrangement of the membraneous discs which are found in the outer segments of retinal rods was described in chapter 3. The function of the rod cells is to convert light energy into an electrical signal. The transduction is mediated by the visual pigment *rhodopsin.* Rhodopsin has been described as a *chromolipoprotein*, comprising a protein (opsin) a chromophore (*11-cis-retinal*) and some tightly bound phospholipids, particularly phosphatidylethanolamine. It is the major protein component of the disc membranes, and in frog retina has been shown to comprise 80% of the membrane protein.

Studies on isolated rhodopsin have revealed some of the details of the molecule's interaction with light. The chromophore is found as 11-*cis*-retinal in native rhodopsin, and is attached through a Schiff's base linkage to the amino group of a lysine residue in the peptide chain of opsin. Illumination results in an isomerization of the chromophore 11-*cis*-retinal, leading to the formation of all *trans* retinal which has a radically-changed conformation [cf. *cis* and *trans* fatty acids (chapter 5, figure 5.4)] and dissociates from the protein. Evidence has recently been produced that a re-orientation of some of the phospholipid molecules of the chromophore also results from illumination. Concomitant with these changes the protein moiety alters its conformation, passing through a number of well-defined intermediate forms until free opsin is produced. Measurements of the Stokes' radius indicate that the molecular volume may increase by over 30% during this sequence. Such a change may have a profound effect on the properties of the membrane of which rhodopsin is a major constituent. J. Heller and his colleagues have shown that the permeability of the disc membrane changes on illumination, resulting in a redistribution of ions between the intradiscal and intracellular spaces. Such ionic changes may well have a role in initiating the nerve impulse.

Detailed investigations of the interactions between rhodopsin and the other membrane constituents have provided information relevant not only to the problem of photo-reception but to membrane proteins generally. Like many membrane proteins rhodopsin is very hydrophobic and can only be extracted from the membrane with detergent solutions. It is not surprising, therefore, that X-ray evidence (see chapter 11) suggests that rhodopsin is partially embedded in the lipid phase of the membrane. R. Cone and his colleagues have provided many of the data relating to the orientation and mobility of rhodopsin in the disc membrane. The acyl chains of the phospholipids of these membranes show a high degree of unsaturation, resulting in a very fluid membrane (see chapters 6 and 11) and Cone has found the viscosity of the lipid phase to be at least an order of magnitude lower than in the erythrocyte membrane. Within this highly fluid environment rhodopsin undergoes rapid lateral diffusion and also spins about an axis perpendicular to the plane of the membrane (see figure 8.5).

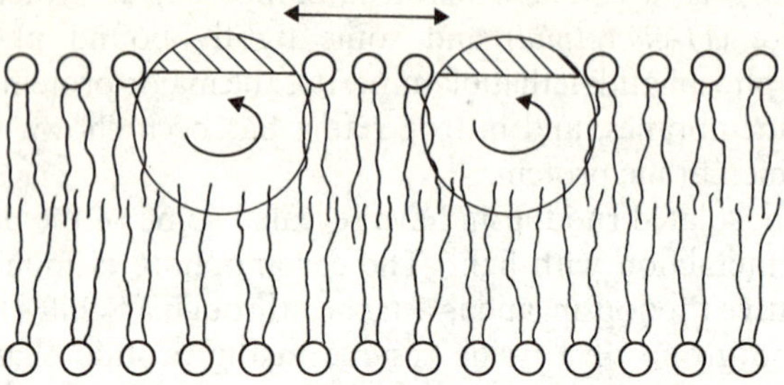

Figure 8.5. The location of rhodopsin in the retinal disc membrane: The spherical rhodopsin molecules are embedded in the lipid bilayer with their hydrophilic regions, ⧹⧹⧹⧹, at the surface. The molecules spin counterclockwise and diffuse laterally through the membrane ↔.

In the native, i.e. unbleached, state the chromophore projects laterally, lying parallel to the surface of the membrane. This permits rhodopsin to spin as shown in figure 8.5, but probably hinders rotation about an axis in the plane of the membrane. The light-induced changes in configuration and the consequent dissociation of the chromophore from the protein may allow such a rotation to occur. Following illumination, rhodopsin has been shown to sink deeper into the membrane, possibly as a result of its conformational change. It has been suggested that in its sunken state rhodopsin could span the membrane and, being free to rotate about an axis in the plane of the membrane (figure 8.6) act as a *diffusional carrier*, picking up ions on one side of the membrane and transporting

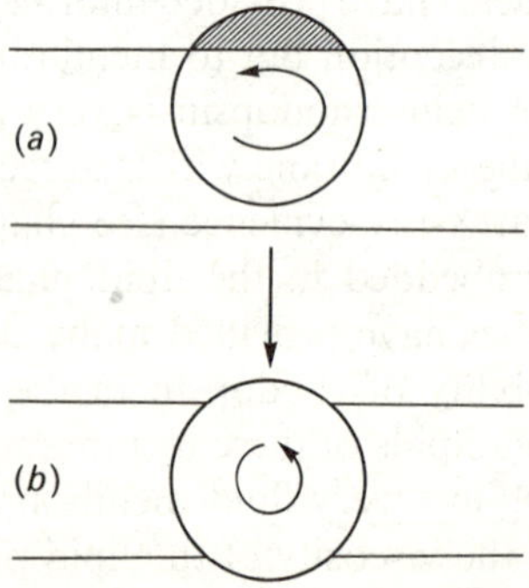

Figure 8.6. Rhodopsin in the retinal disc membrane; the effect of light: In (*a*) rhodopsin is anchored at the membrane surface by its hydrophilic regions. Illumination may result in state (*b*) in which the molecule spans the membrane and can rotate about an axis in the plane of the membrane.

them to the other. There is some evidence that the initial event in the light response is a movement of calcium ions from the intradiscal space into the intracellular space of the outer segment. Cone has suggested that rhodopsin could function as a calcium carrier, and thereby provide the signal for the initiation of the nerve impulse.

The purple membrane of *Halobacterium halobium*

The *Halobacteria* are a group of extreme *halophiles* whose natural habitats are salt flats and stagnant pools at the edge of tropical seas. Under such conditions, salt concentrations close to saturation are maintained, temperature and solar radiation are high, and the oxygen content is low. In order to cope with this environment *Halobacterium halobium* has evolved a fascinating membrane which combines several of the processes described in the preceding sections.

When grown in the light in a high salt medium at low oxygen tension (PO_2) *Halobacterium halobium* synthesizes patches of plasma membrane containing a purple pigment. The purple membrane fragments can be readily isolated and have been shown to contain a single protein species which accounts for about 75% of the membrane mass and occupies some 50% of the surface area. The protein is very similar to rhodopsin and is called *bacteriorhodopsin.* It contains the chromophore retinal bound to a lysine residue via a Schiff's base as in vertebrate rhodopsin. Unlike rhodopsin, bacteriorhodopsin does not show rapid movements within the membrane, but forms a more rigid planar lattice.

Bacteriorhodopsin shows a broad absorption peak at about 570 nm which accounts for the deep purple colour of the patches on the plasma membrane. A flash of visible light converts the native bacteriorhodopsin to a second conformational species, absorbing at about 415 nm, which reverts to the native form within a few milliseconds in the dark. Under conditions of continuous illumination the protein appears to oscillate rapidly between the two conformations. Concomitant with the conformational change, protons are taken up on the inside of the cell and released to the outside. Thus the purple membrane acts as a light-driven proton pump.

The remainder of the plasma membrane of *Halobacterium halobium*, in common with that of other prokaryotes, contains all the constituents of the respiratory electron chain. In conditions of high PO_2 the cell derives its energy from oxidative phosphorylation. Such conditions are only to be found in the upper layers of the stagnant pools which are the natural environment of the organism. Thus the *Halobacteria* have evolved the purple membrane to cope with the anaerobic conditions prevailing in the lower layers of the pools. The trans-membrane proton gradient resulting either from the light-driven pump or from the respiratory chain is coupled to ATP synthesis in the same manner as in chloroplasts and mitochondria. The purple membrane, with its single protein species, is the simplest of the natural chemiosmotic membranes, and is clearly a most attractive system in which to study membrane-mediated energy transduction.

Rhodopsin and bacteriorhodopsin are probably the most well-characterized of the membrane receptors. These are molecules which mediate the transfer of information across the membrane. The rhodopsins receive information as light energy which they convert into a form which can be utilized by the cell. In the following section we will examine some other receptor molecules which recognize and respond to intercellular chemical messengers.

Synaptic membrane receptors

A fundamental prerequisite to the chemical theory of synaptic transmission is the existence of some specialized structure or *receptor* within the post-synaptic membrane (chapter 3) which recognizes the neurotransmitter. Transient interaction of the receptor with the transmitter must initiate a change in the permeability characteristics of the membrane; for it is known that it is in such a permeability change that the 'message' carried by the transmitter is expressed. Over the past few years, much effort has been devoted to isolating and characterizing receptor molecules. Although their precise mode of action is still unknown, we now know what sort of molecules receptors are, and can begin to formulate model systems for their functions. Most of the work so far has been concerned with the receptor for the neurotransmitter *acetylcholine*, although it seems likely that the system will serve as a general model for neurotransmitter-receptor interaction. Indeed, in the few cases where *non-cholinergic* receptors have been isolated, they are found to be very similar molecules to the acetylcholine receptor.

In the mid 1960s an attempt at receptor isolation was made by Eduardo De Robertis and his colleagues. After the success of their isolation of nerve ending membranes (see chapter 4) from cerebral cortex, De Robertis reasoned that the purified synaptic junctions must be enriched in receptor material. Attempts were made to monitor the presence of receptors in the membrane preparations. This was achieved by measuring the binding of radioactively-labelled drugs whose pharmacological properties indicate that they interact with the cholinergic receptor in intact tissue. In this way it was shown that functional receptors are still present in the isolated nerve ending membrane fragments. It was subsequently reported that the components responsible for the binding are very hydrophobic lipoproteins or *proteolipids* (see chapter 5). These protein-lipid complexes have an overall hydrophobicity such that they can only be extracted by dissolution of the membrane with organic solvents. Subsequent studies have revealed that the isolated receptor proteolipid retains many of the characteristics of the native membrane-bound receptor. The natural neurotransmitter acetylcholine and a range of cholinergic drugs show specific high-affinity binding to the proteolipid. Dissociation constants of similar magnitude to those quoted from pharmacological dose-response experiments have been obtained, suggesting that the isolated proteolipid behaves *in vitro* in a similar manner to the receptor *in vivo*. Incorporation of the receptor proteolipid into black lipid films (see chapter 6) leads to increased conductivity of the membrane, and further transient changes in conductivity are elicited by the application of acetylcholine to the membrane surface (see also chapter 9).

Proteolipids are a group of membrane proteins about which relatively little is known. Their extreme hydrophobicity and consequent insolubility in aqueous systems greatly hampers their analysis by any of the established procedures of protein chemistry. For example, estimations of molecular weight by gel filtration, ultracentrifugation or gel electrophoresis cannot be readily made, nor can amino-acid composition be analysed by conventional procedures. Such problems have so far prevented the complete characterization of the proteolipid receptors, and have led other workers to seek alternative methods of receptor isolation. Chief among these workers has been Jean-Pierre Changeux. Changeux used membrane sources which might have been almost tailor-made for the study of receptor-mediated events. These are the electric organs of the electric eel *Electrophorus electricus* and of the electric ray *Torpedo marmorata*. The electric organs of these fishes are made up from many thousands of identical cells or *electroplax*, each one of which may have up to 10,000 synapses on its surface. Furthermore, the synapses all occur on the same face of the electroplax. The opposite face of the cell is *noninnervated* and is particularly rich in Na^+,K^+-ATPase activity (see chapter 9). An homogenate of electric tissue yields two distinct membrane fractions, one of which is derived only from the innervated face, and thus provides an

Figure 8.7*a.* Electron micrograph of a freeze-etched preparation of receptor-rich membranes from electroplax of *Torpedo marmorata.* A hexagonal array of 'rosettes' is seen, and the substructure of the individual particles can be seen in some cases (arrows). The appearance of the rosettes should be compared with the negatively stained preparation of purified receptor protein from the electroplax of *Electrophorus electricus* (figure 8.7*b*). The rosettes are seen to consist of 5 or 6 sub-units some 3 to 4 nm in diameter, with a central pit into

unusually rich source of receptor material. The tissue has a further advantage over mammalian central nervous tissue in that all the synapses are *cholinergic*, resulting therefore in a completely homogeneous population of receptors. Using a combination of detergent extraction and affinity chromatography (chapter 7), Changeux and his colleagues have purified a protein from electroplax membranes which retains the transmitter-binding characteristics of the physiological receptor site. The purified protein consists of two subunits of molecular weights 43,000 and 48,000

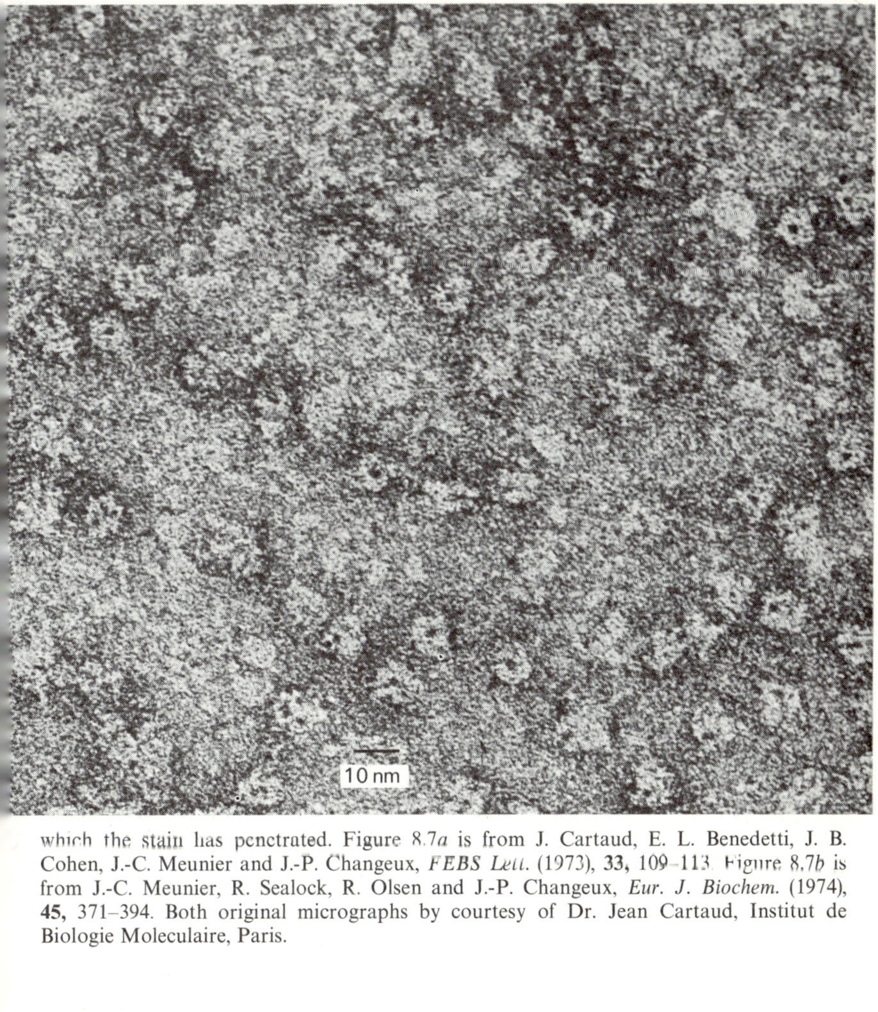

which the stain has penetrated. Figure 8.7*a* is from J. Cartaud, E. L. Benedetti, J. B. Cohen, J.-C. Meunier and J.-P. Changeux, *FEBS Lett.* (1973), **33**, 109–113. Figure 8.7*b* is from J.-C. Meunier, R. Sealock, R. Olsen and J.-P. Changeux, *Eur. J. Biochem.* (1974), **45**, 371–394. Both original micrographs by courtesy of Dr. Jean Cartaud, Institut de Biologie Moleculaire, Paris.

daltons. There is evidence that in the native state the isolated receptor exists as a pentamer or hexamer, giving rise to the appearance of 'rosettes' in electron micrographs of negatively-stained preparations as shown in figure 8.7*b*. These structures bear a striking resemblance to similar patterns seen on the surface of electroplax membranes (figure 8.7*a*). Although the receptor protein can only be isolated and maintained in aqueous solution by using detergents, its overall amino acid content suggests that it is a normal water-soluble globular protein. This emphasizes the point made in chapter 5 that predictions of the overall hydrophobicity of membrane proteins are probably less meaningful than knowledge of the spatial distribution of hydrophobic and hydrophilic amino acid residues within the tertiary structure of the protein.

The binding of a number of cholinergic drugs to the purified receptor protein suggests that the physiological binding site is little changed during the isolation procedure. A group of compounds which has been of great use in monitoring the activity of the cholinergic receptors are toxins found in the venoms of certain snakes. In particular, the polypeptide *α bungarotoxin* from the venom of the Elapidae snake *Bungarus multicinctus* has been extensively used as a marker for the cholinergic receptor from electroplax and from the vertebrate myoneural junction. Chang and Lee showed in 1966 that this toxin blocks the acetylcholine receptor very specifically in vertebrate muscle *in vivo*, and in 1970 Changeux and his colleagues showed an identical effect on the intact electroplax. Both the purified receptor protein of Changeux and the receptor proteolipid of De Robertis show high-affinity binding of α bungarotoxin.

The widely differing isolation procedures of the two groups have led to the common conclusion that the receptor is a hydrophobic *intrinsic* membrane protein. The question then arises: how does this protein initiate the change in membrane permeability which follows receptor-transmitter interaction? Before attempting to answer this question it is necessary to examine in a little more detail the response of the post-synaptic membrane to neuro-transmitters.

Application of neurotransmitter to the post-synaptic membrane initiates a permeability change. This may result in a depolarization of the membrane and generation of an action potential (see chapter 9), in which case the neurotransmitter is said to have an excitatory action. Alternatively, the transmitter may have an inhibitory action leading to an increased membrane potential or hyperpolarization, without the generation of an action potential. It is important to realize that these effects can result only from an interaction of the neurotransmitter with the receptor. Thus neurotransmitter applied at any point on the plasma membrane other than that area covered by the synapse elicits no response whatsoever.

Measurement of the response of an innervated cell to varying concentrations of neurotransmitter allows the construction of a *dose-response curve*. This usually has a sigmoid shape which is indicative of a co-operative effect, that is, the initial binding of neurotransmitter facilitates the response to further transmitter. In the case of the electroplax, the co-operative nature of the transmitter-receptor interaction is maintained in isolated membrane fragments, but is lost in the isolated receptor protein. Therefore the co-operativity must be a feature of the structural organization of the synaptic membrane rather than of the individual receptor molecules. The lattice organization of receptor proteins in the electroplax membranes shown in figure 8.7*a* is consistent with this interpretation.

The question of whether the receptor protein is immediately responsible for the transmitter-induced ion movements, or whether a second protein (the ionophore) is involved, is discussed further in chapter 9. For the present let us consider that a receptor-ionophore unit exists in the membrane. Evidence for a correlation between receptors and discrete ion channels has come from some recent studies on the behaviour of black lipid films into which isolated cholinergic receptors have been incorporated. Of particular interest is the observation that these films show spontaneous quantal changes in conductance. The interpretation of the changes is that individual ion channels are opening and closing spontaneously, and there is a correlation between the number of receptor molecules and the number of unit conductance changes occurring in the membrane.

To explain the co-operative response of the intact receptive membrane, it is postulated that the receptor-ionophore unit exists in two conformations, R and D, which are in reversible equilibrium. R corresponds to the *resting* membrane—it is relatively permeable to potassium ions and largely impermeable to sodium ions. R shows a lowered affinity for the natural transmitter, and an increased affinity for *antagonists*. Thus in the cholinergic system, a compound such as *curare*, which is known to bind to the receptor and to prevent acetylcholine from exerting its effects, would bind readily to R and hold it in its resting state. D corresponds to the depolarized state and shows high permeability to both sodium and potassium ions. The D form shows high affinity for the natural transmitter and other *agonists* which hold the receptor unit in the depolarized state. Depolarization of the whole membrane occurs by a shift in the equilibrium between R and D in the direction of D. Arrangement of the receptor-ionophore units in a lattice, as described above, would allow co-operative mutual interactions to occur. The transition of a given unit from its R to D state would be influenced by the conformations of its neighbours. The co-operative nature of the response to neurotransmitters is a characteristic of the overall structure of the membrane and is likely to be influenced by membrane components other than the receptor units. The isolated receptor is a hydrophobic protein and is likely to be closely associated with lipids in the membrane. It is quite possible, therefore, that the receptor-ionophore unit interactions may be modulated by the membrane lipids. Certainly there is evidence that synaptic transmission may be accompanied by changes in the lipid metabolism of the synaptic membranes (see p. 170), but it is not yet possible to formulate a precise role for lipids in the transmission process.

Receptor localization

It has been emphasized previously that receptors are normally confined to that area of the plasma membrane which forms the synaptic junction. The receptor proteins are presumably synthesized at an intracellular ribosomal site and are then incorporated into the plasma membrane at discrete points. A control system must be present, governing both synthesis and insertion into the membrane. Skeletal muscle provides an interesting system in which to study the mechanism by which the localization of the receptors is achieved.

In the case of a normal vertebrate skeletal muscle, application of the natural transmitter, acetylcholine, to any part of the muscle surface other than the synapse elicits no response. If the nerve to that muscle is cut, a phenomenon known as *hypersensitivity* may be observed. The denervated muscle now responds to the application of acetylcholine at any point on the plasma membrane surface. Pharmacological studies reveal that a new population of *extra-junctional receptors* is formed, whose properties are in many cases identical with those found at the original synapse. It has been clearly demonstrated that the distribution of receptors is under the control of the nerve and not of the muscle. For example, immobilization of the muscle so that contractions are prevented does not lead to hypersensitivity, providing the nerve remains intact. Enforced contraction of a denervated muscle in no way delays the onset of hypersensitivity. Studies made using radioisotopically labelled amino acids have revealed that hypersensitivity is probably achieved by a combination of synthesis of new receptors and unmasking of pre-existing latent receptors. There is also evidence that the lipic composition of the hypersensitive membrane is different, and enhanced phospholipid turnover has been reported.

The details of the mechanism by which the nerve exercises its control over the muscle membrane are not known. Research has so far been centred around the hypothesis that a *trophic substance* is continually being released from the nerve into the muscle cell. This material would then act as a regulator of metabolic activity, probably at the level of gene expression. Elucidation of the control mechanism may reveal something of the nature of membrane synthesis generally. Furthermore, it would have important medical implications, for many of the diseases of muscle are now known to have their origins in a malfunction of the nerve rather than in the muscle itself.

Hormone receptors

The hormone receptors have a similar role to that of the synaptic receptors described above; namely, they must recognize specific chemical messengers, in this case hormones, and then convey the information embodied in the messenger molecule to the cell interior. Unlike neurotransmitters, however, the hormones may be released at sites remote from the receptor, and are carried by the circulatory system throughout the organism. Furthermore, the cellular responses elicited by the hormones are very varied and may impinge upon all aspects of the cell's metabolism.

The alteration of cellular functions by hormones can be considered to occur in three stages.

1. The hormone binds to the receptor at the plasma membrane surface.
2. The interaction initiates changes in a regulatory system within the cell.
3. Some aspect of the cell's activities is changed.

The first two stages of the sequence take place within the domain of the plasma membrane and will be examined in the following sections.

Insulin facilitates the uptake of sugars by a variety of cell types, including striated and cardiac muscle and adipose tissue. Evidence from a variety of experiments suggests that the hormone exerts its effects at the cell surface. The elegant work of Pedro Cuatrecasas particularly is worth mentioning in this respect.

Cuatrecasas attached insulin covalently to large insoluble polymers, such as agarose, and was able to show that the biological activity of the insulin was retained. Furthermore, he demonstrated that the insulin-agarose complex would bind tightly to intact fat cells. The insulin-agarose complex cannot cross the plasma membrane and must therefore act at its surface.

Insulin labelled with ^{125}I has been widely used in binding studies with insulin-sensitive cells. The insulin-receptor complex can be dissociated with acid, and the released insulin is found to be unchanged, indicating that the hormone is not modified as a result of expressing its biological effect. The kinetics of the binding process are consistent with the presence of a finite number of high-affinity sites on the surfaces of cells, such as fat cells, lymphocytes, thymocytes, and mouse mammary cells, and in the case of fat cells the binding sites have been shown to be exclusively located on the outer surface of the plasma membrane. The fat cell plasma membrane can be made to form vesicles in which the original membrane inside-outside relationship is retained, and also vesicles in which this relationship is reversed (*inverted vesicles*). Whereas insulin will bind to 'normal' vesicles (the original outer face of the membrane faces outwards), it will not bind to inverted vesicles unless they are first disrupted by phospholipases or sonication. The insulin binding must accordingly be restricted to the outer face of the membrane, and its biological effects must be mediated by the membrane-bound receptor.

Receptor isolation has been achieved by treatment of cell membranes with non-ionic detergents, and the solubilized receptor retains the binding characteristics of the intact membrane-bound system. The isolated receptor is a rod-like protein whose molecular parameters are reminiscent of those of the detergent-solubilized acetylcholine receptor from electroplax. The mechanism by which the receptor initiates the changes in sugar transport which result from insulin binding is not known. There is evidence that the insulin binding sites and the glucose transport sites reside on different membrane constituents. Thus treatment of fat cells with neuraminidase at low concentrations stimulates glucose transport, with no effect on insulin binding, while increased concentrations of neuraminidase apparently destroy insulin-stimulated glucose uptake, leaving insulin binding and cell membrane permeability unaffected. This indicates that the receptor and sugar transport systems are distinct, and suggests that they may be coupled by a mechanism involving the sialic acid residues of membrane glycoprotein.

Receptor-response coupling

Whereas more is currently known about the nature of the insulin receptor itself than about how it mediates its biological effect, the reverse is generally true for other hormone systems. Thus many hormones are known to exert their effects by stimulating a membrane-bound enzyme, adenylate cyclase, which produces cyclic 3′5′-adenosine monophosphate or cyclic AMP. This molecule affects a wide range of cellular functions and is responsible for the physiological effects of the hormones. Cyclic

AMP is referred to as a *second messenger* responsible for conveying the information carried by the *first messenger*, the hormone, from the plasma membrane to the cell interior. The nature of the changes evoked by cyclic AMP varies widely, ranging from effects on cell motility and morphology to specific regulation of intracellular enzyme systems.

Much of the information on adenylate cyclase comes from studies of the action of *glucagon*, a peptide hormone which acts antagonistically to insulin. It has been established that fat cells and liver parenchymal cells have a glucagon-sensitive adenylate cyclase in their plasma membranes. This was a major step in our understanding of the mode of action of hormones. It provided for the first time an explanation of how a large hormone molecule, unable to cross the plasma membrane, could convey information to the cell interior. Subsequent work has revealed that adenylate cyclase is associated with the plasma membranes of a wide range of cells and can be affected by many different hormones. Thus in fat cells, adrenalin and adrenocorticotrophin, in addition to glucagon, are found to stimulate the membrane-bound adenylate cyclase. How then does a single enzyme at the cell surface elicit the widely differing responses of the cell?

Inhibition studies indicate that different hormones bind to specific receptor sites, which are distinct from the enzyme itself. Solubilization of membranes using detergents has led to the isolation of both receptor and enzyme activities which are associated with quite different membrane

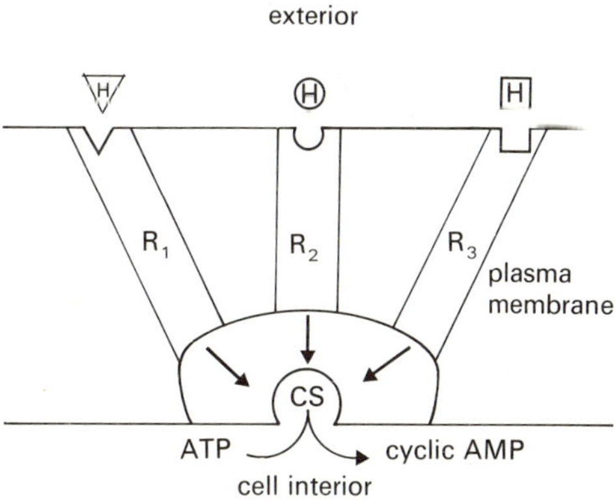

Figure 8.8. Adenylate cyclase-receptor coupling: The enzyme complex spans the membrane. Receptor sub-units R_1 R_2 R_3 have specific binding sites for hormones H at the outer surface of the membrane. The catalytic site CS faces the cell interior and is controlled by the receptor sub-units.

proteins. It has been suggested that adenylate cyclase is located at the inner surface of the plasma membrane, whereas the hormone receptor sites are on its outer surface. The presence of different receptors for different hormones has been confirmed by treatment of fat cells with trypsin, when the adenylate cyclase no longer responds to glucagon but retains its sensitivity to adrenalin.

The mechanism by which the hormone-receptor complex alters the activity of the enzyme has been explained within the framework of established theories of allosteric transformations in multi-sub-unit enzymes. Thus receptor sites are seen as regulatory sub-units of a macromolecular complex having a single catalytic sub-unit (see figure 8.8).

Cuatrecasas has recently suggested that the system as outlined in figure 8.8, and based on conventional models of allosteric enzymes, cannot adequately accommodate current experimental observations. The adenylate cyclase of the fat cell is now known to be stimulated by seven different hormones, and is inhibited by three others. It is difficult to envisage ten discrete receptors, each with a recognition site at the membrane surface, and each contiguous to the catalytic sub-unit. Cuatrecasas therefore proposes an alternative model which does not demand the continuous physical association of the receptors with adenylate cyclase. It is suggested that receptor-hormone complexes have a high affinity for adenylate cyclase, a property not shared with the free receptor. Thus formation of a receptor-hormone-enzyme complex would

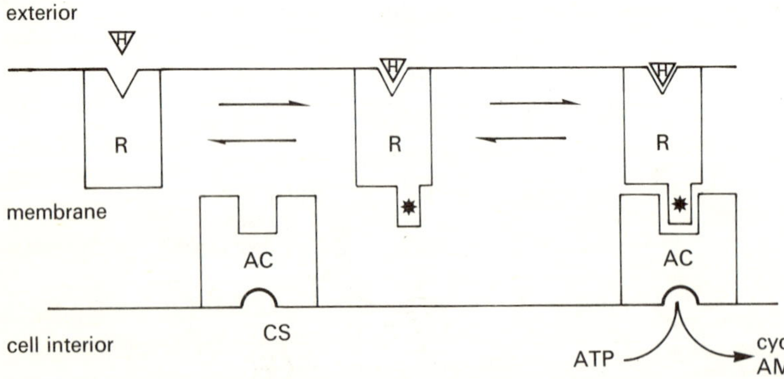

Figure 8.9. Adenylate cyclase-receptor coupling, the alternative model of Cuatrecasas: Hormone H binds to receptor R at the outer surface of the membrane and the complex RH has a high affinity * for adenylate cyclase AC. By lateral diffusion in the plane of the membrane, RH may collide with an AC unit and will bind with it. Concomitant with the binding is a modification of the catalytic site CS.

occur at a rate dependent on the concentration of the receptor-hormone complex. Some receptor-hormone complexes would activate the enzyme, others would inhibit it. It is proposed that the receptor-hormone complexes are free to diffuse laterally in the membrane and to interact with the enzyme by random collision. The scheme is outlined in figure 8.9.

The hypothesis is attractive in that it provides for much greater flexibility than the sub-unit model outlined in figure 8.8. The model suggests a finite time between receptor-hormone binding and the modulation of the enzyme which would depend on the fluidity of the membrane. Cuatrecasas has recently found that temperature-dependent lag periods can be detected in the effects of some hormones on adenylate cyclase, a finding which lends support to the hypothesis. The lipid composition of the membrane could also influence the progress of the events leading up to enzyme modulation, and there is experimental evidence that this is so. Treatment of fat cells with phospholipase A results in loss of sensitivity to glucagon, though the enzyme is largely unaffected.

Although the foregoing discussion has been concerned only with adenylate cyclase, it is emphasized that analogous systems employing other nucleotides are known to occur and to play a similar role. Some of the effects of insulin may be mediated by two such systems in that insulin is reported to inhibit adenylate cyclase and also to activate guanylate cyclase. In accordance with the scheme outlined in figure 8.9, this dual effect could be achieved with a single insulin-receptor species.

The phosphatidylinositol effect

Proteins play the major role in each of the membrane phenomena described in the preceding sections. Although the membrane lipids must influence the progress of the various events occurring within the membrane, it is not yet possible to define precisely their role. It is known that one particular lipid, phosphatidylinositol, is intimately involved in the mediation of many extracellular stimuli by the plasma membranes. This involvement is reflected in a greatly enhanced turnover of phosphatidylinositol following specific stimuli and can be demonstrated in a wide variety of tissues. Isotopic labelling experiments reveal that in most cases only the phosphorylinositol moiety of the phospholipid is affected, and that there is no increased turnover of either the glycerol backbone or the acyl chains. Much of our information on the system has come from studies of nervous tissue, particularly cerebral cortex and sympathetic ganglia but, as may be seen from Table 8.1, the phenomenon is very widespread.

Table 8.1. Tissues showing enhanced phosphatidylinositol turnover in response to specific stimuli (this is not a comprehensive list but serves to illustrate the varied nature of both tissues and stimuli which show the effect).

Tissue	Stimulus
cerebral cortex	acetylcholine
pancreas	acetylcholine; pancreozymin
gastric mucosa	histamine, acetylcholine
adipose tissue	insulin
heart	adrenalin
lymphocytes	phytohaemagglutinin
avian salt glands	acetylcholine
thyroid	thyroid stimulating hormone

It is now generally accepted that the point at which the stimulation of the turnover occurs is the cleavage of phosphatidylinositol to give 1,2-diacyl-*sn*-glycerol and phosphorylinositol. The cleavage is thought to be the first step in a four-stage sequence of reactions:

$$\text{phosphatidylinositol} \rightarrow \text{1,2-diacyl-}sn\text{-glycerol} + \text{phosphorylinositol} \quad (1)$$

$$\text{1,2-diacyl-}sn\text{-glycerol} + \text{ATP} \rightarrow \text{phosphatidic acid} + \text{ADP} \quad (2)$$

$$\text{phosphatidic acid} + \text{CTP} \rightarrow \text{CDP-diglyceride} + \text{PP} \quad (3)$$

$$\text{CDP-diglyceride} + \text{inositol} \rightarrow \text{phosphatidylinositol} + \text{CMP} \quad (4)$$

The enzyme responsible for reaction (1), a phospholipase C has been found in synaptic membranes from cerebral cortex. The enzyme catalyzing reaction (2), diglyceride kinase, has also been shown to be partially localized at the cell surface in cerebral cortex. In many of the stimulated systems, an additional enhanced turnover of phosphatidic acid (as measured by ^{32}P incorporation) can be observed and a precursor-product relationship between the two lipids may be seen. Although the first two steps of the turnover sequence are mediated by plasma membrane-bound enzymes, the remaining two enzymes are associated with intracellular membranes. However it is known that phospholipids may exchange rapidly between intracellular membrane systems. The transfer is mediated by specific soluble proteins which in this case would transport phosphatidic acid to the endoplasmic reticulum, while newly formed phosphatidylinositol would be carried back to the plasma membrane.

The precise role of phosphatidylinositol in the plasma membrane is not yet known. Certainly the increased turnover is associated with transport and secretory processes in a wide variety of tissues. It is not, however, a universal feature of such processes and, for example, does not accompany steroid hormone secretion by adrenal cortex nor bicarbonate secretion in pancreas. There have been suggestions that in nervous tissue the increased turnover is a primary event in neurotransmission. This is now thought to be unlikely, and recent work suggests a role in the release and uptake of neurotransmitters by the synaptic vesicles. The permeability of the plasma membrane would be altered at the sites where the increased turnover occurs, and the breakdown-resynthesis cycle may provide a mechanism for 'opening' and 'closing' discrete sections of membrane. An interesting hypothesis has been put forward suggesting a further role for the phospholipid. The initial cleavage of phosphatidylinositol by the membrane-bound phospholipase C results in the formation of phosphorylinositol as shown in reaction (1) above. It appears that the phosphorylinositol is released as D-inositol 1,2-cyclic phosphate. A specific phosphodiesterase which causes its breakdown to D-inositol-1-phosphate is found in most tissues. The sequence is reminiscent of the cyclic AMP system and, although an intracellular regulatory role for D-inositol 1,2-cyclic phosphate has not yet been found, it emphasizes the key part that phosphatidylinositol may play in membrane-mediated processes.

SUMMARY

1. Membranes participate in a wide variety of cellular activities.
2. The process of oxidative phosphorylation calls for the highly ordered arrangement of the constituents of the inner mitochondrial membrane.
3. The operation of the anisotropically orientated electron transport chain establishes a trans-membrane proton-gradient, the energy of which is utilized for ATP synthesis.
4. Photosynthesis involves the utilization of light energy for ATP synthesis. The light is trapped by photosensitive pigments which are coupled to an electron transport chain. As in the mitochondrion, a trans-membrane proton gradient derives from the chain and is coupled to ATP synthesis.
5. Rhodopsin and bacteriorhodopsin are the major proteins of the retinal disc membranes and the purple membrane of *Halobacterium halobium* respectively. The molecules are very similar and both show light-induced changes of conformation. In the case of rhodopsin, the conformational change may allow the protein to function as a

diffusional ion carrier. Rhodopsin-mediated intracellular ion movements may initiate the generation of an electrical signal in the rod cells. Bacteriorhodopsin operates as a light-driven proton pump, and generates a trans-membrane proton gradient. The proton gradient is coupled to ATP synthesis as in mitochondria and chloroplasts.

6. The synaptic receptors are intrinsic membrane proteins. They interact with neurotransmitters and bring about a permeability change in the post-synaptic membrane.

7. The receptors may be linked to form lattices within which co-operative mutual interactions may occur.

8. The effects of many hormones are mediated by the membrane-bound enzyme adenylate cyclase.

9. The hormone receptors are distinct from the enzyme but may be coupled to it. The coupling may be a transient interaction dependent on the formation of a hormone-receptor complex.

10. Among the phospholipids, phosphatidylinositol clearly has a role in transport and secretion, though the mechanism of its involvement is not yet known.

CHAPTER 9

TRANSPORT SYSTEMS

IN THEIR NATURAL STATE, CELL MEMBRANES ARE BOUNDED ON BOTH SIDES by aqueous environments. Passage of a solute from one side of the membrane to the other can be considered to occur in three stages:

1. The solute must leave the aqueous phase and enter the hydrophobic lipid region of the membrane.
2. The solute must traverse the lipid bilayer.
3. The solute must leave the lipid phase and return to an aqueous environment.

Steps 1 and 2 represent a considerable barrier to most polar molecules, and we saw in chapter 1 how Overton, and later Collander, showed that the rate of entry of many compounds into cells is directly related to their oil-water partition coefficients. Before polar solutes are able to make the transition from an aqueous phase to a hydrophobic lipid phase, it seems that they must lose their water of hydration, and it is this requirement which is the major barrier to their movement.

Simple diffusion

Overton and Collander found a number of compounds which show marked deviations from the general rule that the rate of movement depends on lipid solubility. Thus water, methanol, formamide and ethylene glycol enter cells more rapidly than would be expected from a consideration of their oil-water partition coefficients.

These findings led to the suggestion that there may be discrete pores in the membrane through which small polar compounds pass, thereby circumventing the hydrophobic lipid bilayer. The pores were envisaged as protein-lined channels which penetrate the Danielli-Davson bilayer. With the realization that the lipid bilayer is a highly fluid structure came the concept of the *statistical pore*. The random movement of the acyl chains of the membrane phospholipids (see chapters 5 and 6) leads to the appearance of gaps in the hydrophobic regions of the membrane into which small polar molecules can pass, and thus make their way through the membrane. The gaps or pores will arise spontaneously in a random fashion, and are transitory structures unlike the discrete protein-lined pores in a rigid bilayer that were proposed by earlier workers.

It is not always necessary to invoke any specific membrane structures in order to account for the movement of small polar molecules across the cell membrane. These molecules, along with small lipid-soluble compounds, can cross membranes by simple diffusion. Their net movement is from a high to a low concentration region, and the rate of movement is directly proportional to the concentration gradient as described by Fick's law:

$$J = D\frac{dc}{dx}$$

where J is the rate of movement or flux, D is the diffusion coefficient and $\frac{dc}{dx}$ is the chemical gradient.

The majority of compounds which pass through membranes do so by processes other than simple diffusion. The transfer invariably involves the interaction of the transported molecules with specific transport or carrier systems, and the kinetics of transport are fundamentally different from those of a simple diffusion process as we shall see below.

Facilitated diffusion

The carrier-assisted passive transfer of material is referred to as *facilitated diffusion* and is independent of any energy supply. There are a number of features which distinguish it from the passage of material across the membrane by simple diffusion. Firstly, the activation energy is considerably lower than would be expected for passage of the molecules through the membrane by simple diffusion, and this is reflected in the rate of passage, which is very much higher than would be expected from a consideration of the oil-water partition coefficient. The major difference, however, is that the facilitated diffusion system no longer obeys Fick's law but shows *saturation kinetics*; i.e. increasing the concentration of the material being transported increases the rate of transfer up to an asymptotic value. A graphical plot of transfer rate against concentration has the form of the familiar Michaelis-Menten plot. Measurements of V, the maximum velocity of transfer across the membrane, can be made and an affinity constant K_m determined. A high degree of specificity is seen, and optical isomers or close structural analogues of the transported material show different rates of transfer and different affinity constants.

Considering these features we can formulate a working model of a facilitated diffusion transport system carrying molecules into a cell or organelle. The carrier molecule is free to move back and forth across the membrane, which it does by thermal diffusion, and it has on it a specific binding site for the material to be transported. Thus, at the outer face of the membrane, the carrier can bind to the material, and the complex diffuses across the membrane from a high to low-concentration region. Because of the relatively low concentration of the material being transported at the inner face of the membrane, there will be a tendency for the complex to dissociate; the free material then remains within the cell, while the carrier makes its way back to the outer surface of the membrane. This process will continue so long as a concentration gradient exists across the membrane for the transported material. The scheme is outlined in diagrammatic form in figure 9.1.

This is the system by which glucose enters the erythrocyte and several other vertebrate tissues. In these circumstances it is particularly satisfactory in view of the high concentrations of glucose in plasma. It has been shown that glycerol may also enter human and rat erythrocytes by the same system. Examination of the rate of entry of a number of

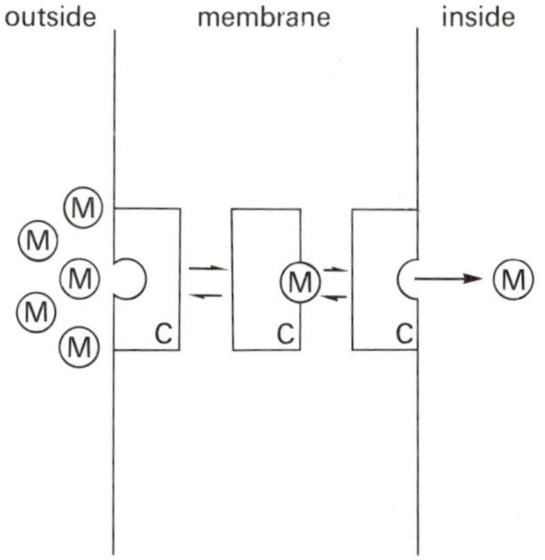

Figure 9.1. Facilitated diffusion: Metabolite M binds to mobile carrier C at the outer face of the membrane. The CM complex diffuses through the membrane and dissociates at the inner surface, releasing M into the cell interior.

sugars into the erythrocyte reveals that the carrier is very specific for D-glucose, the apparent K_m being about 10 × lower than for D-galactose and well over 1000 × lower than for L-glucose.

The precise nature of the carrier is not clear. Evidence points to its being a protein, and we can assume that its conformation is such that it presents a very hydrophobic exterior while maintaining a more hydrophilic region around the sugar binding site. The hydrophilic binding site would replace the hydration shell of the transported molecule, thereby facilitating its transfer from the aqueous phase and giving rise to the lower activation energy compared with simple diffusion. The hydrophobic exterior of the carrier would facilitate the transfer of the complex through the hydrophobic lipid bilayer.

Active transport

Facilitated diffusion will continue only for as long as the concentration gradient for the transported material is maintained; i.e. it is a passive transport system (see chapter 2). However, many transport processes must work against a concentration gradient; in addition to a carrier these active transport systems require an energy source. In its most simple form, active transport requires only a carrier to which an energy supply can be directly coupled, and which in the absence of such a supply will function as a facilitated diffusion system. In the following sections we will examine in detail a variety of active transport systems with widely differing energy-coupling mechanisms.

Simple active transport

Simple active transport involves the transport of material without the apparent concomitant movement of any other substance, and is in many respects identical with facilitated diffusion. Thus the system may show saturation kinetics, and a high degree of specificity is seen. However, the fundamental difference is that simple active transport systems are able to transport material against a concentration gradient. This obviously demands the expenditure of energy.

A system which has received much attention is that of lactose uptake in *E. coli*. It was shown in 1939 by Deere and co-workers that disrupted cells of *E. coli* hydrolyze β-galactosides more rapidly than do intact cells, suggesting that the cell membrane is not freely permeable to the sugars. It was later shown that β-galactosides were transported across the membrane and appeared in the cell chemically unmodified. The fundamental characteristics of the system were established by Cohen and Monod and their co-workers in the Pasteur Institute and have served as a foundation for investigations into the molecular processes of membrane transport in many other systems. Cohen and Monod established that β-galactoside transport depends on a membrane protein, the synthesis of which can be either induced or repressed. This protein was termed a *permease* and was shown to be controlled by two genes in the lac operon of *E. coli.* The characterization of lactose permease and indeed of many other permease systems owes much to enzymology. As in the case of the facilitated diffusion system, the maximum velocity V of the transfer process can be measured and an apparent K_m determined. The K_m is taken to be a measure of the affinity of the permease for the material being transported. The analogy should not be taken too far, however, for there are some fundamental differences between the permease and an enzyme. Firstly, 'substrate' and 'product' are identical, lactose outside an *E. coli* cell appears inside the cell as lactose; no chemical modification whatsoever results from the transport process. Secondly, unlike most enzyme reactions the permease is vectorial: the material is transported from outside the cell through the lipid bilayer of the membrane to the inside of the cell.

Although the permease is considered as an active transport process, it can also function as a facilitated diffusion system. Thus lactose uptake will proceed independently of a source of energy until no concentration gradient exists across the membrane, and even under these circumstances the exchange of extracellular and intracellular lactose is mediated by the permease. By using mutants of *E. coli* lacking the enzymes of lactose metabolism, or by using lactose analogues which are not readily metabolized, active transport can be demonstrated. Under these circumstances lactose or an analogue can be concentrated several hundred times with respect to the extracellular concentration. It can be shown that the active transport process is prevented by inhibitors of energy production and by uncouplers of oxidative phosphorylation. Facilitated diffusion is not affected by such treatment. What then is the nature of the energy source, and how is it coupled to the permease? Two theories have emerged, much as with the problem of oxidative phosphorylation described in chapter 8. These are the *permease model*, which is analogous to the chemical theory of oxidative phosphorylation with its attendant 'high-energy' compounds, and the *chemiosmotic model.*

Proponents of the permease model suggest that ATP or some other 'high-energy' compound connected with the electron transport chain is the energy source. Coupled with this is the assumption that the permease exists in two forms: a high affinity form and a low affinity form. Interaction of one form of the permease with the high-energy compound results in a phosphorylation of the protein, and this in turn switches the permease from high to low affinity or vice versa. There is still disagreement among supporters of the permease model as to whether the energy coupling for transfer of a molecule into a cell or organelle is at the outer surface of the membrane, involving a transition from low affinity to high affinity, or at the inner surface, when the converse would be true. The essential features of the latter form of the permease model are summarized in figure 9.2.

The model described in figure 9.2 might seem to explain satisfactorily the process of simple active transport. However, it is emphasized that the nature of the high-energy compound $H \sim P$ is unknown, and the phosphorylation of the permease is by no means proven. Let us consider the alternative chemiosmotic model which does not involve the direct participation of ATP or of any other high-energy phosphate.

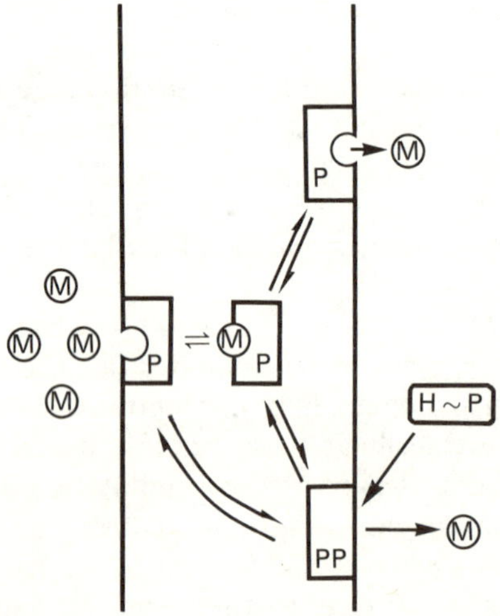

Figure 9.2. Active transport: the permease model: Metabolite M binds to permease P at the outer face of the membrane. The PM complex diffuses through the membrane and at the inner surface P is phosphorylated by the 'high-energy' compound $H \sim P$, resulting in a modified permease PP and in release of M. Alternatively the permease can act as a facilitated diffusion carrier as shown in the upper part of the scheme.

In chapter 8 reference was made to Mitchell's chemiosmotic hypothesis of oxidative phosphorylation. The concepts embodied in this hypothesis are generally applicable to all energy-coupled transport systems. Thus the membrane's *osmotic energy* or *proticity* resulting from a trans-membrane proton gradient can be coupled to the carrier system. This potential energy of the membrane is termed by Mitchell the *proton motive force* and, in the chemiosmotic interpretation of the *E. coli* lactose transport system, it is this which is the driving force for lactose uptake.

E. coli is a prokaryotic organism and so contains the components of the electron transport chain in its plasma membrane. In an analogous manner to the mitochondrion (see chapter 8) a trans-membrane pH gradient is established. Suppose that the lactose carrier, in addition to its binding site for lactose, has a further binding site for protons. The carrier then binds to lactose and to protons at the outer face of the membrane, and the movement of the protons down their concentration gradient drives the accumulation of lactose against its concentration gradient. Thus proticity provides the energy for the active transport of lactose. In this system the permease is said to be acting as a *proton symport*. Supporting evidence for Mitchell's proposal comes from work carried out with uncoupling agents. These compounds dissociate electron transport from oxidative phosphorylation, and in their presence active transport rapidly ceases. This effect on active transport has been explained within the framework of the permease model as being the result simply of a decreased concentration of ATP or some other high-energy compound. There is evidence, however, that the levels of ATP and ATP-dependent processes are not affected by uncoupling agents. The chemiosmotic model proposes a quite different mechanism for the effect of the uncouplers. It is suggested that these compounds act at the level of the membrane, which is relatively impermeable to protons. Uncouplers then act as specific proton carriers within the membrane and lead to a breakdown of the transmembrane pH gradient, with a concomitant diminution of the proton motive force. This effect of uncouplers has been verified experimentally in mitochondria, bacteria and even in synthetic lipid bilayers. In these circumstances the uncoupling agent is acting as an *ionophore* for protons.

Further experimental evidence supporting the chemiosmotic transport model has come from the work of West and Mitchell. It was shown that lactose entering *E. coli* by passive diffusion, i.e. flowing down its concentration gradient, is accompanied by a rise in pH of the external medium. Furthermore, a stoichiometry of 1:1 was found for the proton:

lactose ratio as predicted by the proton symport model of the permease. Evidence was also produced showing that lactose uptake can be stimulated by inducing a pH gradient across the cells.

It is not yet possible to state definitely that the chemiosmotic model is in fact the system which operates *in vivo*. The experimental evidence now coming from examinations of a wide range of transport systems, how-

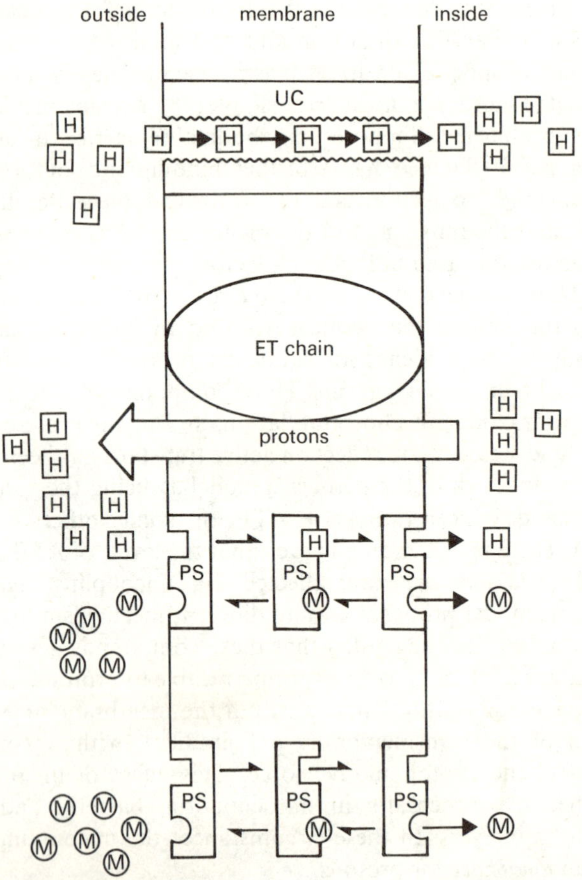

Figure 9.3. Active transport; the chemiosmotic model: The electron transport chain, ET chain, produces a transmembrane proton gradient. Proton symport PS combines with metabolite M and protons H. Protons run down their concentration gradient and power the active uptake of M. Uncoupler UC short-circuits the proton return and diminishes the power source. Under these conditions PS can still function as a facilitated diffusion carrier as shown in the lower part of the diagram.

ever, increasingly favours this interpretation (see chapter 10). Certainly it has the great attraction that it requires no additional membrane components or products of metabolism such as 'high-energy compounds' other than those whose presence is established. The model is summarized in schematic form in figure 9.3.

We have considered both the permease and the chemiosmotic models with reference to lactose transport in *E. coli* but, as was emphasized earlier, their basic principles are applicable to any simple active transport process. At the outset of the discussion, it was stated that a feature of the simple system is that the material being transported is chemically unmodified. Let us now examine a transport mechanism which involves the chemical modification of the transported molecules.

The phosphoenolpyruvate phosphotransferase system

In 1961 Mitchell proposed that transport mechanisms could exist in which the transfer of molecules is directly coupled to metabolic reactions. Membrane-bound enzymes may assume a vectorial character as described in chapter 2. An extreme case of this would be the situation where the product of the reaction is discharged at the opposite face of the membrane from which the substrate approaches. The enzyme would constitute a transport system for the substrate. Kundig in 1964 showed that just such a system occurs in some bacteria, and is concerned with sugar uptake. The system has been very well characterized by Kundig and his colleagues, and more recently Roseman and co-workers have elucidated a lactose phosphotransferase process in *Staphylococcus aureus*.

The system requires the participation of a number of enzymes and proteins and, although some of these are not yet completely characterized, the basic mechanisms are clearly defined.

In essence the chemical energy available in phosphoenolpyruvate is utilized to convert the sugar being transported to its phosphate. This is not a simple one-step transfer of the phosphate from the 'high-energy compound' directly to the sugar. A cytoplasmic enzyme, enzyme I, catalyzes the transfer of the phosphoryl group of phosphoenolpyruvate to a small protein (molecular weight about 10,000 daltons) designated HPr. The phosphorylated protein then enters the membrane and a second enzyme, enzyme II, catalyzes the transfer of the phosphoryl group from HPr to the sugar. Enzyme II is membrane-bound and is now known to be an enzyme complex rather than a single enzyme. Specificity occurs at the enzyme II stage, and separate inducible complexes have been shown for the transport of mannitol, sorbitol and fructose. In the case of *E. coli*, glucose enters the cell by this method, and the glucose-enzyme II complex has been shown to consist of two separate proteins, one of which may act as an intermediate acceptor for the phosphoryl group during the transfer from HPr to glucose. The *E. coli* enzyme II has also been shown to have a specific requirement for phosphatidylglycerol (see chapter 5). In *Staph. aureus* lactose is transported by a slightly modified phosphoenolpyruvate system involving an additional phosphorylated protein, Factor III.

The phosphotransferase system is widespread in bacteria and, although showing a number of variations as outlined above, always uses phosphoenolpyruvate as the energy source. The actual translocation is thought to occur at the enzyme II-phosphoryl transfer step, possibly involving a conformational change in the enzyme II-sugar complex. Evidence has been presented that the system cannot operate in the facilitated-diffusion mode, and therefore differs markedly from the permease or proton symport model. The essential features of the phosphotransferase system are outlined in figure 9.4.

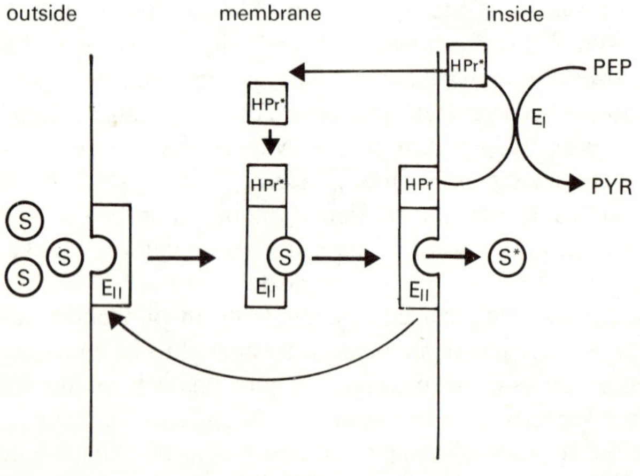

Figure 9.4. The phosphoenolpyruvate phosphotranferase system: Sugar S combines with the membrane-bound enzyme complex E_{II}. Combination of S-E_{II} with phosphorylated protein HPr* occurs within the membrane, and E_{II} catalyzes the phosphorylation of S. The sugar phosphate **S*** is released at the inner face of the membrane along with dephosphorylated HPr. HPr is rephosphorylated by enzyme E_I catalyzing the transfer of phosphate from phosphoenolpyruvate PEP, producing pyruvate PYR. HPr* then re-enters the membrane.

Several other examples of this type of transport system have now been found and are being characterized. Klein has shown that fatty acid uptake by *E. coli* is mediated by an inducible membrane protein which has all the characteristics of AcylCoA synthetase. The transport of purine bases into *E. coli* has similarly been shown to be associated with a phosphoribosyltransferase leading to the intracellular appearance of the corresponding purine nucleoside monophosphate. Although most of the information on the phosphotransferase and associated systems has come from studies of micro-organisms, there is evidence that similar processes may operate in mammalian membranes.

The epithelial cells of the mammalian intestine contain the enzyme sucrase located in their brush-border (i.e. the membrane which lines the lumen of the intestine). There is good evidence that the glucose produced as a result of the sucrase activity enters the epithelial cells more rapidly than does free glucose, suggesting a close coupling of sucrase activity and glucose transport. The sucrase system, although not so well characterized as the phosphoenolpyruvate system, is clearly a further example of *vectorial metabolism*. Storelli and his colleagues have recently incorporated a sucrase-isomaltase complex into a synthetic lipid-bilayer. They were able to show that the complex achieved sucrose transport via its conversion to glucose and fructose. These experiments constitute the first working model of a *vectorial metabolic transporter*.

A system bearing a superficial resemblance to the phosphotransferase system mediates the uptake of glycerol in a number of bacteria. Extracellular glycerol is found in the cells as *sn*-glycerol-3-phosphate. Closer examination of the system reveals that glycerol enters the cells by a *facilitated diffusion* process. Once inside the cells the glycerol is immediately phosphorylated by an ATP-dependent glycerol kinase, and glycerol as its phosphate can be accumulated well beyond the point at which the simple facilitated diffusion system would reach equilibrium. In this case, active transport is achieved by 'trapping' the species being transported. Unlike the phosphotransferase system, however, the enzymic modification of the transported material does not take place in the membrane and is non-vectorial.

So far we have considered the active transfer of a single nutrient across a membrane. There are many systems, however, in which the transfer of a particular molecule is inseparably linked to the trans-membrane movement of one or more different molecules. Such is the case with sodium and potassium ions. Here a tightly-coupled system is present in which both active and passive transfer combine to maintain the trans-membrane distribution of the two ions. Nowhere is this complex relationship better characterized than in the membrane of the nerve cell, and this is the system which we will now examine in detail.

The membrane potential

All living cells show a potential difference across their plasma membranes which is indicative of an unequal distribution of charges across the membrane. In biological systems charges are carried by ions, and any charge flow or current flowing across the membrane means that trans-membrane movement of ions is taking place. The potential difference (E volts), current flow (I amperes) and resistance (R ohms) of cell membranes can be measured, and are found to be related according to Ohm's law ($E = IR$). Measurements of this sort have been of great use in characterizing the ion permeability properties of membranes, although they are limited to rather large cells, and measurements on cells other than those from the nervous system are not yet commonplace.

Measurements of the potential difference across the cell membrane are made by inserting very small *microelectrodes* into the cell. The electrodes are, in effect, glass micro-pipettes with tip diameters of less than 1 μm. The pipettes are filled with a salt solution and may be connected to a range of equipment such as voltmeters, ammeters, voltage sources, etc. If the tip of the pipette is pushed through the plasma membrane of a cell, it is found that the membrane seals itself round the pipette, thus maintaining intact the permeability barrier. Suppose that we have a second electrode, the tip of which is brought close to the membrane surface but not actually pushed through it (see figure 9.5).

If we now measure the potential difference between the tips of electrodes 1 and 2, we find that, in general, electrode 1—the inside of the cell—is more negative than electrode 2—the outside of the cell. This difference in potential may vary between 20 and 200 millivolts in different cells. The potential difference can be changed by passing anions from the microelectrode into the cell, leading to increased internal negativity or *hyperpolarization*; or by adding cations which will reduce the membrane potential—*depolarization.* In the normal state the membrane potential is maintained by the relative distributions of ions, particularly sodium and potassium, across the membrane. In general it is found that the concentration of potassium ions in the cell is much higher than in the extracellular space, the reverse being true for sodium ions. Plasma membranes permit the flow of potassium ions out of the cell and, to a lesser extent,

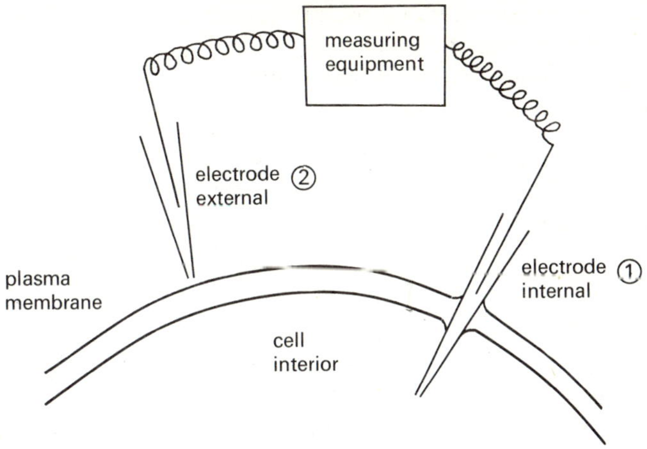

Figure 9.5. Measurement of the membrane potential.

of sodium ions into the cell. How then is the membrane potential maintained? In developing the answer to this crucial question we will assume initially that the movement of ions across the membrane proceeds independently, i.e. we will not consider any effects of sodium ions on potassium transport or vice versa.

Potassium ions are present at higher concentrations inside cells than in the extracellular medium. The tendency is for the potassium ions to flow down their concentration gradient, thereby lowering the internal concentration. Opposing this tendency is the fact that the interior of a nerve cell, for example, is some 50–60 millivolts negative with respect to the outside, which will tend to keep the potassium cation inside the cell. Therefore, a potassium ion is subject to two opposing forces. In order to compare these forces, it is preferable to express them both in the same terms rather than try to relate a concentration gradient to an electrical term. The comparison is achieved by using the *Nernst equation* which relates the concentration of an ion to the voltage resulting from its concentration gradient. It has the following form:

$$E = \frac{RT}{FZ} \log \frac{[\mathrm{I}]_o}{[\mathrm{I}]_i}$$

where E = the electrical gradient in volts,
R = the universal gas constant,
T = the temperature in K,

F = the Faraday (96,500 coulombs/mol),
Z = the valence of the ion,
$[I]_o$ = the concentration of the ion outside the cell,
$[I]_i$ = the concentration of the ion inside the cell.

In practice the Nernst equation can be simplified by converting the natural logarithms to base 10, when, for a univalent ion at a temperature of 20 °C, it becomes

$$E = 58 \log_{10} \frac{[I]_o}{[I]_i}$$

In this form it can be readily appreciated that the potential difference across the membrane can be varied by changing $[I]_o$ assuming a constant $[I]_i$. Furthermore, a tenfold change in $[I]_o$ will result in a change in E of 58 millivolts if the membrane is permeable to the ion I. This fact is widely used to determine whether or not membranes are permeable to particular ions. The membrane potential is measured over a range of $[I]_o$ and the results plotted as in figure 9.6.

If the membrane is 'permselective' for I, then the slope of the line will be 58 millivolts/tenfold change in $[I]_o$. In practice, deviations from the theoretical slope are frequently seen, suggesting that ions apart from I are contributing to the potential, or that interactions occur between I and other ions or molecules.

The substitution of the appropriate values for the internal and external concentrations of potassium into the equation allows the calculation of E, the *equilibrium potential*, which represents the electrical gradient exactly corresponding to the potassium concentration gradient. It is usually found that E for potassium does not correspond to the membrane potential, but is in fact some 10 to 15 millivolts more negative, i.e. 65 to 70 millivolts compared with the measured potential of 50 to 55 millivolts. The potassium ion is subject to a net force, equivalent to 10 to 15 millivolts, which tends to drive it out of the cell. Since the cell membrane is permeable to potassium, we would therefore expect a steady loss of potassium until E was equal to the membrane potential, at which point the net force on the potassium ions would be zero. As this does not happen, there must be further mechanisms which maintain the high internal potassium concentration.

In the early 1950s R. D. Keynes and his colleagues showed that potassium ions are in continuous flux across the membrane. They demonstrated that the movement of potassium out of the cell is inde-

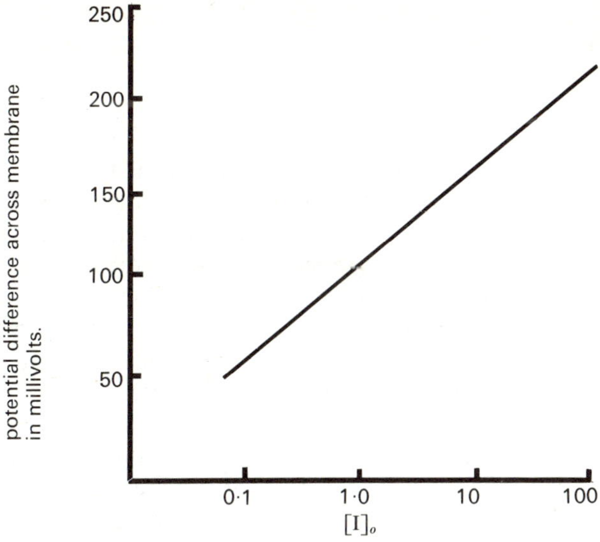

Figure 9.6. The relationship between membrane potential and $[I]_o$, the external ion concentration.

pendent of any energy supply, but movement into the cell is energy-dependent. The passive outward flow of potassium ions down their concentration gradient is counterbalanced by an active energy-requiring system, and in this way the equilibrium potential is maintained. Although these early experiments of Keynes and his co-workers were done using the large axons of crabs and cuttlefish, their findings are relevant to all plasma membranes.

Let us now consider the position of the sodium ion. The membrane potential and the high external sodium concentration both favour the entry of sodium ions into the cell. As in the case of the potassium ion, the concentration gradient for the sodium ions can be expressed in electrical terms by substituting internal and external concentrations into the Nernst equation. Usually this gives a value for the equilibrium potential of about +50 millivolts. This means that the interior of the cell would need to be 50 millivolts more positive than the outside in order to have a zero net flow of sodium ions. As we have seen, nerve cells are 50–60 millivolts more negative than the exterior, so the sodium ion experiences a net force of around 100 millivolts tending to drive it into the cell. Hodgkin and Keynes showed that inhibition of ATP production greatly reduces the exit of sodium from the cell, leaving sodium entry unaffected. Thus we have an energy-requiring system which removes sodium from the cell and maintains the differential concentration gradient across the plasma membrane. The question was immediately asked: are the two energy requiring systems, one pumping sodium out, the other pumping potassium in, linked together? The answer was provided by Hodgkin and Keynes who demonstrated that raising or lowering the external potassium concentration results in a parallel increase or decrease in the active outward flow of sodium ions. Thus ion concentration gradients are maintained by two systems, the passive leakage and the active pumping of the ions across the membrane (figure 9.7).

The symmetrical scheme, as outlined in figure 9.7, cannot develop a membrane potential. In order for this to occur, some disparity in the movement of the two ions must be present. This arises from the greater permeability of the membrane to potassium than to sodium. Potassium ions leak out more rapidly than sodium ions leak in, thereby depleting the interior of the cell of cations and making it more negative than the exterior. This, however, opposes the passive outward flow of potassium ions but assists the inward flow of sodium. Thus the difference in the leakage rates of the two ions is reduced until an equilibrium is established at the membrane potential.

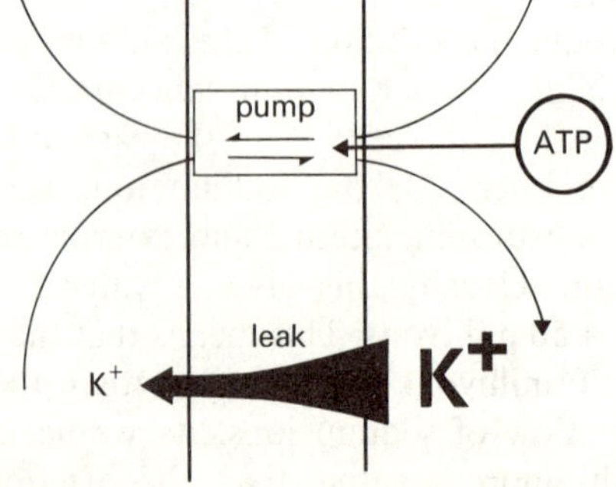

Note: Difference in size of Na^+ and K^+ inside and outside is to emphasise differences in concentrations.

Figure 9.7. The sodium-potassium trans-membrane gradient.

The nerve impulse

The foregoing discussion is generally applicable to all cells. The plasma membranes of nerve cells, muscle cells and certain secretory cells, however, have the unique property of being electrically excitable. What does this mean? Figure 9.5 outlined how it is possible to make electrical measurements on the plasma membrane. If we take some non-excitable cell, such as an erythrocyte, and impale it with a microelectrode, then the membrane potential will be found to be about −50 millivolts. It is possible to change the potential by adding or withdrawing ions from the cell interior via our intracellular pipette, when the membrane potential follows exactly the imposed polarization.

If this experiment is repeated with a squid axon instead of the erythrocyte, we find a very different situation. The membrane potential is about −65 millivolts, and if the membrane is depolarized, say, by adding cations to the cell interior, the membrane potential initially follows the imposed depolarization. As the membrane potential approaches a value of about −15 millivolts, a sequence of events occurs that is unique to excitable membranes. The membrane 'takes over' from the imposed polarization: the membrane potential reduces to zero, and continues beyond, so that the interior of the cell becomes positive, possibly to the extent of +30 millivolts, after which the membrane potential is returned to the original −65 millivolts. This rapid change in the electrical status of the membrane is termed the *action potential* and occurs spontaneously when the membrane potential reaches the threshold value of about −15 millivolts. It can be measured using intracellular electrodes, and its general characteristics are shown in figure 9.8.

This sequence involves a considerable departure from the equilibrium conditions prevailing in the resting nerve with a steady membrane potential of —65 millivolts. The ionic changes giving rise to the action potential were elucidated as a result of a series of now classical experiments in the late 1940s and early 1950s by A. L. Hodgkin, A. F. Huxley and B. Katz. The first change that occurs is a decrease in the resistance of the membrane to the passive in-flow of sodium ions, resulting in a depolarization of the membrane. This seems to be a self-perpetuating process in so far as the continuing depolarization of the membrane seems to lower further the resistance to sodium flow. This process continues until the membrane potential approaches the equilibrium potential for the sodium ions, and Hodgkin and Katz showed that the extent of depolarization was dependent on the external sodium concen-

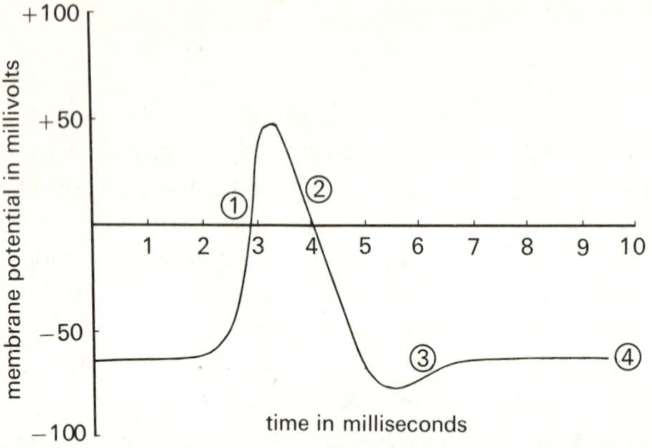

Figure 9.8. The action potential: The main features are: (1) a rapid rising phase; (2) a slower falling phase, combining to give a *spike* of duration about 1 millisecond; (3) a longer hyperpolarization lasting several milliseconds; (4) recovery of the resting potential.

tration; but this is not the whole story. Figure 9.8 shows that the membrane potential rapidly returns to and indeed overshoots, the resting potential. The current in this second half of the action potential seems to be carried by potassium ions, and Keynes showed that this was so using radioactive potassium. The outward flow of potassium increases with increasing depolarization, so that, as the equilibrium potential for sodium is approached, the potassium outflow becomes sufficiently great to reverse the depolarization, which in turn increases the membrane resistance to sodium flow. These events are outlined in figure 9.9.

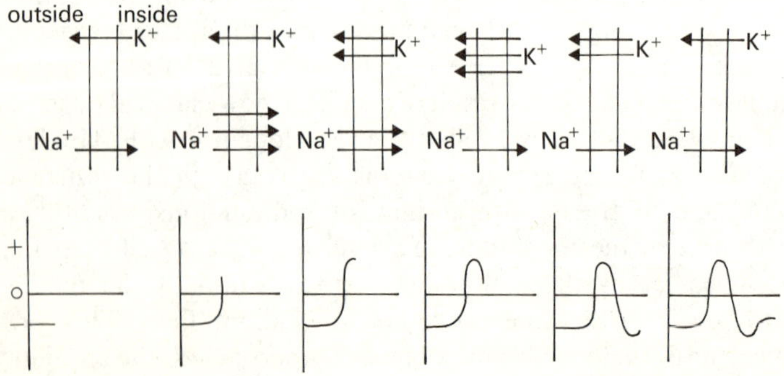

Figure 9.9. Trans-membrane movements of K^+ and Na^+ with the development of the action potential.

The action potential is the form in which information is passed along the axons. The impulse travels as a wave of depolarization, each minutely contiguous section of the membrane being depolarized to its threshold value by the electrical events occurring adjacent to it, and then going through the sequence of events outlined in figure 9.8. After the action potential has passed, the cell is left with a disturbed ion distribution, and it is at this point that the energy-requiring pump takes over. During this brief recovery period the membrane is said to be *refractory* and cannot produce an action potential. It is important to realize, however, that the whole sequence of the action potential occurs as a result of changes only in the *passive movement* of the ions across the membrane. This then raises the question: how is the permeability of the membrane changed? The answer to this question is not yet known. Considerable energy has been expended in searching for the solution, and it is worthwhile reviewing the present situation.

In our previous discussion of the generation of an action potential, reference was made to depolarizing the nerve membrane via microelectrodes. This is not the situation *in vivo*. In chapter 3 we saw how nerve cells communicate with each other and with other cells via specialized contacts or synapses. Neurotransmitters are released from one side of the synapse, and interact with receptors in the apposed post-synaptic membrane. The result of this interaction is a change in the ion permeability of the post-synaptic membrane (see figure 9.10).

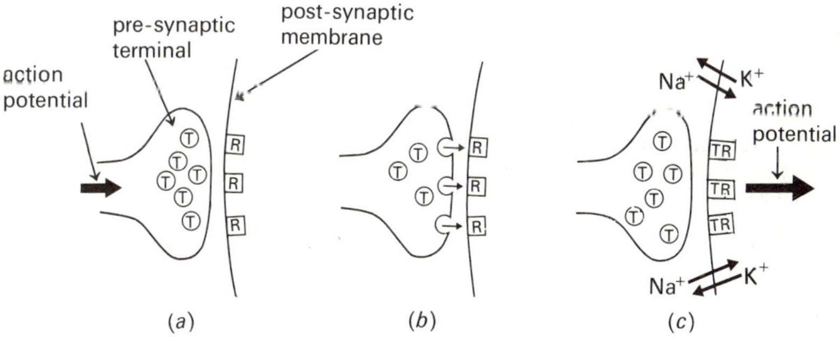

Figure 9.10. The generation of an action potential:
(*a*) The action potential invades the nerve terminal containing transmitter T within the synaptic vesicles.
(*b*) T is released into the synaptic cleft and diffuses across to the receptor sites R on the post-synaptic membrane.
(*c*) Interaction of T and R induces a permeability change such that a new action potential is generated.

The changes in ion permeability are quite specific and are not simply a case of a generally-increased leakiness such as occurs with, say, the erythrocyte membrane during the preparation of erythrocyte ghosts (see chapter 4). There seem to be specific *channels* or *gates* in the membrane which can be opened or closed according to its polarization state. The channels are frequently referred to as *ionophores*, and it is generally agreed that there are distinct molecules or co-ordinated groups of molecules in the membrane which form an ion channel. In the resting state the channels can be thought of as being almost closed, allowing a low leakage of ions through the membrane. The initiation of the action potential requires the sodium channels to be fully opened, and this is triggered by the arrival of the neurotransmitter at the receptor sites on the post-synaptic membrane. A key question arises here: is the receptor for the neurotransmitter the same as the ionophore, or are two discrete membrane units involved? The two alternative situations are outlined in figure 9.11.

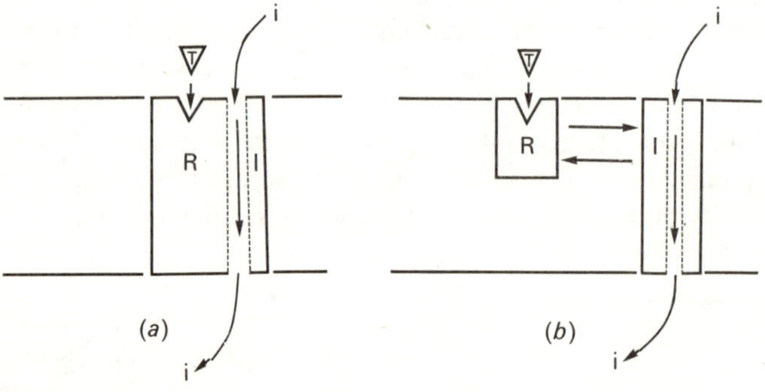

Figure 9.11. Receptor-ionophore coupling: In scheme (*a*) the receptor R and Ionophore I form a single membrane unit. Interaction of transmitter T with R results in a conformational change such that I opens and allows ions i to flow through. In (*b*) R is a discrete membrane constituent separate from I. The information carried by T and expressed as a conformational change in R must be transmitted through the membrane to I.

The work leading to the isolation and characterization of that component of the synaptic membrane which functions as a receptor was described in chapter 8. What of the ionophore? Changeux and his colleagues have recently shown that it is possible to reconstitute a functional excitable membrane from a solution of its constituent parts. Membranes were prepared from the electric organ of *Torpedo marmorata* (see chapter 8) and completely dissolved in detergent solutions. The solubilized membrane preparation was then subjected to a long dialysis procedure, when a spontaneous reassembly of membranes occurred resulting in the formation of small membrane-bound vesicles. The small vesicles or *microsacs* are osmotically sensitive, and can be shown to change their permeability to sodium ions when treated with an acetylcholine-like compound.

These experiments have far-reaching implications for membrane research, but let us confine ourselves at present to a consideration of the receptor-ionophore situation. The experiments tell us a number of things. Firstly, the receptor must orientate itself correctly in the reconstituted membrane, i.e. with its transmitter recognition site facing the outside. Secondly, the ionophore aligns itself so as to connect the vesicle interior with the outside. Thirdly, the receptor and the ionophore are functionally linked. While not providing absolute proof that the receptor and the ionophore are a single unit, the experiments indicate that they are very closely associated. That the two are in fact a single membrane protein is suggested by experiments from the group of De Robertis. They have prepared black-lipid membranes (see chapter 6) into which have been incorporated isolated receptor proteins. The electrical resistance of the membranes can be measured and undergoes a transitory reduction when neurotransmitter is put onto the membrane surface. Concomitant with the decrease in membrane resistance there is a reversible change in the structure of the membrane. This takes the form of the appearance of 'holes' in the membrane (see figure 9.12) and has been interpreted as an opening of ion-channels in the receptor-ionophore units.

The resistance change is the result of increased conductance to cations, and thus is analogous to the changes in the synaptic membrane *in vivo*. Therefore, in a phospholipid membrane containing only a single protein species, a change in ion permeability results from interactions of neurotransmitter and receptor, suggesting that under these conditions the receptor also functions as the ionophore. Evidence from several sources suggests that the receptor molecules are arranged in groups (see figure 8.7) in the membrane, and each group may constitute a receptor-ionophore unit allowing transmitter-controlled passive movement of ions across the membrane. Separate ion pumps are also present to restore the ionic gradients after the nerve impulse has passed, and these are described below.

Ion pumps

Reference has already been made to the experiments of Keynes and his colleagues demonstrating an energy requirement for sodium efflux

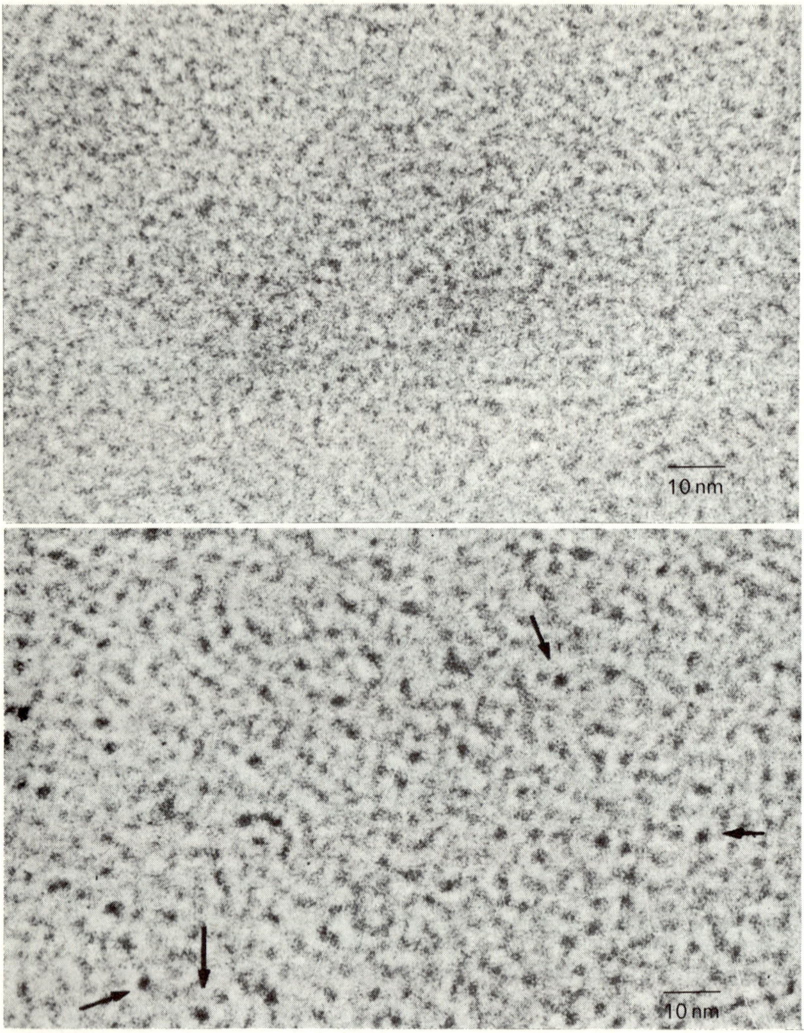

Figure 9.12. Electron micrographs of negatively-stained black-lipid films containing the cholinergic receptor proteolipid of De Robèrtis. The black-lipid films are seen in surface view after fixation with glutaraldehyde and exposure to osmium vapours. In the upper micrograph the appearance of the resting membrane is seen. The membrane has an amorphous appearance with no clearly defined structure. In the lower micrograph the membrane is seen at the peak of the conductance change elicited by acetylcholine. Discrete pores have appeared into which the negative stain has penetrated (arrows). As the conductance falls to the resting level, the appearance of the membrane reverts to that shown in the upper micrograph. Original micrographs were kindly supplied by Dr. E. De Robertis, Instituto de Biologia Celular, Universidad de Buenos Aires.

and potassium influx in squid giant axons. In 1960 Caldwell and collaborators produced increased efflux of sodium from cyanide-poisoned squid axons by direct injection of ATP, GTP, arginine phosphate or phosphoenolpyruvate. Later work established that the active pumping of both sodium and potassium specifically required ATP. Earlier, in 1957, Skou had discovered an ATPase in the leg nerve of a crab which showed a specific requirement for sodium and potassium. This finding was soon followed by reports of similar ATPases from a whole range of tissues, among them, cerebral cortex of guinea pigs, frog toe muscle, toad urinary bladder, seagull salt gland, and the electric organ of the electric eel. All these ATPases, usually referred to as Na^+,K^+-ATPases, were found to be inhibited by a group of compounds called *cardiac glycosides*. These compounds had been shown to be specific inhibitors of sodium and potassium transport in 1953 by Schatzmann, and the idea developed that the Na^+,K^+-ATPase and the ion pump were one and the same. It is still to be demonstrated unequivocally that this is so, but the evidence certainly favours such an interpretation. Much of the evidence has come from studies on erythrocyte ghosts and is summarized here.

In intact ghosts, the pump and the Na^+,K^+-ATPase require the simultaneous presence of both potassium and sodium, and the effect of changing the concentration of either ion is the same on the pump and on the ATPase. It can be shown that sodium activates both the pump and the Na^+,K^+-ATPase only from the inside of the ghost, whereas potassium exerts its effects only from the outside. The cardiac glycosides inhibit both the pump and the Na^+,K^+-ATPase only from the outside, and the effects on both can be reversed by raising the external potassium concentration, suggesting that the glycosides and potassium may compete for a common external site. Thermodynamic considerations demand that the Na^+,K^+-ATPase should be able to run backwards, thereby synthesizing ATP. Garrahan and Glynn have shown that this is possible by using ghosts with high internal potassium concentrations incubated in high external sodium buffer. Glycolysis was poisoned using iodoacetate, and these workers were able to show an incorporation of ^{32}P into ATP when the pump was running backwards. Furthermore, the ATP synthesis was sensitive to cardiac glycosides. Very recently Jain and his colleagues have been trying to incorporate an Na^+,K^+-ATPase from rat brain into an artificial lipid bilayer and to show that it confers electrogenic properties on the membrane. The successful completion of such experiments could provide the final proof that the pump and the Na^+,K^+-

ATPase are the same molecular entity. In spite of this lack of ultimate proof, however, a clear picture of the pumping mechanism and its orientation within the membrane is beginning to emerge.

Consideration of the points detailed above allows us to state quite definitely that the Na^+,K^+-ATPase spans the membrane (see chapter 5) and has functional sites exposed on both membrane surfaces. Attachment of sodium and potassium ions to their respective binding sites must be followed by a reorientation of the enzyme within the membrane, so that the ions are transferred to the opposite membrane face. It is firmly established that the enzyme has a specific requirement for phospholipids, probably phosphatidylcholine and phosphatidylserine, though there is still some discussion on this point. While the role of the phospholipids is not at all clear, it is usually assumed that they assist the protein to maintain its conformation. Metcalfe and his group have presented data from experiments on a Ca^{++},Mg^{++}-ATPase from sarcoplasmic reticulum which may well be relevant to the Na^+,K^+-ATPase. They find that the Ca^{++},Mg^{++}-ATPase, which functions as a calcium transporter, has specific phospholipids associated with it which are necessary for full functional activity. Metcalfe has shown that these phospholipids exchange relatively slowly with other membrane phospholipids which normally undergo rapid lateral diffusion as described in chapter 6. The suggestion is that the phospholipids associated with the ATPase form a bilayer shell around the protein. In this way a discrete *microenvironment* could be maintained within the general hydrophobic area of the membrane which particularly suits the requirements of the ATPase.

As long ago as 1960 Skou suggested that one of the steps in the overall reaction of sodium and potassium transport and ATP hydrolysis might be the phosphorylation of the enzyme itself. Subsequent work has shown this to be so. The phosphorylation of the protein may be measured by observing the transfer of ^{32}P from ATP $\gamma^{32}P$, and it is found that this step is dependent on sodium ions. Subsequent addition of potassium ions to the system results in loss of ^{32}P from the enzyme. Thus a cyclic phosphorylation-dephosphorylation stimulated by sodium and potassium respectively would seem to operate during the functioning of the Na^+,K^+-ATPase. There is still some discussion as to whether the potassium-stimulated phosphatase is part of the Na^+,K^+-ATPase, or whether it is a quite separate enzyme. Evidence certainly favours the former situation, and it seems that the phosphorylation-dephosphorylation sequence is an integral part of the ion-transport ATPase process.

Let us now try to integrate all the data outlined above and fabricate a working model of the ion pump. The current view is that the Na^+,K^+-ATPase undergoes a series of conformational changes which bring about translocation of the ions. The changes in conformation are initiated by the phosphorylation-dephosphorylation process. In the dephosphorylated conformation, sodium acceptor sites are available on the inner membrane surface. Binding of sodium to these sites permits

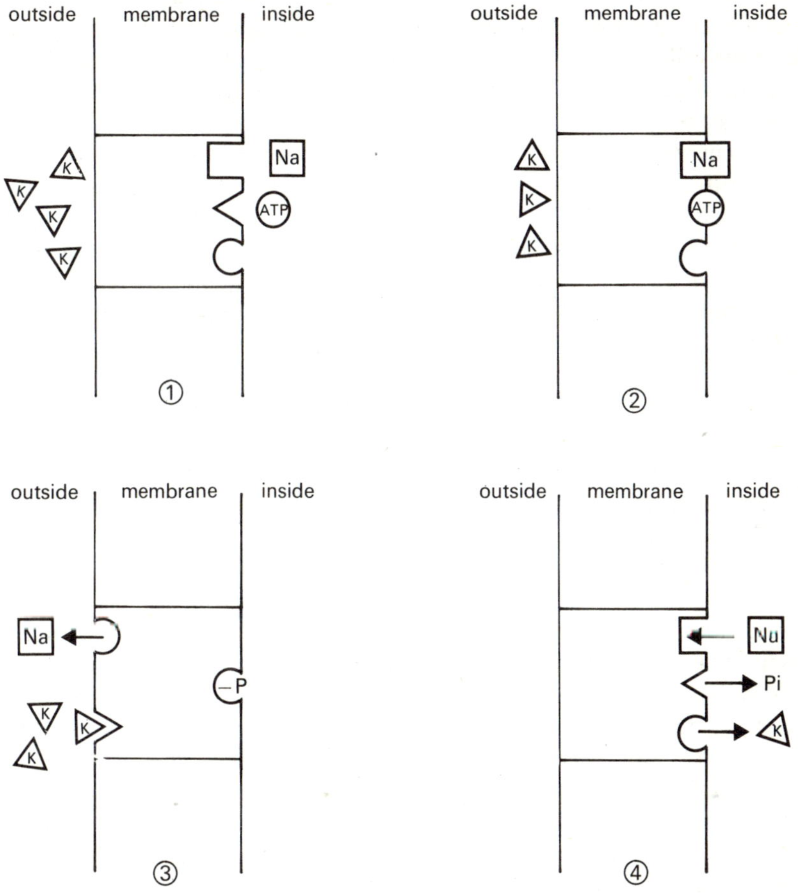

Figure 9.13. The Na^+,K^+-ATPase pump: In (1) Na^+ and ATP approach the inner face of the ATPase complex and bind to specific sites (2). In (3) phosphorylation of the ATPase results in a re-orientation of the binding sites for Na^+ and K^+. In (4) dephosphorylation of the protein results in a reversion of the conformation to that of stage (1), and the whole process may then be repeated.

ATP to phosphorylate the enzyme. This phosphorylation is known to occur at a glutamyl residue in the ATPase active site. The phosphorylation results in a change in conformation, such that potassium binding sites are exposed on the outer surface, and the bound sodium is carried to the outer surface also. The external-facing sodium sites have a lower affinity, and thus sodium is lost to the exterior. Meanwhile, binding of potassium stimulates dephosphorylation, and the enzyme reverts to its original conformation. The reversion carries potassium to the inner membrane and lowers the affinity of the sites, thus releasing potassium into the cell. Parallel with this the sodium sites regain their high affinity, sodium binds to the sites and the whole cycle of events is repeated. The sequence is presented in schematic form in figure 9.13.

A scheme has recently been put forward by Lieb and Stein which attempts to define more precisely the functioning of the ATPase. They propose that the ATPase is arranged as a tetramer, each unit of which has a binding site at the membrane surface. Ions can bind simultaneously at both membrane surfaces. The binding is accompanied by a conformational change in the monomers, such that the ions are moved to the centre of the membrane, where they are passed on to a complementary binding site on another monomer. The monomers then revert to their original conformation. The model has the attractions that it does not require the physical movement of a binding site across the entire width of the membrane. Furthermore, it is in accordance with experimental observations made using erythrocytes that transport occurs when cations are bound simultaneously at both sides of the membrane.

The pump as described above is not *electrogenic*, i.e. it does not alter the net charge distribution across the membrane. There are indeed examples of *non-electrogenic* pumps, one being the epithelial cells of frog skin, where one sodium ion is exchanged for one potassium ion. We know that in many membranes there is not an exactly equivalent exchange of the two ions. Thus, in the case of the erythrocyte, there is a net efflux of three sodium ions for a net influx of two potassium ions, with the concomitant hydrolysis of one molecule of ATP. In this case the pump *is* electrogenic, as is that of the nerve cell membrane. Although the primary features of the sodium-potassium pumping system are satisfied by the model described above, the fine details of its mechanism remain to be elucidated.

The operation of the Na^+,K^+-ATPase maintains the gradients for the two ions. The transport of a number of amino acids and sugars is dependent on the presence of sodium ions, and it seems that this mode of transport may operate in an analogous manner to the proton symport model of the facilitated diffusion carrier.

Sodium-linked amino acid and sugar transport

A specific dependence on sodium ions has been observed for the transport of glycine and alanine into duck erythrocytes, tyrosine and phenylalanine in frog small intestine, alanine into thymus nuclei, various sugars in guinea pig and rat intestine, and into mucosal cells from rabbit ileum and amino acids into bacteria. Much of our information on sodium-dependent transport systems has come from the work of Crane and his colleagues on sugar transport in intestinal cells, but the amino-acid transporting systems probably have the same basic mechanism. In several cases the uptake is inhibited by potassium ions, and the cardiac glycoside ouabain

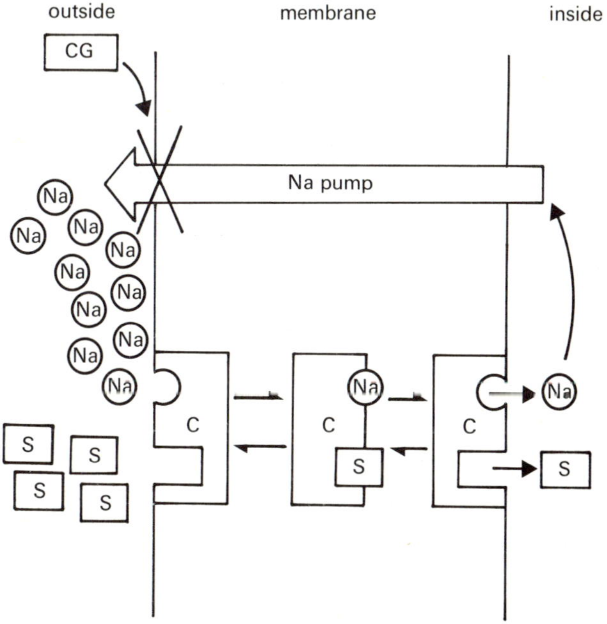

Figure 9.14. Na^+-linked sugar transport: The sodium pump, Na pump, maintains a transmembrane Na^+ gradient. Carrier C has binding sites for both sugar S and Na^+. Thus the Na^+ gradient provides the power for active uptake of S in analogous manner to the proton-driven transport system shown in figure 9.3. Cardiac glycosides CG diminish the Na^+ gradient by inhibiting the pump, thereby removing the energy source for the transport process.

inhibits the uptake of sugars and of amino acids in some of the systems. The suggestion is that there exists in the membrane a carrier for the sugar or amino acid which has an additional binding site for sodium. Recalling the nomenclature of the chemiosmotic model, such a carrier might be termed a *sodium symport.* The sodium pump maintains a high-external low-internal sodium concentration which results in a continuing tendency for sodium to enter the cell, which it does in the form of a carrier-sugar/amino acid complex. Thus the energy potential of the sodium concentration gradient or the *sodium motive force* is used to drive the active accumulation of the sugar or amino acid. The scheme is outlined in figure 9.14.

It should be noted that alternative models for the involvement of sodium in sugar and amino acid transport have been put forward. This is particularly so for some of the bacterial systems in which several workers have demonstrated that co-transport of sodium does not occur: i.e. the carrier is not functioning as a sodium symport. There have been several suggestions that in these systems sodium exerts its stimulatory effect by acting on the carrier, so as to increase the affinity of the sugar binding site. This would occur at the outer face of the membrane, and the sodium would not then form part of the carrier complex.

A variation of the sodium-linked transport system in which the sodium symport and the sodium pump reside in different membranes of the same cell is found in mucosal cells of the small intestine. These cells have one surface in contact with the lumen of the intestine, while the opposite face

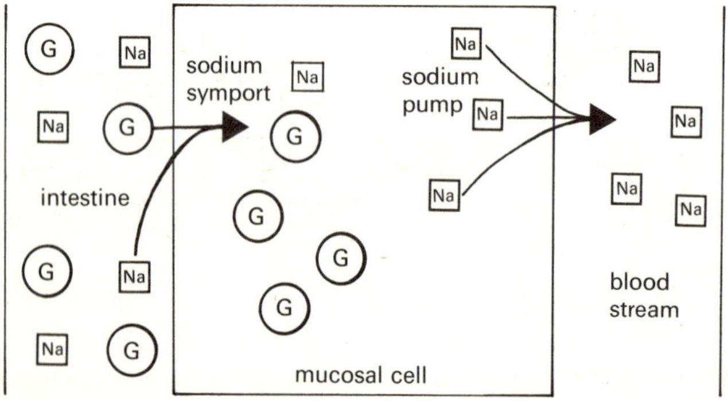

Figure 9.15. Na^+-linked glucose transport in intestinal mucosal cells: Glucose G enters the mucosal cell from the intestinal lumen on a sodium symport (see figure 9.14). The sodium gradient is maintained by a sodium pump in the other membrane of the cell pumping Na^+ out into the blood stream.

borders the blood stream. The sodium pump is located in the serosal membrane and pumps sodium out of the cell into the blood. The carrier or symport is located in the mucosal membrane. It can be shown that in the resting state the lumen of the intestine is about 3 millivolts negative with respect to the blood. This can be accounted for by leakage of sodium ions through the mucosal membrane into the cell, and their active transfer via the pump into the blood. On the addition of glucose to the lumen, the potential differences rises to about 10 millivolts. This occurs due to the entry of sodium along with glucose on the carrier; the intracellular concentration of sodium therefore increases, and the pumping rate of the serosal membrane similarly increases. Thus in this system the transport of one molecular species across a membrane is effectively coupled to the active transport of another molecule across a different membrane (see figure 9.15).

SUMMARY

1. The removal of water of hydration from polar solutes must precede their entry into the lipid phase of membranes. This constitutes a major barrier to their movement across the membrane.
2. Carriers provide the solute molecule with an environment which replaces the hydration shell. The carrier-solute complex can present a hydrophobic exterior which facilitates trans-membrane movements of polar molecules.
3. Facilitated diffusion provides a simple energy-independent method for the specific transfer of material across the membrane. Transport continues so long as a concentration gradient is maintained.
4. More sophisticated transport systems involve the coupling of an energy source to the carrier mechanism, and are able to transfer material against a concentration gradient.
5. Simple active transport entails a single carrier molecule which may utilize the energy of either a 'high-energy' phosphate or the osmotic energy of the membrane. The detailed mechanism of energy coupling is still open to debate.
6. Alternative methods of active transport involve the integration of the transfer mechanism with an initial metabolic step. The material being transported is chemically modified during the transport process, and therefore this system differs markedly from simple active transport.
7. An integrated system of passive and active transport is frequently found to occur and is best exemplified by the Na^+,K^+-ATPase. This system may be electrogenic and is responsible for the maintenance of the membrane potential of a wide variety of cells.
8. The potential energy of the sodium concentration gradient resulting from the operation of the ion pump may be utilized in sodium-dependent transport systems. In these circumstances the transport process is analogous to the chemiosmotic model of simple active transport, but with the sodium ion replacing the proton. An alternative view is that sodium acts as a modifier of the carrier conformation but does not particpate directly in the transfer process.

CHAPTER 10

THE IONOPHORIC ANTIBIOTICS

IN THE PREVIOUS CHAPTER SEVERAL DIFFERENT MODEL TRANSPORT SYSTEMS were presented, some of which have a mobile carrier migrating through the membrane. Other models were dependent on specific pores or channels which provide a passage across the lipid bilayer. The presence of either carriers or specific pores in biological membranes has yet to be verified.

In 1964 C. Moore and B. C. Pressman discovered that an antibiotic, valinomycin, shows great specificity for the transport of potassium into mitochondria. Since that time several naturally occurring antibiotics have been found to function as highly specific carriers for alkali metal cations. Other compounds, also of bacterial origin, are able to function as *anion selective pores* when introduced into phospholipid bilayers.

The compounds are collectively referred to as *ionophores* and their transport characteristics have been studied in a wide range of natural and artificial membranes. Many of them are naturally-produced antibiotics, and their ion-carrying ability may be the basis of their biological activity. The suggestion has also been made that these compounds enable some micro-organisms to maintain trans-membrane ion gradients. It must be emphasized that, except for a recent report of the isolation of a peptide ionophore from electroplax membranes, similar molecules have never been found in membrane preparations from higher organisms. Nevertheless, the ionophores have provided valuable research tools, and have enabled the construction of working models of membrane transport systems. It is, therefore, well worth while to examine more closely both their structure and mode of action.

The ion-carriers

The ion-carrying ionophores fall into two main classes: the *valinomycin* group and the *nigericin* group. Members of the former group are electrically neutral and form a charged complex with alkali metal cations, whereas those of the latter group have a carboxylic acid grouping which is dissociated over the physiological pH range, leading to the formation of electrically neutral complexes.

Most members of the valinomycin ionophore group are cyclic compounds. Valinomycin and the enniatins are cyclic depsipeptides, with an alternating sequence of α amino and α hydroxy acids joined by alternating amide and ester bonds. The macrotetrolides are polycyclic tetralactones having a 32-membered heterocyclic ring structure. The gramicidins are also classified within the valinomycin group; they are acyclic pentadecapeptides which may nevertheless assume a ring-like tertiary structure which is stabilized by hydrogen bonding. A group of synthetic compounds, the crown polyethers, is also incorporated into the valinomycin group. Valinomycin and the macrotetrolides have been used more extensively in permeability studies than the other ionophores. Structures of valinomycin and nonactin, a macrotetrolide, are shown in figure 10.1.

The nigericin group comprises nigericin, monensin, griseorexin, X-206, and X-537A. These compounds consists of a series of linked heterocyclic

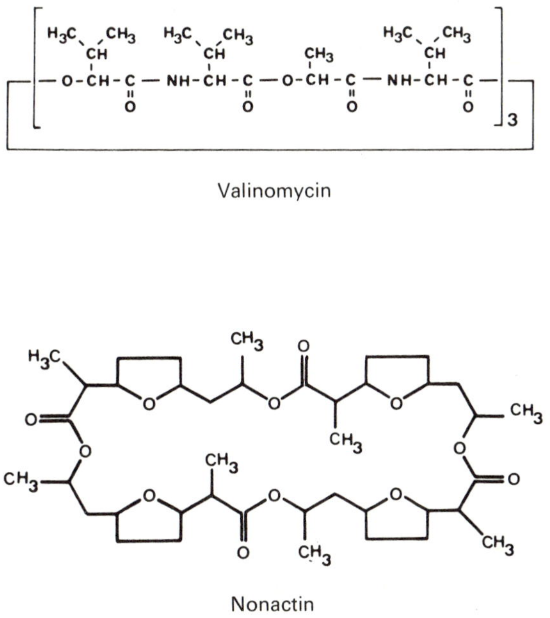

Figure 10.1. Structures of valinomycin and nonactin.

rings having a carboxyl group at one end and a hydroxyl group at the other. A tertiary cyclic structure is maintained by hydrogen bonding between the two terminal groupings. The structure of nigericin is shown in figure 10.2.

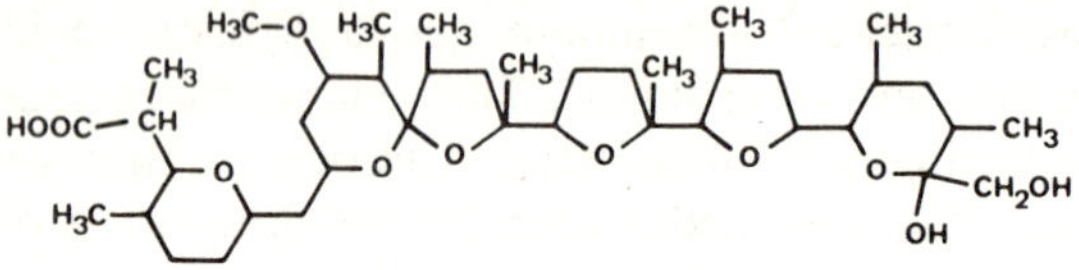

Figure 10.2. Nigericin.

Structure of the ion-carrier complexes

The ionophores all form 1:1 crystalline complexes with a number of alkali metal cations, and the structures of these complexes have been analyzed in some detail by X-ray crystallographic methods. The ionophores have the common feature of a number of oxygen atoms linked through a ring system of varying size. In the crystalline complexes all the oxygens point to the interior, forming a polar cavity into which the cation fits. The nonpolar groups are turned to the exterior, and thus the complex has a hydrophobic shell. The overall structure of the complex is maintained by hydrogen bonding between the various groups of the ring system. The importance of this hydrogen bonding is emphasized by experiments in which the optical configuration of one of the constituent acids of valinomycin is changed when the stability of the ion-carrier complex is found to be drastically reduced. The polar cavity formed in the ionophore is about the same size as the particular unhydrated alkali metal cation for which the carrier shows specificity. Thus it is thought that the ionophore presents an internal environment which closely resembles the normal hydration shell of the cation. The structures of three of the crystalline complexes are shown in schematic form in figure 10.3.

Membrane activity of the ion-carriers

In 1964 Pressman and his colleagues found that addition of valinomycin to preparations of rat liver mitochondria resulted in a depletion of the potassium in the incubation medium. It was shown that this was due to movement of the ions into the mitochondria. A simultaneous counter-movement of protons was seen, thereby maintaining the electrical status of the mitochondrial membrane. Similar experiments using erythrocytes revealed that the ionophoric effect of valinomycin was not unique to mitochondria. Moreover, the macrotetrolides were found to have similar effects. Most of the detailed information on the behaviour of the ionophores in membranes has been obtained using artificial phospholipid bilayers. As the reader will by now appreciate, biological membranes are highly complex structures and it is not yet possible to define precisely the influence of each of the many constituents on the behaviour of an ionophore. The situation in a synthetic lipid bilayer is very much simpler; thus the lipid composition can be defined, and both trans-membrane potentials and ionic gradients can be varied at will. In black-lipid films (see chapter 6) valinomycin brings about a marked

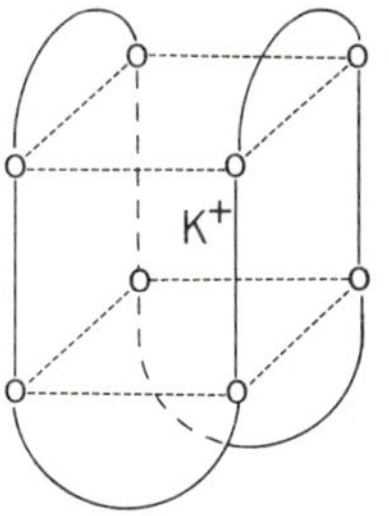

(*a*) Nonactin-K^+ complex;

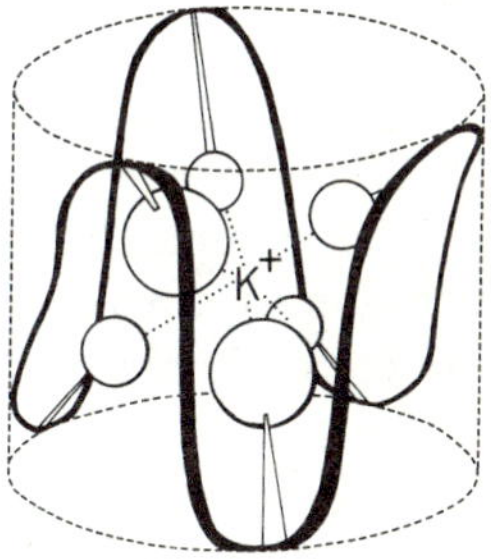

(*b*) Valinomycin-K^+ complex;

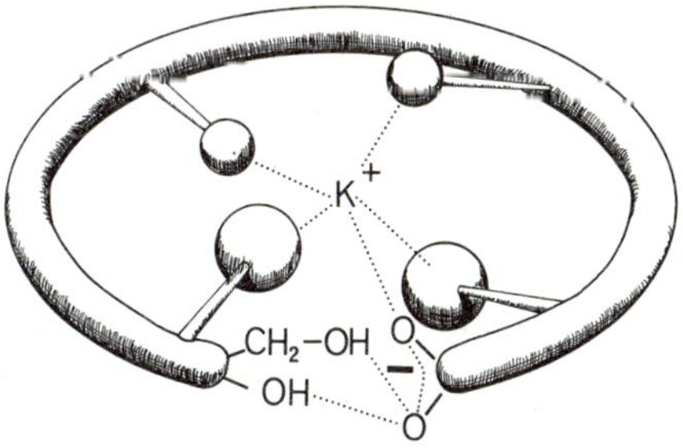

(*c*) Nigericin-K^+ complex.

Figure 10.3. Schematic representation of ionophorecation crystalline complexes: (*a*) In the nonactin complex the potassium ion is held in quasi-cubic symmetry. (*b*) Valinomycin forms a complex in octahedral co-ordination with the potassium ion. (*c*) The potassium-nigericin complex shows no such symmetry. Hydrogen bonds hold the nigericin in a ring-like structure and the potassium is co-ordinated by the oxygen atoms projecting into the ring.

increase in the permeability of the membranes to potassium ions. The specificity of the ionophore for potassium may be seen when the ion is replaced by sodium; under these conditions the resistance of the membrane is some $10^3 \times$ higher. The highly specific nature of the ionophore is further emphasized by experiments in which the trans-membrane gradient of potassium ions is varied. Under these conditions a membrane potential develops, and this may approach very closely the value of 58 millivolts predicted by the Nernst equation (see chapter 9) for a tenfold difference in potassium concentration. Thus the lipid bilayer-ionophore system behaves like an ideal permselective membrane.

A number of hypotheses on the mode of action of the ion-carriers has been put forward. It has been suggested that several molecules may link together to form a pore through the membrane, with the ions flowing through the lumen. Alternatively, they have been likened to a 'bridge' with several molecules linked together to span the membrane, the ions being passed along from one ionophore to the next. A number of pieces of evidence suggest that they usually function as mobile carriers with a single molecule forming the basic transporting unit. The conductivity of lipid bilayers is directly proportional to ionophore concentration over a very wide range. Similarly a direct linear relationship between conductivity and ion concentration is seen up to a point at which saturation occurs. Thus the ionophore behaves as a *facilitated diffusion carrier*. Recently it has been shown that the conductivity of lipid bilayers containing valinomycin drops markedly if the temperature is lowered to that of the phase transition for the acyl chains in the membrane (see chapter 6); this again is in keeping with the mobile carrier concept. The formation of the 1:1 crystalline complexes referred to above also favours the suggestion that the transporting unit is a single ionophore molecule.

Ion-carriers and the chemiosmotic theory

The chemiosmotic interpretation of simple active transport enables a mobile carrier to accumulate transported material against a concentration gradient without any direct coupling of energy to the carrier (see chapter 8). Is it then possible for the ionophores to function effectively as active transport systems? The answer is that under certain circumstances this is indeed possible, and the ionophores can provide a direct working model of a chemiosmotic transport process.

Compounds of the valinomycin group form a positively charged complex with potassium ions. If a potential is applied across a lipid bilayer containing valinomycin, potassium ions will be carried across the membrane from the positive to the negative side. The ions will be transported against their concentration gradient so long as the membrane potential is maintained. Thus the valinomycin-potassium carrier complex may be coupled to the membrane potential gradient, and in effect becomes a simple active transport system.

Ionophores of the nigericin group complex with potassium, or in the case of monensin, sodium, to form an electrically neutral complex. These compounds serve not only to carry alkali metal cations but also protons. Thus addition of nigericin to an erythrocyte suspension results in loss of potassium from the erthrocyte with a concomitant fall in internal pH. It is suggested that the carboxyl group of the nigericin compounds serves as a counterion for metal cations in one direction, and in its undissociated form carries protons in the opposite direction. The net result of this is an electrically neutral exchange of metal cations for protons. The transport of alkali metal cations by the nigericin compounds can be 'driven' by proticity, and this constitutes a further verification of the chemiosmotic theory of transport.

Pore-forming antibiotics

The pore-forming ionophores have not yet been as well characterized as have the ion-carriers. The group is collectively known as the *polyene antibiotics*. Nystatin is one of the most widely used members of the group and its structure is shown in figure 10.4.

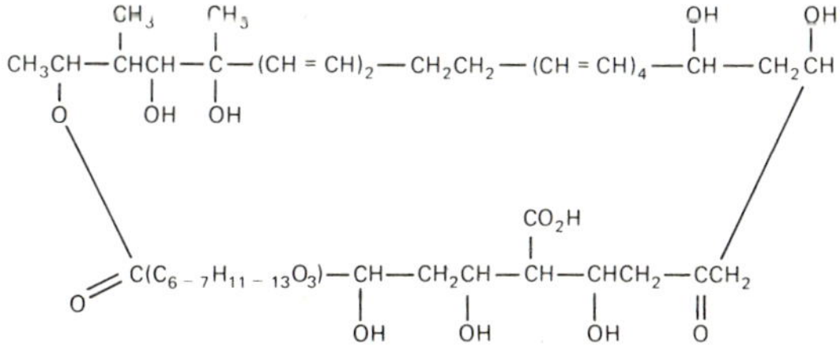

Figure 10.4. Nystatin.

The major difference between the polyene pore-formers and the ion carriers is that the former have hydrophilic groups projecting both into and out of the ring. Thus the polyenes are much more soluble in aqueous systems than are the ion-carriers.

Incorporation of nystatin into a phospholipid bilayer greatly lowers the resistance of the membrane. Unlike the ion-carriers, the change in membrane permeability takes the form of increased conductance to anions. Thus an electrical potential of about 50 millivolts will develop across a nystatin-containing membrane which has a tenfold gradient of chloride ions across it. This figure is not far removed from the 58 millivolts predicted by the Nernst equation (see page 206 and chapter 9). A major difference between the polyenes and the ion-carriers is their effect on the trans-membrane movement of water and small non-electrolytes. Nystatin greatly increases the permeability of phospholipid bilayers to water, and the kinetics of the transfer process are consistent with the presence of continuous channels through which the water can flow. Further support for this suggestion comes from examinations of the trans-membrane movements of small molecules such as urea and glucose to which phospholipid bilayers are normally impermeable. Nystatin however, renders the membrane permeable to these molecules provided their radius does not exceed 0·4 nm, and in fact their permeability is inversely related to their radius. Thus it is suggested that the polyenes form pores which completely traverse the phospholipid bilayer. The size of the nystatin molecule is insufficient to span the membrane, and the relationship between conductance and polyene concentration is not consistent with the stacking of several molecules to form a pore.

The current view is that the polyenes exert their effects as the result of interactions with cholesterol, some of which is always present in the phospholipid bilayers used in this work. The suggestion is that the interaction results in the spontaneous formation of transient lipid micelles which would leave gaps in the bilayers. Thus the polyenes may produce transient pores with a lifetime of several milliseconds. The polyene-induced conductance of bilayers increases markedly at low temperatures, which, by increasing the viscosity of the acyl chains of the bilayer, would tend to stabilize the pores.

The antibiotic ionophores possess many of the properties of the various carriers and ion gates or channels described in chapter 9. Thus a phospholipid-cholesterol bilayer containing both polyenes and ion carriers would have anion-selective water-filled channels and highly-selective cation carriers, properties which are shared by all biological membranes.

SUMMARY

1. A number of naturally occurring antibiotics change the permeability characteristics of membranes.
2. The ion-carriers behave as highly selective mobile carriers for alkali metal cations. They have a polar interior into which the metal cation fits, and a hydrophobic exterior shell.
3. The pore-forming ionophores result in the formation of channels which traverse the membrane through which water and anions can pass.
4. Both types of ionophore show almost ideal permeability characteristics as predicted by the Nernst equation.
5. The ion-carriers may be coupled to a trans-membrane gradient of potential or of protons, thereby providing experimental verification of the chemiosmotic theory of transport.

CHAPTER 11

PHYSICAL METHODS USED IN THE STUDY OF MEMBRANES

IN THIS CHAPTER THE MAJOR PHYSICAL METHODS WHICH ARE APPLICABLE to the study of membranes will be outlined. It is not possible in the space available either to treat fully the theoretical basis of the methods or to give a comprehensive coverage of their applications. Accordingly, the principles of the methods will be dealt with, only in so far as is necessary to indicate the physical significance of the parameters which are measured in membrane studies. The examples of application of the methods are chosen so as to give an idea of the range of information which can be obtained by use of each technique, and to indicate the potential and relative values of the methods.

Nuclear magnetic resonance (n.m.r.)

An atomic nucleus may be regarded as a positively charged spinning ellipsoid and, as such, can have both a magnetic moment and spin angular momentum. When a nucleus with magnetic moment μ is placed in a magnetic field H_0, the magnetic moment will precess about the H_0-direction, inclined to H_0 at a constant angle θ—just as a gyroscope precesses about the direction of the earth's gravitational field (figure 11.1*a*). The spin angular momentum is quantized and defined by the spin number $I = \frac{1}{2}$, 1, $1\frac{1}{2}$ ... For nuclei with spin number $I = \frac{1}{2}$, only two $(2I+1)$ orientations or *spin states* are possible (figure 11.1*a* and *b*). In the lower-energy spin state, the magnetic moment μ is inclined at an angle θ to the positive direction of the field H_0 (figure 11.1*a*) and, in the higher-energy state (figure 11.1*b*), the magnetic moment is inclined at the same angle θ to the negative direction of H_0. The energy associated with orientation (*a*) is $-\mu_z H_0$ and with orientation (*b*) is $+\mu_z H_0$, where μ_z is the component of μ along H_0. Accordingly, the separation of the two energy levels or spin states is $2\mu_z H_0$, and transitions between the two

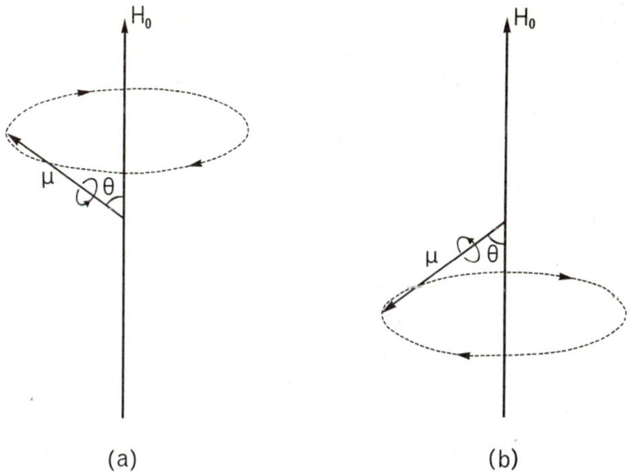

Figure 11.1. Precession of nuclei with spin number $I = \frac{1}{2}$ and magnetic moment μ about the direction of a magnetic field H_0. Two orientations are allowed, one of lower energy (*a*) and one of higher energy (*b*), each inclined at an angle θ (54° 44′) to H_0.

levels can be induced by applied electromagnetic radiation of frequency ν, where

$$h\nu = 2\mu_z H_0 \qquad (1)$$

and h is Planck's constant.

For values of H_0 of the order of 1 tesla (10^4 gauss), which are used in the n.m.r. experiment, ν falls in the radiofrequency range. The probabilities of induced transitions between the two energy levels are equal but, because there will initially be a slight excess of nuclei in the lower spin state (figure 11.1*a*), transition from lower to higher spin states will predominate, giving rise to a net absorption of energy from the applied radiofrequency radiation. This can be detected and recorded as an absorption peak. For nuclei of a given type (i.e. constant μ), only one value of ν will cause transitions at a given field strength H_0 (equation 1). Conversely if, as in one possible n.m.r. experiment, ν is fixed and the magnetic field H is swept over a suitable range, we might expect all the nuclei of a given type to undergo transitions (*resonate*) when a single value H_0, corresponding to equation (1), is reached. If this were so, no distinction could be made between any of the nuclei of a given type (e.g. protons), and n.m.r. spectrometry would be of little practical value. However, each nucleus is more or less shielded from the applied magnetic field H by its immediate electronic environment, and the field actually experienced at the nucleus (H_{eff}) is not H but $H(1-\sigma)$ where σ is a *shielding constant* characteristic of each individual nucleus in a molecule. Consequently the resonance condition $H_{eff} = H_0$, where H_0 satisfies equation (1), will be met for different values of the applied field H such that $H(1-\sigma) = H_0$. As the applied magnetic field is swept, a spectrum of resonance or absorption peaks will be obtained, and each individual nucleus will have a characteristic position or *chemical shift* in the spectrum.

When specific nuclei have been identified, further information can be obtained from other parameters. The area under a resonance peak, for example, corresponds to the number of chemically identical nuclei giving rise to that peak. Information concerning the mobility of the nucleus can also be obtained from n.m.r. experiments. A nucleus in the higher-energy spin state (figure 11.1*b*) can revert to the lower state (*relax*) by exchange of energy with its neighbours. The rate of relaxation is characterized by the *spin relaxation times* T_1 and T_2, and depends upon the rate of tumbling of the section of the molecule which contains the nucleus being studied. The relationship is such that the rate of relaxation increases as the rate of tumbling decreases. As a high relaxation rate means a low spin relaxation time, T_1 and T_2 decrease as molecular motion becomes slower. T_1 and T_2 can be measured directly by sophisticated n.m.r. experiments in which the radiofrequency radiation is applied in pulses rather than continuously. T_2 can also be obtained directly from the standard n.m.r. experiment in which the line width (width of the absorption peak at half its maximum height) is inversely proportional to T_2. Accordingly, broad lines are indicative of low values of T_2 and of slow motion of the nucleus.

Nuclei in solid systems generally give rise to very broad absorption peaks. Although the use of special wide-line n.m.r. techniques has given considerable information about lamellar lipid systems, it is more usual to try to obtain high resolution n.m.r. spectra with much narrower absorption peaks. Such spectra can be obtained from hand-shaken dispersions of lipids in water, which contain multilamellar vesicles (chapter 6). Higher-resolution spectra are, however, generally given by sonicated lipid-water systems, when vesicles bounded by a single bilayer (chapter 6) can be obtained. High-resolution proton n.m.r. spectra of sonicated dispersions of dipalmitoyl phosphatidylcholine (dipalmitoyl lecithin) in D_2O (H_2O gives complicating proton signals) at different temperatures are shown in figure 11.2. Because lipid molecules are complex and contain very many protons with similar chemical environ-

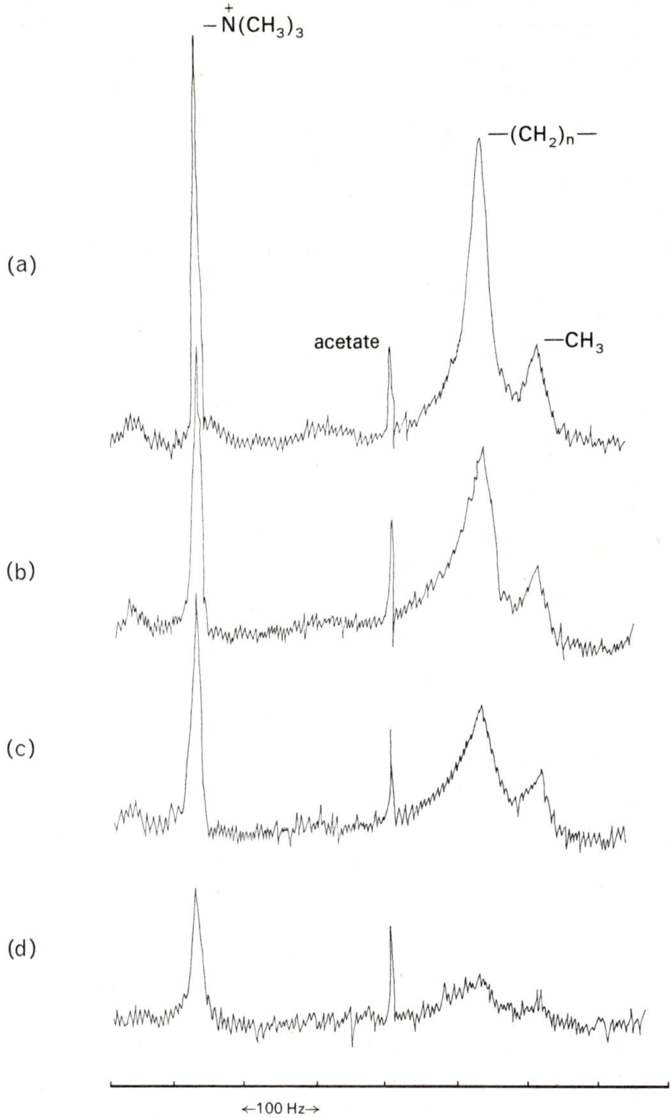

Figure 11.2. High-resolution proton n.m.r. spectra of sonicated dispersions of dipalmitoyl phosphatidylcholine in D_2O at different temperatures, (*a*) 67 °C; (*b*) 52 °C; (*c*) 42 °C; (*d*) 39 °C: from A. G. Lee *et al., Biochim. Biophys. Acta* (1972), **255,** 43–56. The acetate peak arises from the use of acetate-containing buffers.

ments (e.g. CH_2 protons), envelopes of peaks with similar chemical shifts are mostly obtained. Peaks corresponding to the $-\overset{+}{N}(CH_3)_3$, chain-CH_2- and chain-CH_3 protons can be distinguished in the spectrum at 67 °C (figure 11.2*a*). Dipalmitoyl phosphatidylcholine containing approximately 20% water undergoes a liquid crystalline-gel phase transition at 43 °C, and both the choline head groups and aliphatic chains will be fairly mobile at 67 °C. As the temperature is dropped (figure 11.2*b*, *c*, *d*), a progressive broadening of all the major peaks occurs, until at 39 °C the -CH_2- and CH_3 peaks have almost disappeared. This corresponds to the very much more restricted movement of the aliphatic chains in the gel phase below the transition temperature. Although a plot of line-widths of the $\overset{+}{N}(CH_3)_3$ protons against temperature shows a sharp upward inflexion as the temperature decreases through the transition point, it is evident from figure 11.2*d* that the $\overset{+}{N}(CH_3)_3$ group retains considerable mobility even when the aliphatic chains are frozen in the gel phase.

The exact reason why higher resolution is obtainable from sonicated than from unsonicated lipid dispersions is not known. It has been suggested both that rapid tumbling of the sonicated vesicles and that structural rearrangement resulting from curvature of vesicle bilayers might account for the observed line narrowing. The presence of a single bilayer in sonicated vesicles has been demonstrated by selective line-broadening experiments. Paramagnetic ions, such as Mn^{++}, cause line-broadening of nearby protons which depends upon the inverse sixth power of the distance of a given proton from the metal ion. Addition of Mn^{++} to a sonicated lipid-water system caused some 70% of the protons of the $\overset{+}{N}(CH_3)_3$ signal to be broadened out so as effectively to disappear. This corresponds to the proportion of the choline groups which are located on the outside of the vesicle and close to the external Mn^{++} ions. Sonication of the lipid in the presence of Mn^{++} allowed the metal ions to occur both inside and outside the vesicles when all the $\overset{+}{N}(CH_3)_3$ signals disappeared. The conclusions drawn from these experiments were not only that the sonicated vesicles were bounded by a single lipid bilayer, but also that they were effectively sealed (chapter 6).

Proton magnetic resonance spectra of complex systems suffer from the confusion of a large number of overlapping resonances. ^{13}C n.m.r. spectra tend to be simpler, having larger chemical shifts and narrower lines, and can be observed from the natural ^{13}C content of lipids if the sensitivity of the n.m.r. spectrometer is enhanced by computer accumulation of repeated spectral scans. The scan time is reduced in practice by simultaneously exciting nuclei over the whole spectral range using a short intense radiofrequency pulse and converting the information obtained into a conventional n.m.r. spectrum by a Fourier transform operation carried out by computer. ^{13}C n.m.r. spectra of sonicated aqueous dispersions of dipalmitoyl phosphatidylcholine have been obtained which allow several methylene carbons in the aliphatic chains to be individually distinguished. As with proton spectra the immobilization of the aliphatic chains as the temperature is dropped below the transition temperature can be observed. Moreover direct measurement of T_1-values above the transition temperature has established that the mobility of the carbon atoms increases outward from the glycerol backbone toward both the terminal $-CH_3$ of the chains and the $\overset{+}{N}(CH_3)_3$.

Fourier transform has allowed ^{31}P n.m.r. resonance signals to be used to analyze the distribution of components of binary phospholipid mixtures between inside and outside surfaces of single-bilayer vesicles. The chemical shifts of the ^{31}P resonances of the two phospholipid types were found to be sufficiently separated to allow their identification. Moreover, resonances from phospholipids on either the inner or outer surface of the vesicle could be separately examined by removal of the resonances from the alternate surface by peak broadening reagents (see above). In this way, phosphatidylcholine and sphingomyelin were both found to show a preference for the outer surface, while phosphatidylserine, phosphatidylethanolamine and phosphatidylinositol preferred the inner surface. The asymmetry was related to the steric requirements of the bulky head groups of phosphatidylcholine and sphingomyelin which are less crowded at the outer surface. Phosphatidylcholine and sphingomyelin also predominate on the outer surface of erythrocyte membranes, and the suggestion was made that biological membranes could possess areas of high curvature which would mimic the artificial situation in small phospholipid vesicles.

Increasing use is also being made of deuterium magnetic resonance which has been applied in studies of the molecular motion of chain-deuterated phospholipids. ^2H has spin number $I = 1$, unlike ^1H, ^{13}C, ^{31}P and ^{19}F, all of which have spin number $I = \frac{1}{2}$.

Introduction of probe molecules into a lipid bilayer tends to simplify the spectroscopic information received, while carrying the risk of disturbing the original bilayer structure. Molecules of the type $CH_3(CH_2)_mCHF(CH_2)_{n-2}$ COOH, where $n = 4$, 7 and 12, have been incorporated into sonicated vesicles of hens egg lecithin (phosphatidylcholine) and the ^{19}F resonances studied as a probe of molecular movement at various points in the aliphatic chain. Values of T_2 were determined

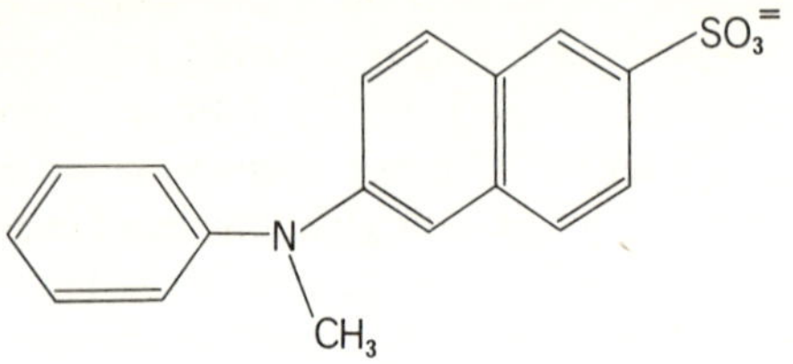

Figure 11.3. The fluorescent probe MNS (*N*-methyl-2-anilino-6-naphthalene sulphonate).

from the line-widths of ^{19}F peaks in the three compounds and were found to increase sharply as *n* increased, indicating again that the motion of the lipid chain becomes greater toward the centre of the bilayer.

An interesting application of n.m.r. has been found in helping to establish the location of a fluorescent probe (see p. 230) within a bilayer. The n.m.r. spectrum of MNS (N-methyl-2-anilino-6-naphthalene sulphonate, figure 11.3) allows assignation of peaks to specific protons, and all peaks are broadened following incorporation of the probe into sonicated vesicles of dipalmitoyl phosphatidylcholine as a consequence of the restricted motion of the membrane-bound molecule. If Mn^{++} is now added to the system, it binds to the phosphate head groups on the outer surface of the vesicles, and the n.m.r. peaks of the MNS protons nearest to the $SO_3^=$ group are preferentially broadened. This is interpreted as showing that the polar end of the MNS molecule (near the $SO_3^=$ group) is located at the outer surface of the lipid bilayer and close to the MN^{++} binding sites on the phosphate head groups of the lipid. The non-polar end of the MNS molecule containing the phenyl ring is located well into the bilayer away from the Mn^{++} ions.

The effect of incorporation of cholesterol into phospholipid bilayers has been examined using both proton and ^{13}C n.m.r. The high resolution ^{13}C n.m.r. spectra of unsonicated aqueous dispersions of egg lecithin (figure 11.4*a*) and egg lecithin-cholesterol (1:1) (figure 11.4*b*) at 18 °C are shown. The spectrum of egg lecithin above its phase transition temperature (figure 11.4*a*) is much better resolved than comparable proton spectra from unsonicated dispersions. Peaks corresponding to —CO—, —CH=CH— (from unsaturated aliphatic chains), $\overset{+}{N}(CH_3)_3$, —CH_2— and CH_3 can all be distinguished. Addition of cholesterol (figure *b*) causes considerable broadening of the —CO— and CH=CH peaks, whereas the $\overset{+}{N}(CH_3)_3$ signal from the choline heat group is apparently unaffected. Although some broadening of the CH_2 peak has occurred,

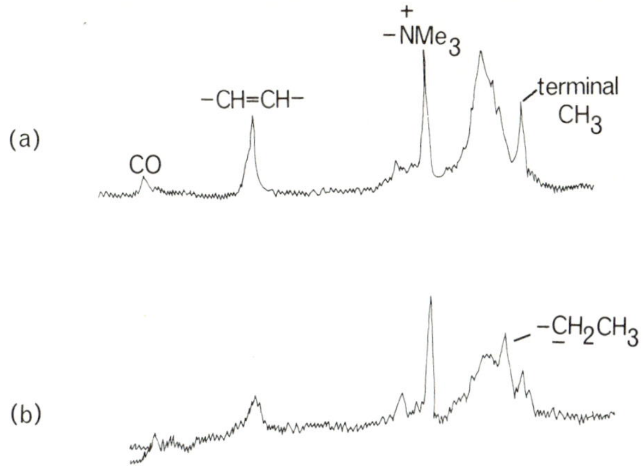

Figure 11.4. High-resolution ^{13}C spectra at 25·2 MHz of unsonicated dispersions in D_2O at 18 °C of (*a*) egg lecithin and (*b*) egg-lecithin-cholesterol (1:1): from K. M. Keough *et al.*, *Chem. Phys. Lipids* (1973), **10,** 37–50.

signals from the penultimate $—CH_2—$ and terminal $—CH_3$ groups are still well resolved. These effects are consistent with the close association of cholesterol molecules with the middle and polar sections of the fatty acid chains in the phospholipid bilayer, leading to immobilization and consequent line broadening of those sections of the chain most closely associated with the steroid molecule. No resonances can be assigned in this spectrum to the cholesterol carbons, many of which may be so broad as to be submerged in the baseline because of their immobility. The selective restriction of certain methylene groups of phospholipid by added cholesterol has also been demonstrated by wide line proton n.m.r. studies (chapter 6, figure 6.18).

All the n.m.r. spectra discussed to this point have been obtained from model bilayer systems. Biological membranes, particularly those containing high levels of cholesterol, present more difficulties. High-resolution proton n.m.r. spectra have been obtained from sonicated dispersions of erythrocyte membrane which are in many ways comparable with spectra from phospholipid models. In view of possible changes in the membrane structure brought about by sonication, attention has been increasingly directed toward unsonicated membrane preparations. While proton n.m.r. has not been particularly successful with such preparations, quite well-resolved ^{13}C n.m.r. spectra have been obtained from erythrocyte

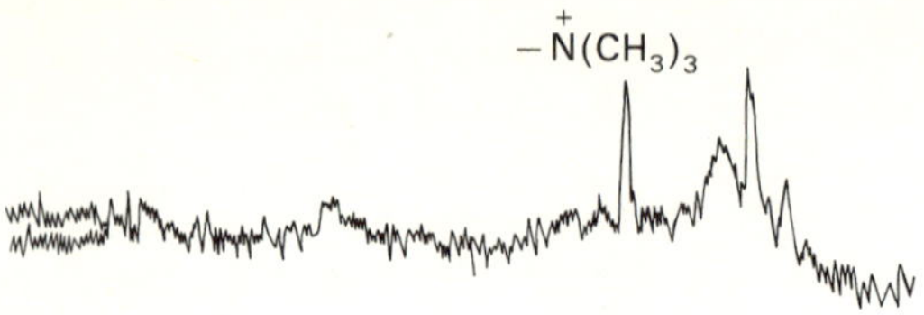

Figure 11.5. High-resolution ^{13}C spectrum at 25·2 MHz at 37 °C of unsonicated erythrocyte ghosts: from K. M. Keough *et al.*, *Chem. Phys. Lipids* (1973), **10**, 37–50.

ghosts. Such a spectrum (figure 11.5) shows considerable similarity to that of the egg lecithin-cholesterol model bilayer (figure 11.4*b*).

Mitochondrial membranes give better resolved proton and ^{13}C n.m.r. spectra than do erythrocyte membranes, possibly because of the lower cholesterol content of the former (chapter 5). A ^{13}C spectrum of unsonicated mitochondrial membrane is shown in figure 11.6 where peaks corresponding to —CH=CH—, $—\overset{+}{N}(CH_3)_3$ and chain-terminal $—CH_3$ groups can be clearly distinguished. The complex signals in the $—CH_2—$ region are believed to arise partly from lipid $—CH_2—$ and partly from protein. ^{13}C spectra have also been obtained from chloroplast membranes and sarcoplasmic reticulum membrane.

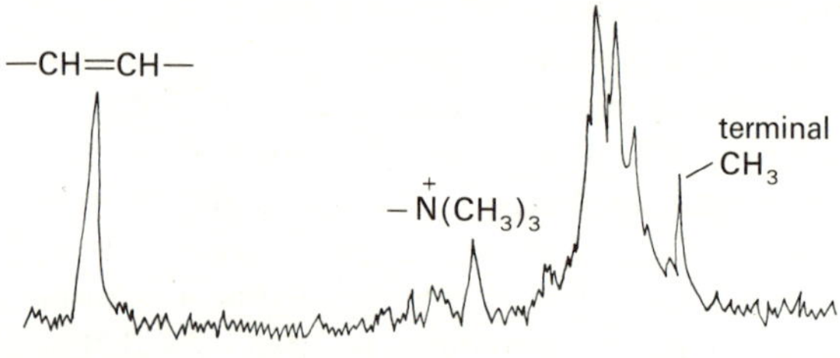

Figure 11.6. High-resolution ^{13}C n.m.r. spectrum at 25·2 MHz at 37 °C of unsonicated mitochondrial membrane: from Keough *et al.*, *Chem. Phys. Lipids* (1973) **10**, 37–50.

Electron spin resonance (e.s.r.)

The nitroxide free radical ($> N—\dot{O}$), by virtue of its unpaired electron spin, gives rise to an electron spin resonance signal which is sensitive both to the detailed motion of the radical and to the polarity of its environment. If a molecule containing this radical is incorporated into a bilayer or membrane, therefore, information can be obtained concerning its surroundings. The technique has the advantage that only the signal from the probe itself need be considered, and the disadvantage that insertion of the probe could disturb the molecular relationships of the system it is intended to describe.

Like an atomic nucleus with spin number $\frac{1}{2}$, the unpaired electron has both a magnetic moment and a spin angular momentum, and when placed in a magnetic field can adopt only two orientations relative to the field (cf. figure 11.1 but note that the particle spin-magnetic moment relationship is reversed). As in the case of the nucleus, the energy difference between the two orientations is proportional to both the magnetic moment and the field strength, and transitions between the two levels can be induced by electromagnetic radiation of suitable frequency. For field strengths of 0·34 tesla (3400 gauss) such as are commonly used in e.s.r. equipment, ν is of the order of 10^{10} Hz, which is microwave frequency. At resonance, microwave radiation is absorbed and recorded as an absorption peak, or more commonly, as its first derivative (figure 11.7).

The nitrogen nucleus ^{14}N has a spin number $I = 1$ and, as such, can itself assume three $(2I+1)$ possible orientations in the magnetic field. Each orientation of the nitrogen nucleus will correspond to a slightly different magnetic environment for the unpaired electron, which accordingly shows not one, but three, resonances as the magnetic field is swept and ν is held constant. The oxygen nucleus ^{16}O is non-magnetic with spin

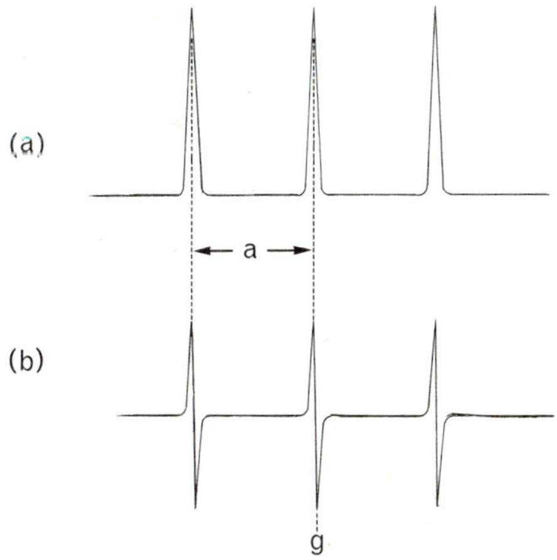

Figure 11.7. Freely tumbling nitroxide radical e.s.r. spectrum shown as (*a*) absorption peaks and (*b*) their first derivatives.

number $I = 0$ and does not further split the three lines. The e.s.r. spectrum of a freely-tumbling nitroxide radical is shown in figure 11.7, both as absorption peaks and as their corresponding first derivatives.

The position of the middle peak in the spectrum as the field is swept is specified by the g-value, a measure of the magnetic moment, and the line separation by the *coupling constant a*. The nitroxide radical is a resonance hybrid of the structures:

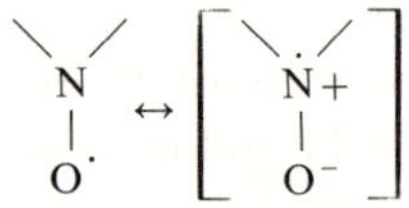

and the contribution of the charged form increases with the polarity of the medium. Thus transfer of the radical from a non-polar to a polar environment results in a higher spin density on the nitrogen atom and the coupling constant a increases. The g-value is rather less sensitive to medium polarity and decreases as the polarity increases. When a radical or *spin-label* partitions between an aqueous and a hydrocarbon environment, two superposed spectra can be seen, provided that the exchange between the two media is slow. The spectrum arising from the partition of the spin-label TEMPO (2,2,6,6-tetramethylpiperidine-1-oxyl) (figure 11.8) into rabbit vagus nerve is shown in figure 11.9. In the hydro-

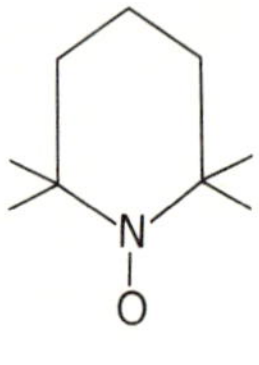

Figure 11.8 The nitroxide spin-label TEMPO (2,2,6,6-tetramethylpiperidine-1-oxyl).

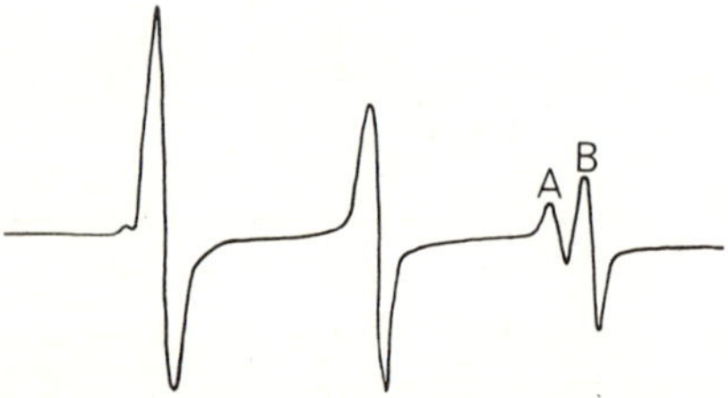

Figure 11.9. Partition of the spin-label TEMPO in a rabbit vagus nerve. A and B are the high field lines in hydrophobic and aqueous regions respectively: from W. L. Hubbel and H. M. McConnell, *Proc. Natl. Acad. Sci.* (*US*) (1968), **61,** 12–16.

carbon medium *g* is increased and the coupling constant *a* is decreased relative to water. The increase in *g*-value causes a shift of the middle e.s.r. line to low field (to the left) and maximum separation is accordingly seen in the high field line. Line A corresponds to the signal from the spin-label in the nerve membrane, and line B to that in water. The ratio of the signal heights gives the partition of the label in the two environments. Such experiments have been used to study the effect of various treatments (e.g. addition of anaesthetics, temperature changes, etc.) on the solubility of labels in the non-polar regions of the membrane.

Three sharp lines as in figure 11.7 are obtained in an e.s.r. spectrum of spin-label undergoing rapid *isotropic* tumbling, i.e. with equal probabilities in all directions. If, however, the molecules are fixed so that the magnetic field is aligned along one of three mutually perpendicular axes defined relative to the nitroxide group, a different three-line spectrum results with parameters *g* and *a* specific for the orientation. Intermediate fixed orientations give spectra for which the parameters can be calculated in terms of the three extreme cases. When immobilized molecules are randomly oriented, a *rigid glass spectrum* such as that in figure 11.10*f* is obtained; it is the sum of the superposed spectra from each of the randomly oriented spin-labels. The effect of progressively slowing down an isotropically-tumbling spin-label is shown in the e.s.r. spectra of figure 11.10. To some extent the mobility of the spin-label can be calculated from the shapes of the spectra and, as in the case of n.m.r., wide lines are generally indicative of slow motion.

Anisotropic motion refers to molecular reorientation that does not occur with equal probability in all directions. Data for fixed alignments of the magnetic field relative to the nitroxide group can be used to compute

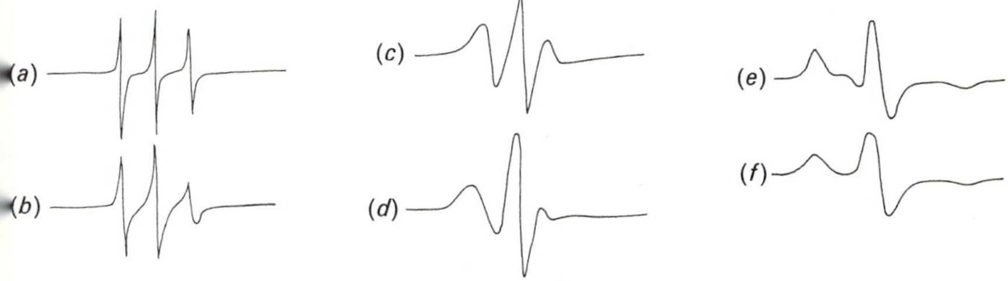

Figure 11.10. The effect on the e.s.r. spectrum of progressively slowing down an isotropically-tumbling spin-label. The spectra are given by the spin-label TEMPO in glycerol. As the temperature falls the viscosity of the medium increases, and the motion of the spin-label decreases. (*a*) 43 °C; (*b*) 26 °C; (*c*) 9 °C; (*d*) 0 °C; (*e*) −36 °C; (*f*) −100 °C: from P. Jost *et al.* in *Structure and Function of Biological Membranes* (1971), (ed. L. I. Rothfield), New York, Academic Press, pp. 83–144.

simulated spectra for certain forms of anisotropic motion, which can be compared with spectra of spin-labelled probe molecules in lipid bilayers. In this way a much clearer idea of the motion of bilayer components can be obtained than is possible using n.m.r. methods.

The mobility of lipid chains in sonicated vesicles of dipalmitoyl phosphatidylcholine has been examined using spin-labels attached at various points along stearic acid molecules (figure 11.11) which were

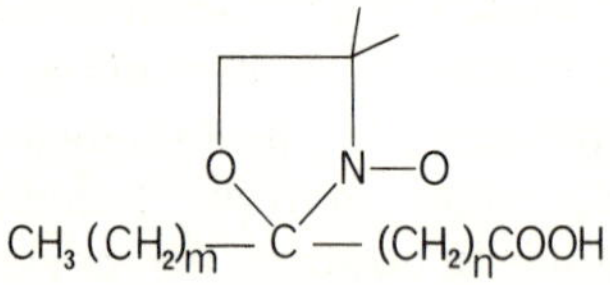

Figure 11.11. Nitroxide spin-label attached to a stearic acid molecule.

intercalated in the lipid bilayer. An index of motion of the spin-label was obtained from a crude analysis of e.s.r. line shapes and is shown plotted against temperature for the three labelled stearic acids *m*, *n* = 12, 3; *m*, *n* = 5, 10 and *m*, *n* = 1, 14 (figure 11.12). When the label is at the

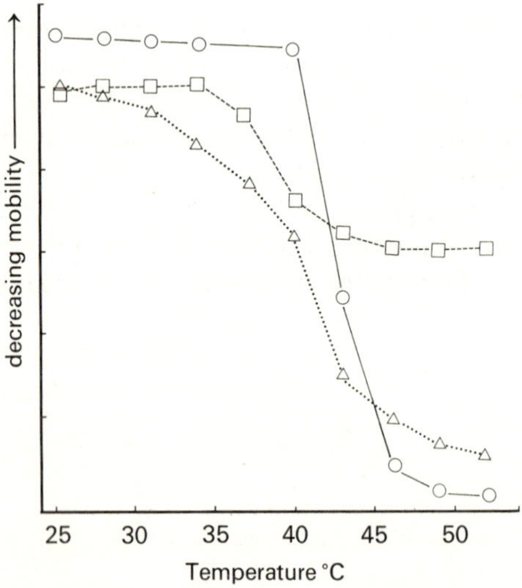

Figure 11.12. Temperature variation of the motion of spin-labels in a sonicated dispersion of dipalmitoyl phosphatidylcholine in water. The spin-labels are attached to stearic acid molecules as shown in figure 11.11 where *m*, *n* = 12, 3 (□--□--□), *m*, *n* = 5, 10 (△···△···△) and *m*, *n* = 1, 14 (○ – ○ – ○): from P. Jost *et al.* in *Structure and Function of Biological Membranes* (1971), (ed. L. I. Rothfield), New York, Academic Press, pp. 83–144.

methyl end of the chain ($m, n = 1, 14$) an abrupt loss of motion is apparent as the temperature is decreased through the transition temperature. The loss of motion is less dramatic when the spin-label is nearer the polar head group ($m, n = 5, 10$ and $m, n = 12, 3$) and occurs over a wider range of temperature. Comparison of relative mobilities above the transition temperature shows decreasing mobility as the label moves toward the polar head group ($1, 14 > 5, 10 > 12, 3$). These data are all consistent with the location of the probe acids in the lipid bilayer with the polar head groups facing outward, and give considerable information about motions within the bilayer.

Spin-labelled stearic acids of the type shown in figure 11.11 have been incorporated into dispersions of egg lecithin-cholesterol (2:1). The e.s.r. spectra from spin-labels at various points along the fatty acid chain were analyzed in terms of a model of chains undergoing rapid segmental anisotropic motion. It was suggested, on the basis of such studies, that the lipid chains are relatively 'rigid rods' up to about C-8, with increasing segmental motion farther along the chains. Selective immobilization of lipid chains by cholesterol in this way has been shown by n.m.r. studies (see p. 112).

The effect of anaesthetics on the fluidity of phospholipid bilayers has been examined using spin-labelled phosphatidylcholine molecules of the type shown in figure 11.13 which contain the spin-label at various positions along the C-2 fatty acyl chain. Addition of inhalation anaesthetics to phosphatidylcholine-cholesterol liposomes containing the probe molecules was found to cause general fluidization of the entire hydrophobic region of the bilayer. The effect could be reversed by application of high pressures ($1{\cdot}5 \times 10^4$kPa, 150 atmospheres) of helium or hydrostatic pressure; conditions which are known to reverse the effect of anaesthetics in several organisms. These results are consistent with the theory that anaesthetic action *in vivo* involves disordering of membrane lipid regions

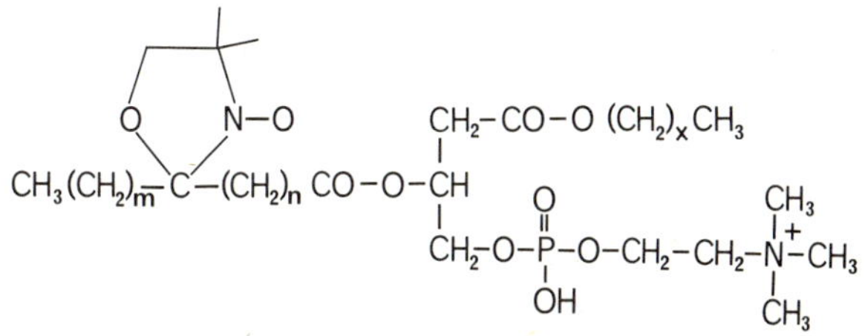

Figure 11.13. Phosphatidylcholine containing a spin-label in the C-2 fatty acyl chain.

and that the demonstrated high-pressure reversal of anaesthesia arises through reimposition of order in the membrane.

An indication of the rate of interchange of phospholipid molecules across a membrane bilayer by a '*flip-flop*' mechanism has been examined using spin-labelling techniques. Hubbell and McConnell sonicated egg lecithin in the presence of the small water-soluble tempocholine (figure 11.14) and obtained single bilayer-bounded vesicles with the spin-labelled

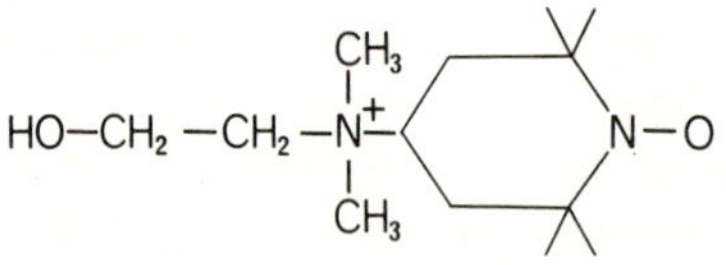

Figure 11.14. Spin-labelled choline (tempocholine).

choline trapped in the internal aqueous space. The vesicles were freed of external tempocholine and exposed to ascorbic acid solutions which reduce nitroxides, removing the paramagnetism. Very little of the signal from internally-trapped tempocholine was destroyed, indicating that the vesicles were impermeable to ascorbate (cf. p. 214). Egg lecithin vesicles were then prepared in the presence of the spin-labelled phosphatidylcholine shown in figure 11.15, which was incorporated into both sides of the vesicle bilayer with its spin-label at the internal and external aqueous interfaces. Treatment with ascorbic acid now rapidly destroyed the signal from all the externally facing spin-labels (65% of the total). Subsequent ascorbic acid treatments of the vesicles at various time intervals demonstrated, however, that progressively more spin-label could be destroyed, showing that the labelled phospholipid molecules were undergoing 'flip-flop' transfer from inside to outside of the vesicles. The transfer was slow, with an estimated probability of internal to external transfer of a spin-labelled molecule of 0·07 per hour at 30 °C.

Lateral diffusion of the spin-labelled phosphatidylcholine (figure 11.15) in the plane of a phospholipid bilayer has been studied by Devaux and

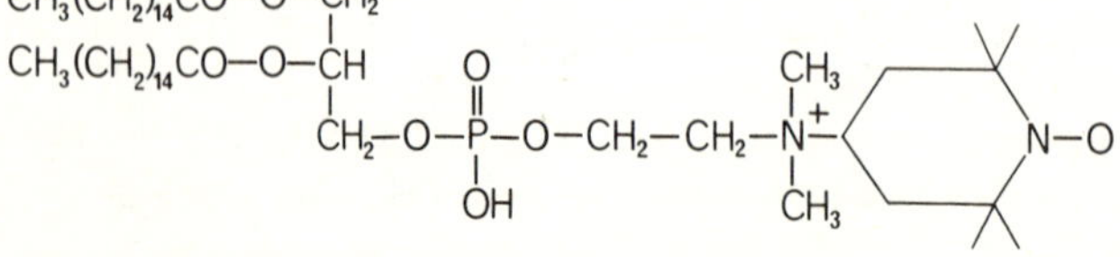

Figure 11.15. Phosphatidylcholine containing a spin-label in the choline head group.

McConnell who incorporated the spin-labelled molecules into multilayers (a series of parallel planar phospholipid bilayers) of phosphatidylcholine. At high concentrations of spin-labelled molecules, the e.s.r. line shapes change as a result of interaction between neighbouring spin-labels, and an empirical relationship can be established between line shape and label concentration. A small region of concentrated spin-labels was introduced into the multilayer, and the fall off in local concentration caused by lateral diffusion was followed by e.s.r. line-shape analysis. In this way a neighbour-exchange frequency of 10^7 per second was calculated. Lateral diffusion of phospholipid molecules in biological membranes has also been demonstrated using spin-labels. When viable *Acholeplasma laidlawii* (see p. 242) were incubated with sonically-produced vesicles containing spin-labels of the type shown in figure 11.13, the artificial and natural membranes apparently fused. Following fusion, changes in the e.s.r. spectrum were observed corresponding to the diffusion of the probe molecules into the unlabelled phospholipids of the mycoplasma membrane.

As with n.m.r., the bulk of spin-label work in bilayers has been carried out in artificial lipid model systems, but applications to biological membranes are increasing. Spin-labelled fatty acids and steroids have been diffused into erythrocyte and nerve membranes, and biosynthetically incorporated into the membranes of micro-organisms. The evidence from such studies is generally that the incorporated probes find themselves aligned with phospholipid molecules in a bilayer, and that their motion is somewhat more restricted than in artificial phospholipid systems, possibly because of the presence of protein.

Optical rotatory dispersion (ORD) and circular dichroism (CD)

Plane-polarized light can be resolved into two circulatory-polarized beams of equal intensity rotating in opposite senses, right- and left-handed. Disymmetric molecules (i.e. non-superimposable on their mirror images) have different refractive indices for left- and right-handed circularly-polarized light, and when a solution of disymmetric molecules is interposed in a beam of plane-polarized light, one of the two circularly-polarized beams will be slowed down relative to the other. This leads to a phase difference between the two beams, and the result will be light polarized in a plane which is rotated relative to the plane of the incident light. The angle through which the plane of plane-polarized light is rotated by the sample is known as its *optical rotation* and can be positive or negative, depending upon the direction of rotation. The variation of optical rotation with wavelength of incident light is the *optical rotatory dispersion* (ORD).

In the region of an absorption band, the sample may preferentially absorb one of the two circularly-polarized beams, in which case incident plane-polarized light will emerge elliptically polarized. The ellipticity can be defined in terms of the axial ratio of the ellipse e, or as θ, where $e = \tan \theta$. The variation of θ with wavelength is known as the *circular dichroism* (CD) spectrum and in contrast to the ORD spectrum, is seen only in the wavelength interval where absorption takes place. Because of this, CD spectra are not complicated by overlapping between neighbouring absorptions, and with the development of sensitive new

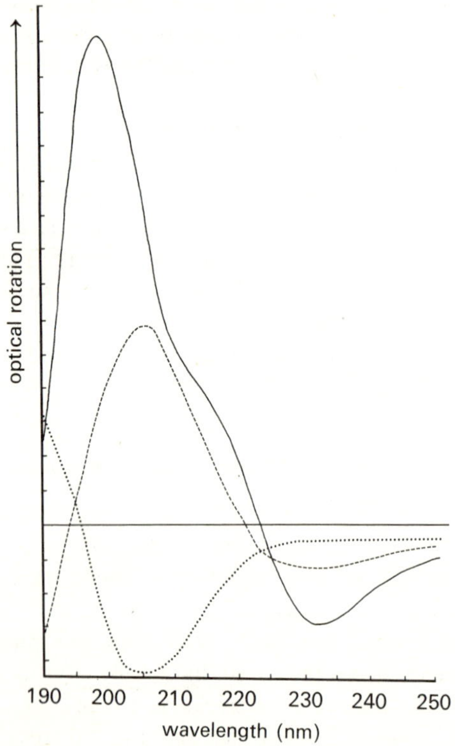

Figure 11.16. ORD spectra of synthetic polypeptides in the α-helical (———), β-pleated sheet (— — —) and random coil (.......) conformations: from N. Greenfield *et al.*, *Biochemistry* (1967), **6**, 1630–1637.

wide-range instruments have become increasingly used in conformational studies of protein, particularly in membranes.

The peptide linkages of proteins show two absorption bands in the region 190–250 nm. Proteins and polypeptides contain many peptide bonds, and the resultant ORD and CD spectra are not simply the sums of the individual peptide contributions, but depend critically on their spatial relationships. Thus distinctive ORD and CD spectra have been obtained from polypeptides known to exist in α-helical, β-pleated sheet or random coil conformations (chapter 6). Such spectra are shown in figures 11.16 and 11.17.

Membrane optical activity in the accessible spectral regions has been found to arise predominantly from peptide chromophores with very little

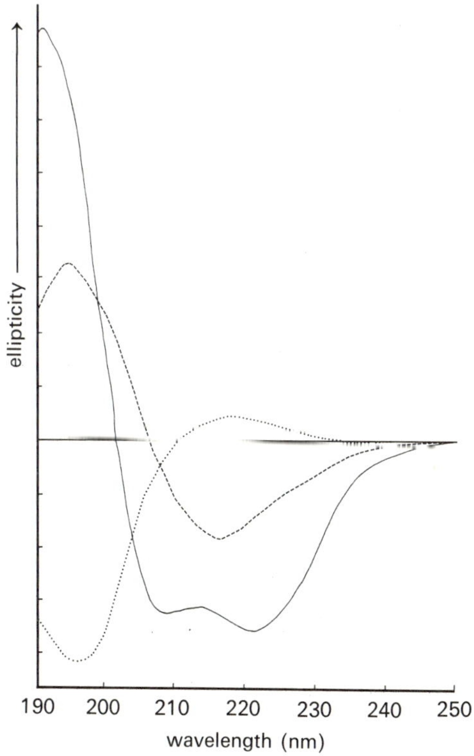

Figure 11.17. CD spectra of polypeptides in α-helical (———), β-pleated sheet (— — — —) and random coil (.......) conformations: from N. Greenfield and G. D. Fasman, *Biochemistry* (1969), **8,** 4108–4116.

contribution from amino acid side chains, lipids, carbohydrate or RNA. Accordingly information concerning conformations of membrane proteins has been sought using ORD and CD techniques. Both ORD and CD spectra of a range of membranes show shapes very similar to those obtained from polypeptides in a right-handed α-helical conformation (figure 11.18) but with anomalously low amplitude and with displacements to longer wavelengths. The spectra appear as if most of the optical activity of the membrane protein were masked, with only the right-handed α-helix being expressed. This alone would not account for the observed band shifts, and several factors (particularly light scattering) have been suggested as giving rise to the anomalous effects which remain the subject

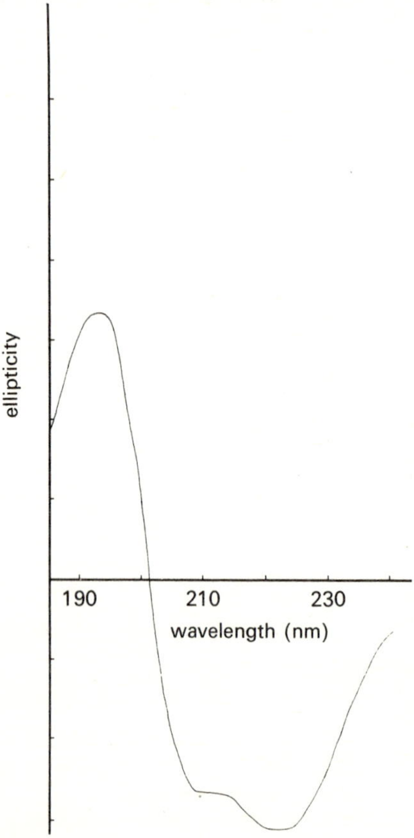

Figure 11.18. CD spectrum of erythrocyte membranes: from M. Glaser and S. J. Singer, *Biochemistry* (1971), **10,** 1780–1787.

of considerable discussion. Although estimates vary, there is general agreement that most membranes contain more than 30% of their peptide linkages in right-handed α-helical conformation, and contents as high as 60% have been quoted, depending on the reference spectra and method of analysis. The remaining protein is believed to exist largely in the random coil conformation, with generally very little in the β-conformation, although significant β-conformation has been reported in membranes of mitochondria and of some micro-organisms. The situation is clearly complex and, while accurate conformational analysis of membrane proteins is still not possible using ORD and CD techniques, early results in this area have done much to clarify problems of membrane structure (chapter 6).

Fluorescence

All molecules have a series of *electronic energy states* which take account of all the electrons in the molecule. Such overall energy states can be classified as *singlet* or *triplet*. In a singlet state all the electrons in the molecule have paired spins, whereas in a triplet state two electron spins are unpaired. At room temperature most molecules are in the ground electronic state S_0, which is a singlet state (figure 11.19). Irradiation of the molecule with ultraviolet or visible light of frequency ν leads to

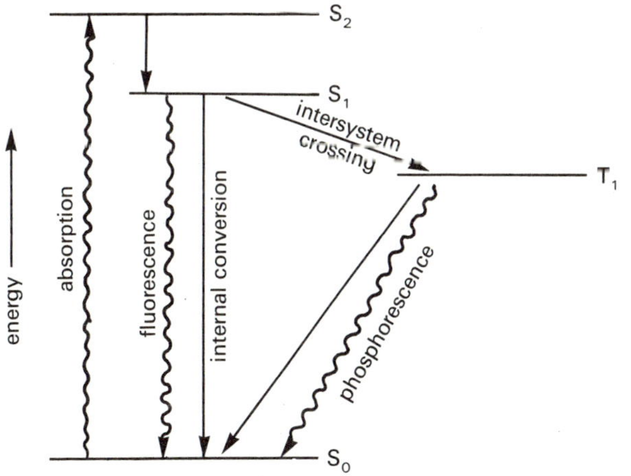

Figure 11.19. Electronic transitions leading to fluorescence and competing processes: S_0 = ground electronic state; S_1 = lowest excited singlet state; S_2 = higher excited singlet state; T_1 = lowest triplet state. Wavy arrows denote transitions with absorption or emission of radiation. Straight arrows denote non-radiative transitions.

absorption of energy E ($= h\nu$ where $h =$ Planck's constant) and the molecule is excited to an upper electronic state such as S_2. The energy level to which the molecule is raised depends on the frequency of the absorbed radiation. After excitation the molecule very rapidly reverts to the lowest excited singlet state S_1 (figure 11.19) without emission of radiation, after which the molecule can return to the ground state by a number of pathways. Direct demotion to the ground electronic state S_0 can occur with emission of light, and this is the process known as *fluorescence*. Because the energy change is less than that involved in the initial absorption (figure 11.19), the frequency of light emitted in fluorescence will be lower than that of the incident light, i.e. *fluorescence is at longer wavelength than the absorption band*, and irradiation with ultraviolet light commonly leads to fluorescence in the visible region. Non-radiative demotion to the ground state S_0 (*internal conversion*) and *intersystem crossing* to the lowest triplet state T_1 (figure 11.19) compete with fluorescence. Reversion from T_1 to the ground state occurs mainly by non-radiative emission for molecules in solution at room temperature, when radiative emission (*phosphorescence*) does not successfully compete. The relative rates of the competing processes will determine the efficiency of fluorescence, which is measured as the quantum yield

$$q = \frac{\text{quanta emitted as fluorescence}}{\text{quanta absorbed from incident light}}$$

The fluorescent properties of many polycyclic hydrocarbons are very sensitive to the environment of the molecule, and such compounds find a use as *fluorescent probes* of which the best known is 1-anilinonaphthalene-8-sulphonate (ANS, figure 11.20). Transfer of ANS from a polar to a non-polar environment leads to a dramatic increase in the quantum

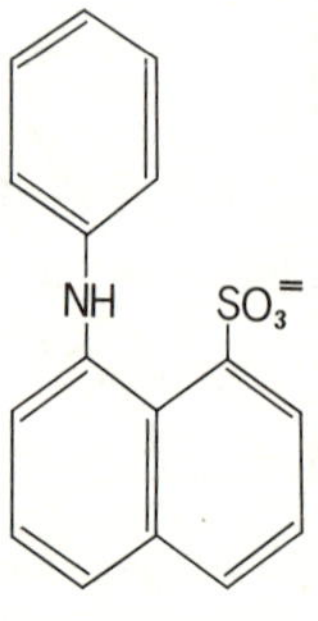

Figure 11.20. The fluorescent probe ANS (1-anilinonaphthalene-8-sulphonate).

yield of fluorescence, and to a shift of fluorescence to shorter wavelengths (blue shift). Some understanding of these changes can be gained from a consideration of the first excited singlet state. In ANS-type compounds this state (S_1) is more polar than either the ground state S_0 or the triplet state T_1, and is relatively more stabilized by dipole interactions in polar media. Consequently, on transfer from a polar to a non-polar environment, S_1 is destabilized more than S_0, and the S_1-S_0 energy gap increases, leading to the blue shift of fluorescence (shift to higher frequency, i.e. shorter wavelength). Moreover, the S_1-T_1 energy gap is also increased, and the probability of intersystem crossing is reduced, giving rise to higher quantum yields for fluorescence.

The fluorescent probes are not only sensitive to the polarity of their environment, but also to the viscosity. A probe molecule which has been newly promoted to its excited state will be stabilized by rearrangement of solvent molecules around it. If the viscosity of the medium is increased, this stabilization may be slowed down, resulting in an increased S_1-S_0 energy gap and a blue shift in fluorescence. For reasons explained above, decreased stability of S_1 can also lead to increased quantum yield of fluorescence. It can be difficult to distinguish such effects caused by *orientation constraint* from those caused by solvent polarity. However, if incident light is applied in nanosecond pules, the time dependence of the emission spectrum during the lifetime of the excited state can be measured, and this allows the orientation constraint to be assessed directly.

The mobility of the probe molecule itself can be measured by irradiation with plane-polarized light. The *polarization of fluorescence* is defined as

$$p = \frac{I_{\parallel} - I_{\perp}}{I_{\parallel} + I_{\perp}}$$

where $I\|$ and $I\perp$ represent the intensities of emitted light parallel and perpendicular to the direction of excitation. The value of p will decrease as the probe molecules reorientate during the lifetime of the excited state. If a nanosecond flash of plane-polarized light is applied, the variation of p with time can be observed directly, and a measure of the rotational mobility of the probe molecule obtained. Alternatively, similar information can be gained from the steady-state polarization of fluorescence caused by continuous irradiation.

Various fluorescent probes have been designed to sample lipid bilayers and membranes at specific locations. Thus ANS contains both a charged

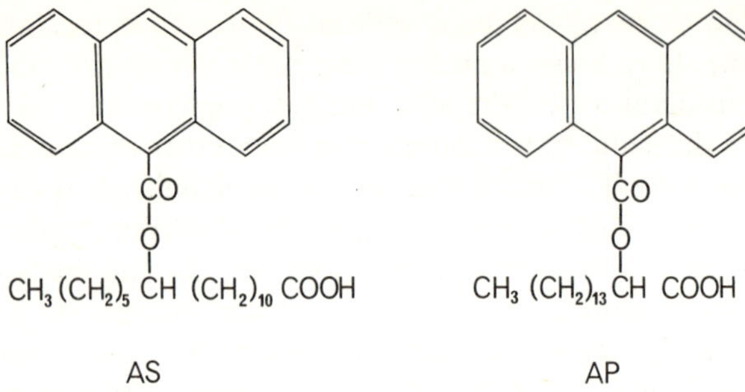

Figure 11.21. Fluorescent probes AS [12-(9-anthranoyl)-stearic acid] and AP [2-(9-anthranoyl)-palmitic acid].

$SO_3^{=}$ group and non-polar phenyl rings, and will be located at the lipid-water interface. For the same reasons the probe MNS (figure 11.3) would be expected to be similarly located, and this has been shown by n.m.r. (see p. 216). As in the case of spin-labels (p. 222), fluorescent probes have been covalently linked to different points in fatty acid chains, and the anthranoyl probes of AS and AP (figure 11.21) are believed to sample the hydrocarbon interior of lipid bilayers approximately 1·5 nm and 0·5 nm respectively inwards from the phosphate head groups.

ANS and other probe molecules have been partitioned, both into phospholipid vesicles and into a range of membranes when a blue shift in fluorescence and increased quantum yields are observed, consistent with non-polar environments of the bound probes. The fluorescence of ANS is further enhanced in the presence of cations, which are believed to increase partition of the probes into the lipid bilayers by counter-ion shielding of the negatively-charged phosphate groups.

AS and AP have been incorporated into phospholipid vesicles. As the temperature is raised through that of the phase transition, sharp increases in the mobilities are detected by fluorescence polarization studies. The fluorescence of AS simultaneously shifts from 430 nm to 442 nm, indicating a decrease in orientation constraint in the more mobile medium. Above the transition temperature, the mobility of the AS probe is higher than that of AP, which probes closer to the head groups, consistent with the idea of a flexibility gradient down the lipid chain.

Information of this kind is, of course, also obtainable from n.m.r. and e.s.r. techniques. The potential of fluorescence probes lies in their ability to reflect small conformational changes within a membrane. The probes are sensitive to small localized changes in the dielectric state of the environment, and the kinetics of even very rapid changes of this kind can be followed.

An illustration of the potential of fluorescent probes as reporters of biochemical processes is provided by their detection of structural changes in mitochondrial membranes. ANS, probing the bilayer-water interface region, indicates a structural change in the membrane by an increased quantum yield under conditions of electron transport and energy coupling. The conformational change appears to be associated with the coupling mechanism. AP and AS probe further into the mitochondrial membrane and show fluorescence changes which are associated with electron transport and are energy-independent. The time constants for the changes detected by ANS, AP and AS decrease in that order, i.e. as the probe location moves further from the head groups. The overall picture which emerges from detailed study of these phenomena is of rapid electron transport-linked changes in the centre of the mitochondrial membrane which slow down as we move toward the head groups, where the slowest process is associated with energy coupling. It is most probably in detection of structural changes at such a level of sensitivity that fluorescent probes will be of greatest value.

X-ray diffraction

Stacked arrays of parallel membranes or polar lipid bilayers behave like an optical diffraction grating in forming diffraction patterns from a beam of X-rays. The X-rays are randomly scattered from the atoms in the bilayers, but it can be shown that the conditions for constructive interference of scattered radiation can be derived by considering the incident X-rays as being reflected by successive planes in the array (figure 11.22). Constructive interference will occur between radiation 'reflected' from equivalent points A and B in adjacent bilayers, provided that the path length difference (CB + BD, figure 11.22) is an integral number of wavelengths. For radiation incident at an angle θ to the plane of the bilayers, this condition, known as Bragg's law, may be written as:

$$2d \sin \theta = n\lambda$$

where d (figure 11.22) is the lamellar spacing, λ is the wavelength of the X-rays, and n is an integer.

Constructive interference will give a diffracted beam which may be detected on a photographic film. The Bragg condition will be met for a

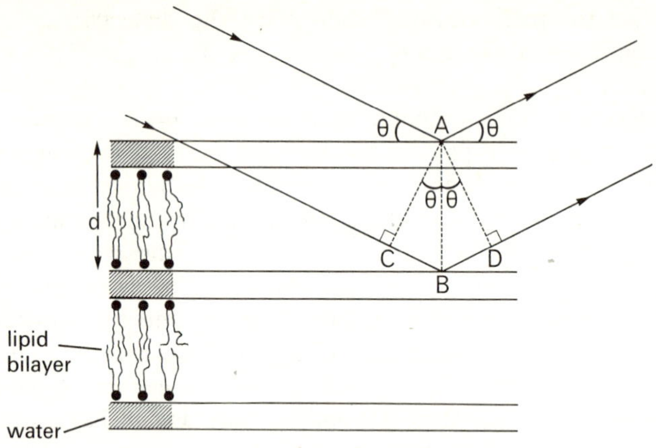

Figure 11.22. Diffraction of an X-ray beam from stacked polar lipid bilayers. Hydrated phospholipids contain water in the hydrophobic head group regions separating the bilayers. The lamellar spacing *d*, corresponding to the repeat distance in the array, includes both the lipid bilayer and the water layer.

series of values of θ, each corresponding to a different integral value of n, and a point X-ray beam will give rise to a series of points in a line perpendicular to the plane of the array. Provided the values of n can be assigned, the value of d may be calculated from measurement of θ for a given point [the angle between the transmitted and diffracted beams is 2θ (figure 11.22)]. The lamellar spacing of approximately 5·0 nm gives rise to rather low diffraction angles in the vertical plane, and special techniques are generally necessary to record diffractions from macromolecular systems such as membranes.

In addition to the lamellar diffractions, an ordered array of hydrocarbon chains in the bilayers of figure 11.22 will give rise to a diffraction pattern in the horizontal axis, parallel to the planes of the bilayers. An X-ray diffraction pattern from multilamellar arrays of egg lecithin above its phase transition and at 14% water content is shown in figure 11.23. A series of sharp arcs cutting the vertical axis (perpendicular to the planes of the bilayers) corresponds to diffractions from lamellae 4·97 nm apart, while two diffuse 0·46 nm bands located about the horizontal axis arise from hydrocarbon chains oriented largely perpendicular to the lamellar planes. Despite this marked orientation of the hydrocarbon chains, there is a broad wide-angle diffraction band of low intensity cutting the vertical axis of the diffraction pattern corresponding to regions in which short segments of the hydrocarbon chains lie nearly parallel to

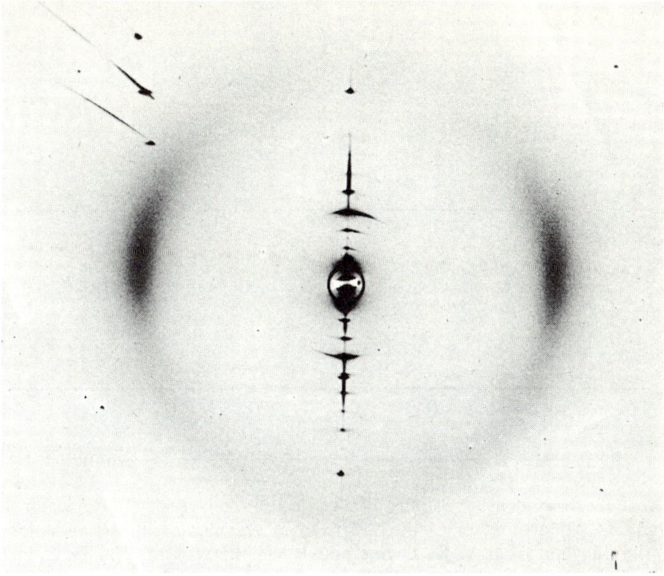

Figure 11.23. Diffraction pattern from oriented bilayers of egg lecithin at 14% water content: from Y. K. Levine and M. H. F. Wilkins, *Nature New Biology* (1971), **230,** 69–72, by courtesy of Professor M. H. F. Wilkins, School of Biological Sciences, University of London, King's College.

the plane of the bilayer. This presumably corresponds to disorder of methyl terminal segments of the chain in the liquid crystalline state. Increased hydration of the bilayer leads to increasing disorder of the chains, and the diffraction pattern at 21% hydration shows the equatorial orientation of the wide-angle 0·46 nm band to be less marked than that at 14% hydration.

Similar diffraction patterns have been obtained from bilayers of synthetic phospholipids. As the temperature of dipalmitoyl phosphatidylcholine is lowered through that of the phase transition, the diffuse 0·46 nm band changes to a sharp 0·42 nm diffraction characteristic of fully extended alkyl chains packed in a two-dimensional lattice. Direct measurements from the diffraction patterns indicate that the extended chains tilt away from a direction perpendicular to the plane of the bilayer with increasing hydration to a maximum of 60° (chapter 6, figure 6.17). This is confirmed by calculations of the average area occupied by each phospholipid in the plane of the bilayer. The thickness of the bilayer increases by

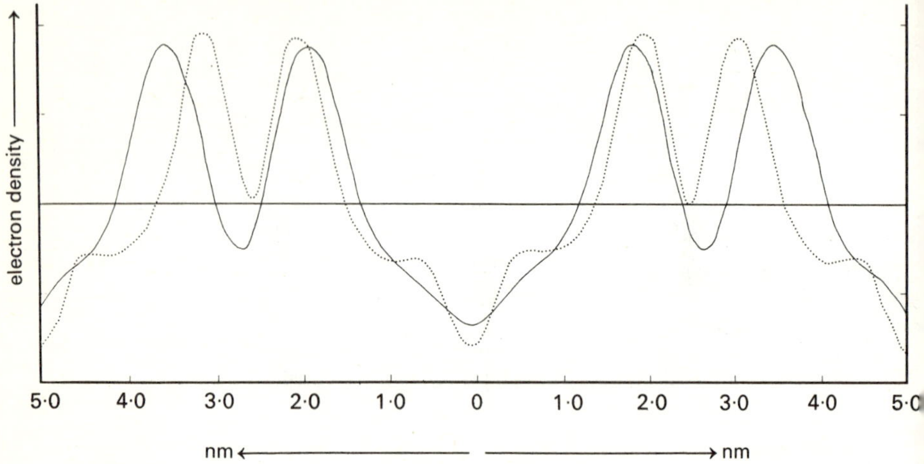

Figure 11.24. Electron density profiles of egg lecithin bilayers at 14% water content (.......) and 21% water content (———). Distances are measured perpendicular to the planes of the bilayers: from Y. K. Levine and M. H. F. Wilkins, *Nature New Biology* (1971), **230,** 69–72.

some 0·5 nm on transition to the gel phase as the alkyl chains assume fully extended conformations.

Measurements of the intensities of the diffracted beams can be used to calculate *electron density profiles* in the bilayers. Two such profiles from the egg lecithin bilayer that gave the diffraction pattern of figure 11.23, are shown in figure 11.24. The peaks of electron density correspond to lipid head groups, and the central troughs of low electron density to the terminal methyl groups of the alkyl chains. At 14% hydration these methyl groups appear to be quite localized in the centre of the bilayer (the shoulders immediately bordering the central trough are artefacts of the calculation procedure). Addition of water causes delocalization of the terminal methyl groups, and the central trough is broadened at 21% hydration. This corresponds to the increasing disorder of the terminal chain segments suggested by the decreased equatorial orientation of the 0·46 nm diffraction observed with increasing hydration.

Whereas X-ray diffraction methods have been used extensively in studies of the phase behaviour of model lipid systems, considerably less information is available concerning true biological membranes. Myelin has the advantage for X-ray studies that it is naturally formed from stacked arrays of pairs of Schwann cell membranes (chapter 3). The system has

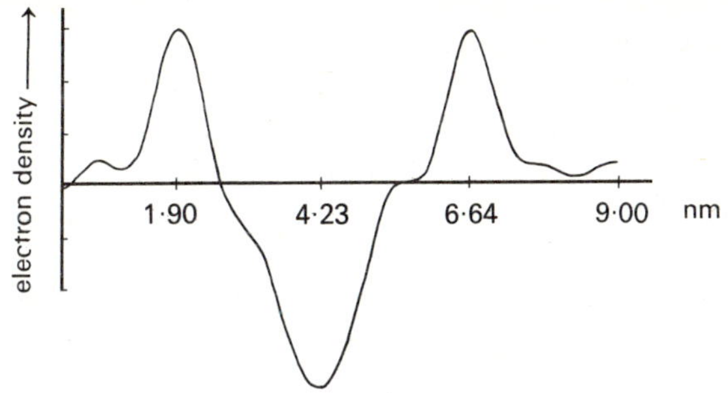

Figure 11.25. Electron density profile for myelin from rabbit sciatic nerve. Distances are measured perpendicular to the plane of the bilayers: from D. L. D. Caspar and D. A. Kirschner, *Nature New Biology* (1971), **231,** 46–52.

been extensively studied, and an electron density profile of myelin from rabbit sciatic nerve is shown in figure 11.25. The similarity to the pattern of the central lipid bilayer unit of figure 11.24 is obvious. Again the high-density peaks correspond to lipid head groups, and the terminal methyl groups of the hydrocarbon chains occupy a central trough about 1·5 nm wide. In this case it is believed that the shoulders bordering the central trough are significant, and they occur in the same position as the symmetric steps identified with steroid rings in artificial phospholipid-cholesterol bilayers. In the myelin profile, however, the steps are asymmetric and indicate a higher concentration of cholesterol in the outer half of the membrane bilayer.

In general, little information has been obtained from X-ray diffraction studies concerning the distribution of protein molecules in membranes. Retinal rods (chapters 3 and 8) are amenable to X-ray studies, as they contain stacked arrays of discs, each containing a double membrane unit. Diffraction patterns from both intact retinae and isolated disc membranes oriented by sedimentation indicate a well-defined disc-to-disc repeat distance of approximately 30 nm. A diffuse diffraction, oriented at right angles to the main lamellar pattern, occurs in the 5–8 nm region, and this has been attributed to the organization of the rhodopsin complexes which contain some 80% of the membrane protein. Detailed X-ray examination has indicated that the rhodopsin 'molecules' are spheres of uniform density with diameters of about 4 nm. Moreover, recent X-ray data suggest that the spherical complexes in unbleached membranes (chapter 8) are partially embedded in the lipid hydrocarbon layer and that, after bleaching, the protein sinks further into the membrane.

Such studies represent a significant contribution to the knowledge of functional aspects of membrane protein.

Recently it has been found possible to obtain useful diffraction patterns from dispersions of single membranes, as opposed to the stacked arrays of myelin or retinal rods, and patterns consistent with lipid bilayer structure have been obtained in this way from erythrocyte and *Mycoplasma laidlawii* membranes. *Mycoplasmas* have the experimental advantage that their membrane lipids can be artificially enriched in certain components by choice of growth medium, and X-ray diffraction has been used to correlate phase transitions and lamellar spacings with predominance in the bilayers of specific fatty acids.

Thermal techniques

As the temperature of a lipid system is raised through that of its gel to liquid crystalline phase transition, the mobility of the hydrocarbon chains suddenly increases, and a corresponding abrupt rise in heat absorption occurs. This heat absorption can be monitored by application to the lipid system of the general techniques of *differential thermal analysis* (DTA) and *differential scanning calorimetry* (DSC). In DTA the lipid sample and an inert reference substance are heated or cooled at the same rate, and the temperature difference between them is plotted against the temperature of the sample. The differential temperature remains constant until the phase transition of the sample, when the sample will absorb heat without corresponding rise in temperature, while the temperature of the control continues to rise, thus giving a peak in the differential temperature/sample temperature curve. DSC involves controlling the heat flow to sample, and reference in such a way that the temperatures of the two substances are raised or lowered while remaining either equal or at a fixed differential. The heat flow necessary to maintain this relationship is recorded and plotted against sample temperature. At the phase transition of the sample the extra heat flow will be recorded as a peak. In both DTA and DSC a peak is therefore obtained, the direction of which indicates whether the transition is exothermic or endothermic. The area of the peak can be related to the heat of transition in both techniques, but DSC is generally preferred for such quantitative studies.

DTA of diacyl phosphatidylcholines has shown that the transition temperature increases with the chain length of the fatty acid and is considerably reduced by the presence of unsaturation in the chains (Table 11.1).

Table 11.1. Transition temperatures for gel to liquid crystalline phase transitions in diacyl phosphatidylcholines containing two identical chains at maximum hydration.

Fatty acid chain	*Transition temperature (°C)*
C_{22} saturated	75
C_{18} saturated	58
C_{16} saturated	41
C_{14} saturated	23
C_{18} unsaturated	−22

Both the transition temperature and the heat of transition depend upon the state of hydration of diacyl phosphatidylcholines. In the DSC curves of figure 11.26 it can be seen that the transition temperature of distearoyl

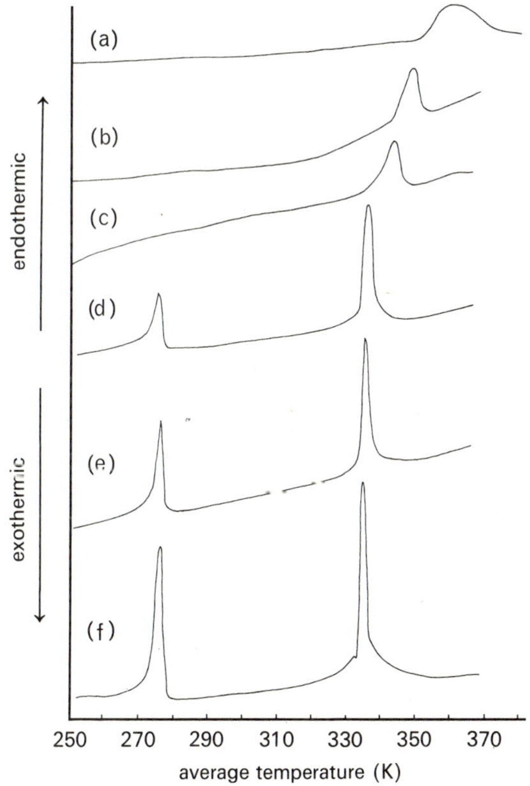

Figure 11.26. DSC curves showing the effect of the state of hydration on the gel to liquid crystalline phase transition for distearoyl phosphatidylcholine. Water contents by weight are (*a*) 3%; (*b*) 10%; (*c*) 20%; (*d*) 25%; (*e*) 30%; (*f*) 40%; from R. M. Williams and D. Chapman, *Progr. Chem. Fats and Other Lipids* (1970), **11**, 1–79.

phosphatidylcholine (right-hand peak) decreases with increasing hydration to a limiting value, at about 25% water content, while the heat of transition increases continuously with increasing water content. The main transition peak arises from the change of the hydrocarbon chains from their state in the gel to that in the liquid crystalline phase. It has been shown by X-ray diffraction (see p. 236) that the states of the chains in both phases vary with degree of hydration, and so the corresponding DSC peak-hydration dependence is expected. At 40% hydration the main transition peak can be seen to be preceded by a small endothermic transition which is believed to arise from conformational changes in the polar head groups. A further endothermic transition (left-hand peak), corresponding to the melting of ice, is present at and above 25% water content. It can be shown that at 20% water content all the water (10 molecules of water per phosphatidylcholine molecule) is bound to the

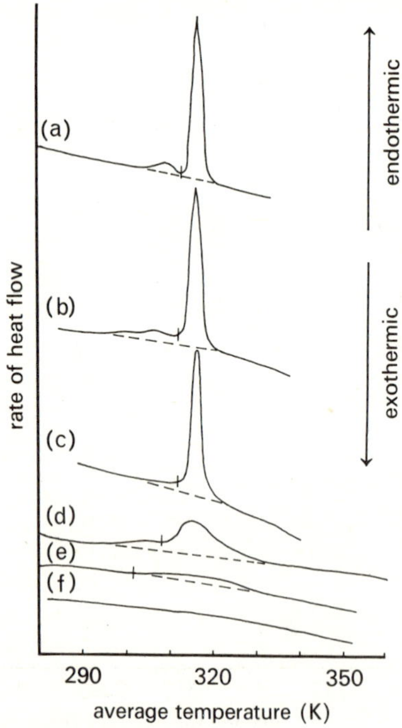

Figure 11.27. DSC curves for 50% (by weight) dispersions in water of dipalmitoyl phosphatidylcholine-cholesterol mixtures containing (*a*) 0·0; (*b*) 5·0; (*c*) 12·5; (*d*) 20·0; (*e*) 32·0; (*f*) 50 mole % cholesterol: from B. D. Ladbrooke *et al.*, *Biochim. Biophys. Acta* (1954), **150,** 333–340.

phospholipid and does not freeze, even if the mixture is cooled to −100 °C.

The thermal behaviour of binary mixtures of phospholipids varies. Whereas mixtures of two phospholipids containing chains of widely different lengths or degrees of unsaturation usually show two transition peaks, mixtures of components with similar chains or intramolecular mixed chains have single sharp peaks. Mixing of polar head groups has been shown to lead to broad intermediate phase transitions, indicating the presence of clusters of gel and liquid crystalline lipid in the bilayer, and to a reduction in heat of transition characteristic of reduced co-operativity of the transition.

The effect of adding cholesterol to dipalmitoyl phosphatidylcholine is shown in figure 11.27. Addition of increasing amounts of cholesterol leads to broadening first of the small pretransition peak and then of the main peak until at 1:1 molar ratio of cholesterol to phospholipid, no transition is visible. Cholesterol has been shown not only to restrict the motion of the hydrocarbon chains of bilayers in the liquid crystalline state but also to disrupt the ordered array of chains in the gel phase leading to increased fluidity in the gel. The tendency is to make the two phases more similar and to abolish the phase transition.

In view of the relatively high levels of cholesterol in myelin and erythrocytes, it is not surprising that no phase transitions have been detected in the hydrated membranes. Dehydration of myelin below 20% water content leads to disappearance of the ice peak and appearance of a small endothermic transition at 35 °C (figure 11.28) which broadens and shifts with increasing dehydration to a limiting value at 55 °C. At very low water levels, a further peak appears at 35 °C. The 55 °C peak is a phospholipid transition, while that at 35 °C is attributed to crystalline cholesterol. It appears that the presence of 20% bound water in myelin is necessary to prevent separation of individual components and to preserve the structural organization of the membrane. The total lipid extract from myelin shows similar thermal behaviour to that of myelin itself. Removal of cholesterol leads to a broad chain-melting transition spanning the physiological range, and part of the myelin phospholipid is crystalline at body temperature in the absence of cholesterol.

Erythrocyte ghosts do not show a phase transition but, as in the case of myelin, the cholesterol-depleted lipids do. It seems, therefore, that part of the function of cholesterol in erythrocyte membrane, as in myelin, is to fluidize lipid gel areas, and possibly also to make liquid crystalline areas less fluid.

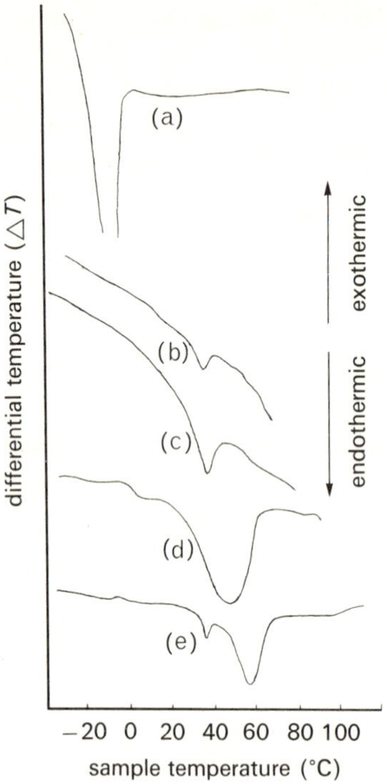

Figure 11.28. DTA heating curves for samples of myelin with approximate water contents (*a*) 30%; (*b*) 15%; (*c*) 10%; (*d*) 5%; (*e*) 3%: from B. D. Ladbrooke *et al.*, *Biochim. Biophys. Acta* (1968), **164,** 101–109.

Membranes of *Mycoplasma* and the closely related *Acholeplasma* species (*Acholeplasmas* differ in not being dependent on sterol for growth) normally show a phase transition. Fatty acids and sterols can be incorporated into membranes of strains of both species by appropriate supplementation of the growth media, and the effect of specific membrane components may then be examined. Thus membranes of *Mycoplasma laidlawii*, which generally have a low cholesterol content, show a phase transition at 30–40 °C, depending on conditions of growth, and the transition can be increased to 60 °C following stearate incorporation, or reduced to −20 °C by corresponding oleate enrichment. When *Acholeplasma laidlawii* are grown in unsupplemented media a broad phase transition occurs in the membrane over a temperature range of some 30 °C, encompassing the growth temperature. This suggests that at the growth temperature both gel and liquid crystalline phases co-exist in the membrane lipids. Similar results have been obtained from membranes of *Escherichia coli*, and it may be that the occurrence of patches of phospholipids in the gel state in membranes at physiological temperatures is commoner than was originally envisaged. It should always be borne in mind that data concerning membrane fluidity obtained from probe molecules could be misleading in that the probe might (*a*) seek out fluid areas of the membrane or (*b*) itself promote fluidization of its immediate environment.

SUMMARY

1. Nuclear magnetic resonance spectra of ^{1}H, ^{13}C, ^{31}P, ^{2}H and ^{19}F nuclei have been used to gain information concerning the mobility and location of the relevant nuclei in phospholipid bilayers and membranes. High resolution n.m.r. spectra are best obtained from sonicated dispersions containing single-bilayer vesicles, although the physiological significance of such preparations from membranes is in doubt. ^{13}C has so far proved to be the most useful nucleus for n.m.r. studies of non-sonicated membranes.

2. Nitroxide spin-labels can be incorporated into lipid bilayers when their electron spin resonance signals can be used to report on the polarity of their environment, and also on the detailed mobility of the probe in the bilayer. Spin-labelled lecithin molecules have been used to measure both 'flip-flop' and lateral motion of phospholipids in bilayers.

3. Different protein conformations give rise to different optical rotatory dispersion and circular dichroism spectra. Both types of spectra have been used to establish the predominance of α-helical and random coil conformations of proteins in membranes.

4. The fluorescence spectrum of a fluorescent probe is sensitive to the polarity and viscosity of the probe's environment, and also to the mobility of the probe. Probes have been incorporated into specific locations in lipid bilayers and membranes, and their major potential is probably as very sensitive indicators of small conformational changes within membranes.

5. X-ray diffraction allows accurate measurement of lamellar spacing and interchain distances in stacked arrays of lipid bilayers or membranes. Such measurements and electron density profiles have been used to provide detailed information on lipid molecule orientation both in gel and liquid crystalline phases. The arrangement of the protein complex, rhodopsin, in retinal disc membranes has been studied in this way. Recently it has been shown that useful diffraction patterns can be obtained from dispersions of single membranes.

6. Thermal techniques, such as differential thermal analysis and particularly differential scanning calorimetry, have been used to study phase transitions in lipid bilayers and membranes. Variations of temperatures and heats of transitions in lipid bilayers with factors such as hydrocarbon chain type, degree of hydration, mixture composition, etc., have been examined in this way. Phase transitions in cholesterol-rich membranes cannot generally be detected.

FURTHER READING

Chapter 1

Branton and Park, R. B. (1968) *Biological Membrane Structure*, Little, Brown & Co., Boston, USA.

De Robertis, E. D. P., Nowinski, W. W. and Saez, F. A. (1970) *Cell Biology*, 5th ed. (Chapters 1–9), W. B. Saunders, Philadelphia, USA.

Chapter 2

Coleman, R. (1973) 'Membrane Bound Enzymes and Membrane Ultrastructure', *Biochim. Biophys. Acta.*, **300,** 1–30.

Cook, G. M. W. (1971) 'Membrane Structure and Function', *Ann. Rev. Plant Physiol.*, **22,** 97–120.

Korn, E. D. (1968) 'Structure and Function of the Plasma Membrane', *J. Gen. Physiol.*, **52,** 257.

Chapter 3

Daemen, F. J. M. (1973) 'Vertebrate Rod Outer Segment Membranes', *Biochim. Biophys. Acta* (*Reviews on Biomembranes*), **300,** 255–288.

De Robertis, E. (1964) *Histophysiology of Synapses and Neurosecretion*, Pergamon Press, Oxford.

Heller, J. and Ostwald, T. (1972) 'Rhodopsin: Conformational Changes in a Membrane Protein', *Ann. N.Y. Acad. Sci.*, **195,** 439–449.

Kirk, J. T. O. (1971) 'Chloroplast Structure and Biogenesis', *Ann. Rev. Biochem.*, **40,** 161–196.

Munn, E. A. (1974) *The Structure of Mitochondria*, Academic Press, London.

Chapter 4

De Duve, C. (1971) 'Tissue Fractionation, Past and Present', *J. Cell Biol.*, **50,** 20D–55D.

De Pierre, J. W. and Karnovsky, M. L. (1973) 'Plasma Membranes of Mammalian Cells. A review of methods for their characterization and isolation', *J. Cell Biol.*, **56,** 275–303.

Emmelot, P. (1968) 'Plasma Membranes', *Excerpta Medica Internat. Cong. Ser.*, **166,** 16.

Hannahan, D. J. (1973) 'The Erythrocyte Membrane. Variability and Membrane Enzyme Activity', *Biochim. Biophys. Acta* (*Reviews on Biomembranes*), **300,** 319–340.

Suomalainen, H. and Nurminen, T. (1973) 'Structure and Function of the Yeast Cell Envelope' in *Proceedings of the Third International Symposium on Yeast Protoplasts, Salamanca 1972*, (ed. Villanueva, J. R., Garcia-Acha, I., Cascon, S. and Uriburu, F.), Academic Press, N.Y. pp. 167–186.

Wallach, D. F. H. and Lin, P. S. (1973) 'A Critical Evaluation of Plasma Membrane Fractionation', *Biochim. Biophys. Acta* (*Reviews on Biomembranes*), **300,** 211–254.

Chapter 5

Ansell, G. B., Hawthorne, J. N. and Dawson, R. M. C. (eds.) (1973) *Form and Function of Phospholipids*, 2nd ed., Elsevier, Amsterdam.

Bean, G. A. (1973) 'Phytosterols', *Advan. Lipid Res.*, **11,** 193–214.

Goldfine, H. (1972) 'Comparative Aspects of Bacterial Lipids', *Advan. Microb. Physiol.*, **8,** 1–58.

Guidotti, G. (1972) 'Membrane Proteins', *Ann. Rev. Biochem.*, **41,** 731–752.

Hakomori, S-i (1973) 'Glycolipids of Tumour Cell Membrane', *Advan. Cancer Res.*, **18,** 265–315.

Helenius, A. and Simons, K. (1975) 'Solubilization of Membranes by Detergents', *Biochim. Biophys. Acta*, **415,** 29–79.

Juliano, R. L. (1973) 'The Proteins of the Erythrocyte Membrane', *Biochim. Biophys. Acta*, **300,** 341–378.

Rouser, G., Nelson, G. J., Fleischer, S. and Simon, G. (1968) 'Lipid Composition of Animal Cell Membranes, Organelles and Organs' in *Biological Membranes, Physical Fact and Function* (ed. D. Chapman), Academic Press, London, 5–69.

Singer, S. J. (1971) 'Molecular Organisation of Biological Membranes', in *Structure and Function of Biological Membranes* (ed. L. I. Rothfield), Academic Press, New York, 145–222.

Winzler, R. J. (1972) 'Glycoproteins of Plasma Membranes, Chemistry and Function', in *Glycoproteins. Their Composition, Structure and Function Part B*, (ed. A. Gottschalk), Elsevier, Amsterdam, 1268–1293.

Chapter 6

Bangham, A. D. (1968) 'Membrane Models with Phospholipids', *Progr. Biophys. Mol. Biol.*, **18,** 31–95.

Bretscher, M. S. (1973) 'Membrane Structure: Some General Principles', *Science*, **181,** 622–629.

Capaldi, R. A. (1974) 'A Dynamic Model of Cell Membranes', *Scientific American*, **230,** 26–33.

Goldup, A., Ohki, A. and Danielli, J. F. (1970) 'Black Lipid Films', *Recent Progr. Surface Sci.*, **3,** 193–260.

Gulik-Krzywicki, T. (1975) 'Structural Studies of the Associations between Biological Membrane Components', *Biochim. Biophys. Acta*, **415,** 1–28.

Lenaz, G. (1973) 'Lipid-Protein Interactions in the Structure of Biological Membranes' in *Membrane Structure and Mechanisms of Biological Energy Transduction*, (ed. J. Avery), Plenum Press, London, 455–526.

Phillips, M. C. (1972) 'The Physical State of Phospholipids and Cholesterol in Monolayers, Bilayers and Membranes', *Progr. Surface Membrane Sci.*, **5,** 139–221.

Pinto Da Silva, P. and Nicolson, G. L. (1974) 'Freeze-etch Localization of Concanavalin A Receptors to the Membrane Intercalated Particles of Human Erythrocyte Ghost Membranes', *Biochem. Biophys. Acta*, **363,** 311–319.

Singer, S. J. (1971) 'Molecular Organisation of Biological Membranes', in *Structure and Function of Biological Membranes*, (ed. L. I. Rothfield), Academic Press, New York, 145–222.

Singer, S. J. and Nicolson, G. L. (1972) 'The Fluid Mosaic Model of the Structure of Cell Membranes', *Science*, **175,** 720–731.

Stockenius, W. and Engelman, D. M. (1969) 'Current Models for the Structure of Biological Membranes', *J. Cell. Biol.*, **42,** 613–646.

Tanford, C. (1973) *The Hydrophobic Effect: Formation of Micelles and Biological Membranes*, John Wiley and Sons, New York.

Ti Tien, H. (1974) *Bilayer Lipid Membranes (BLM), Theory and Practice*, Marcel Dekker Inc., New York.

Vanderkooi, J. (1974) 'Organisation of Proteins in Membranes with Special Reference to the Cytochrome Oxidase System', *Biochim. Biophys. Acta*, **344,** 307–345.

Chapter 7

Cook, G. M. W. and Stoddart, R. W. (1973) *Surface Carbohydrates of the Eukaryotic Cell*, Academic Press, London.

Ginsburg, V., Hickey, C., Kobata, A. and Sawicka, T. (1971) 'Biochemical Basis for Blood Types in Man', in *Glycoproteins of Blood Cells and Plasma*, (ed. G. A. Jamieson and T. J. Greenwalt), J. B. Lippincott Co., Philadelphia, 114–126.

Hakomori, S-i (1973) 'Glycolipids of Tumour Cell Membrane', *Advan. Cancer Res.*, **18,** 265–315.

Hughes, R. C. (1973) 'Glycoproteins as Components of Cellular Membranes', *Progr. Biophys. Mol. Biol.*, **26,** 191–268.

Mehrishi, J. N. (1972) 'Molecular Aspects of the Mammalian Cell Surface', *Progr. Biophys. Mol. Biol.*, **25,** 3–68.

Sharon, N. and Lis, H. (1972) 'Lectins: Cell-agglutinating and Sugar Specific Proteins', *Science*, **177,** 949–959.

Wallach, D. F. H. (1973) *The Plasma Membrane. Dynamic Perspectives, Genetics and Pathology*, Heidelberg Science Library, Heidelberg.

Watkins, W. M. (1972) 'Blood Group Specific Substances', in *Glycoproteins, Their Composition, Structure and Function*, (ed. A. Gottschalk), Elsevier, Amsterdam, 830–891.

Winzler, R. J. (1972) 'Glycoproteins of Plasma Membranes: Chemistry and Function', in *Glycoproteins, Their Composition, Structure and Function*, (ed. A. Gottschalk) Elsevier, Amsterdam, 1268–1293.

Chapter 8

Avruch, I. and Pohl, S. L. (1973) 'The Plasma Membrane Initiator Systems for the Actions of Insulin and Glucagon' in *Biological Membranes*, Vol. 2, (ed. Chapman, D. and Wallach, D. F. H.), Academic Press, London, 185–220.

Changeux, J.-P. and Sealock, R. E. (1975) 'Biochemistry of Purified Receptor Protein', *Biochim. Biophys. Acta* (*Reviews on Biomembranes*), **415** (in press).

Cuatrecasas, P. (1974) 'Membrane Receptors', *Ann. Rev. Biochem.*, **43,** 169–243.

Clarkson, D. T. (1974) *Ion Transport and Cell Structure in Plants*, McGraw-Hill, London.

Danon, A. and Stoeckenius, W. 'Photophosphorylation in *Halobacterium halobium*', *Proc. Nat. Acad. Sci. USA*, **71,** 1234–1238.

De Robertis, E. and Schacht, J. (1974) *Neurochemistry of Cholinergic Receptors*, Raven Press Publ., N.Y.

Ernster, L., Estabrook, R. W. and Slater, E. C. (eds.) (1974), *Dynamics of Energy Transducing Membranes*, Elsevier, Amsterdam.

Michell, R. H. (1975) 'Inositol Phospholipids and Cell Surface Receptor Function', *Biochim. Biophys. Acta* (*Reviews on Biomembranes*), **415,** 81–147.

Mitchell, P. D. (1973) 'Performance and Conservation of Osmotic Work by Proton-Coupled Solute Porter Systems' in *Membrane Structure and Mechanisms of Biological Energy Transduction*, (ed. J. Avery), Plenum Press, London, 265–293.

Poo, M. and Cone, R. A. (1974) 'Lateral Diffusion of Rhodopsin in the Photoreceptor Membrane', *Nature*, **247,** 438–441.

Slifkin, M. A. and Caplan, S. R. (1975) 'Modulation Excitation Spectrophotometry of Purple Membrane of *Halobacterium halobium*', *Nature*, **253,** 56–58.

Palmier, J. M. and Hall, D. O. (1972) 'The Mitochondrial Membrane System' in *Progress in Biophysics and Molecular Biology*, **24,** (ed. J. A. V. Butler and D. Noble), Pergamon, London, 125–176.

Chapter 9

Clarkson, D. T. (1974) *Ion Transport and Cell Structure in Plants* (chapters 3, 4, 5, 6), McGraw-Hill, London.

Haydon, D. H. and Hladky, S. B. (1972) 'Ion Transport across Thin Lipid Films: a Critical Discussion of Mechanisms in Selected Systems', *Quart. Revs. Biophys.*, **5**, 127–282.

Hokin, L. E. (1972) *Metabolic Pathways*, 3rd Ed., Vol. VI, *Metabolic Transport* (chapters 2, 3, 5, 8, 11) Academic Press, N.Y.

Lieb, W. R. and Stein, W. D. (1974) 'Simultaneity, Occlusion, and the Sodium Pump', *Nature*, **252**, 730.

Lin, E. C. C. (1971) 'The Molecular Basis of Membrane Transport Systems' in *Structure and Function of Biological Membranes*, (ed. L. I. Rothfield), Academic Press, N. Y., 285–341.

Chapter 10

Cass, C., Finkelstein, A. and Krespi, V. (1970) 'The Ion Permeability induced in Thin Lipid Membranes by the Polyene Antibiotics Nystatin and Amphotericin B', *J. Gen. Physiol.*, **56**, 100–124.

Eisenman, G. (ed.) (1973) *Membranes—A Series of Advances*, Vol. 2, *Lipid Bilayers and Antibiotics*, Marcel Dekker, N.Y.

Lauger, P. (1972) 'Carrier-mediated Ion Transport', *Science*, **178**, 24–30.

Chapter 11

Chapman, D. (1973) 'Some Recent Studies of Lipids, Lipid-cholesterol and Membrane Systems', in *Biological Membranes*, Vol. 2 (ed. D. Chapman and D. F. H. Wallach) Academic Press, New York, 91–144.

Chapman, D. and Dodd, G. H. (1971) 'Physicochemical Probes of Membrane Structure', in *Structure and Function of Biological Membranes*, (ed. L. I. Rothfield), Academic Press, New York, 13–81.

Chapman, D. and Wallach, D. F. H. (1968) 'Recent Physical Studies of Phospholipids and Natural Membranes', in *Biological Membranes: Physical Fact and Function*, (ed. D. Chapman), Academic Press, London, 125–202.

Jost, P., Waggoner, A. S. and Griffith, O. H. (1971) 'Spin Labelling and Membrane Structure', in *Structure and Function of Biological Membranes*, (ed: L. I. Rothfield), Academic Press, New York, 84–144.

Ladbrooke, B. D. and Chapman, D. (1969) 'Thermal Analysis of Lipids, Proteins and Biological Membranes. A Review and Summary; Some Recent Studies', *Chem. Phys. Lipids*, **3**, 304–356.

Levine, Y. K. (1972) 'Physical Studies of Membrane Structure, *Progr. Biophys. Mol. Biol.*, **24**, 3–74.

Oseroff, A. R., Robbins, P. W. and Burger, M. M. (1973) 'The Cell Surface Membrane: Biochemical Aspects and Biophysical Probes', *Ann. Rev. Biochem.*, **42**, 648–682.

Radda, G. K. (1973) 'Membrane-water Interfaces', in *Membrane Mediated Information*, Vol. 2: *Structures*, (ed. P. W. Kent), MTP Medical and Technical Publishing Co. Ltd., Lancaster, 14–26.

Radda, G. K. and Vanderkooi, J. (1972) 'Can Fluorescent Probes tell us Anything about Membranes?', *Biochim. Biophys. Acta*, **265**, 509–549.

Shipley, G. G. (1973) 'Recent X-ray Diffraction Studies of Biological Membranes and Membrane Components', in *Biological Membranes*, Vol. 2, (ed. D. Chapman and D. F. H. Wallach), Academic Press, New York, 1–89.

Wallach, D. F. H. and Springer, R. J. (1974), *Evolving Strategies and Tactics in Membrane Research*, Springer Verlag, New York.

INDEX